Fundamental
Concepts
of Analysis

PRENTICE-HALL MATHEMATICS SERIES

PRENTICE-HALL INTERNATIONAL, INC., *London*
PRENTICE-HALL OF AUSTRALIA, PTY., LTD., *Sydney*
PRENTICE-HALL OF CANADA, LTD., *Toronto*
PRENTICE-HALL OF INDIA (PRIVATE) LTD., *New Delhi*
PRENTICE-HALL OF JAPAN, INC., *Tokyo*

Fundamental Concepts of Analysis

ALTON H. SMITH

Professor of Mathematics
California State College at Long Beach

WALTER A. ALBRECHT, JR.

Professor of Mathematics
California State College at Long Beach

PRENTICE-HALL, INC.

Englewood Cliffs, New Jersey

© 1966 by Prentice-Hall, Inc.
Englewood Cliffs, N.J.

Current printing (last digit):

10 9 8 7 6 5 4 3 2 1

Library of Congress Catalog Card Number: 66—12117

Printed in the United States of America
33212C

Preface

Our object is to provide a text which is both rigorous and thoroughly understandable, dealing with the fundamental concepts of analysis. We have considered it important to ease the difficulty that many students experience in making the transition from problem solving to theory. The student should have some background in the calculus.

Chapter 1 deals with the customary set operations and introduces the student to the simple type of mathematical proofs associated with set theory.

Chapter 2 starts with a section on mathematical logic which is useful in the development of a better understanding of the nature of mathematical proof. Subsequent sections in this chapter develop properties of the real number system based on the field, order, and completeness axioms.

Chapter 3 presents the definitions of relation and function using the concept of cartesian product. Numerous examples are provided. Basic theorems establish the extent to which set operations are preserved by a function and its inverse. A study of cardinality of sets is also included.

In Chapter 4 the concept of metric set is introduced, and three types of limits are carefully defined: limit points of a set, the limit of a sequence, and the limit of a function. Again, many examples and illustrations are used to aid the reader in understanding the definitions given. The classical theorems are presented with modern proofs which are very readable.

Chapter 5 begins with a discussion of continuous functions defined on a metric set. The theory follows naturally from the study of limits of functions. In the latter part of this chapter special attention is given to functions defined on E^1, and the derivative, as a special case of functional limit, is discussed.

In Chapter 6 the integral is defined in terms of step functions. We first consider the properties of integrals of step functions, and then extend these properties to integrals of bounded functions in general. The Fundamental Theorem is preceded by a discussion indicating plausibility before a formal proof is given. Repeated integration as an evaluation technique for double integrals is also justified.

Throughout the text, modern techniques are used to make explanations clear. The transition to more difficult concepts is gradual. Exercises relate directly to the theory, and solutions normally take the form of a proof rather than a numerical answer. Preceding theorems indicate the pattern of proof. Solutions or hints are given for approximately one-half of the exercises.

Our manuscript has been class tested for several years prior to publication. We gratefully acknowledge the many valuable suggestions given by our colleagues who have used preliminary drafts of this text in their classes.

A. H. SMITH
W. A. ALBRECHT

Contents

vii

6 INTEGRATION   118

Fundamental Concepts of Analysis

1

Introductory
Set
Theory

1-1 INTRODUCTION

The word *set* (or *collection*) is a primitive term or undefined term in mathematics. We do not attempt to define the word "set" but merely state that a set is specified by a property which any single object does or does not have. Those objects which have this property are called *elements* or *members* of the set. The collection of books in the college library, the freshman class, the natural numbers, and the automobiles on a given parking lot at a given moment are examples of sets. The elements of a set need not be related to one another in some simple or obvious way. A perfectly good set is the one consisting of the number 5, the River Nile, and the planet Saturn.

1-2 NOTATION

Elements are usually designated by lower-case letters while sets are designated by capital letters. The symbol $\in$ indicates membership in a set, while the symbol $\notin$ indicates that an object is not in the set. Thus, we would write $x \in A$ to point out that "the object x is a member of the set A" and $y \notin B$ to state that "the object y is not a member of set B".

I-3 SPECIFYING OR DESIGNATING SETS

Sets may be specified in several different ways. For small sets, one way, called *tabulation*, is simply to list the elements of the set and enclose them in braces, such as $A = \{a, e, i, o, u\}$ or $B = \{1, 4, 9, 16, 25, 36, 49\}$. The order in which the elements are listed is immaterial. Thus, $S = \{b, d, c, a\}$ and $T = \{a, b, c, d\}$ describe the same set since the elements are the same in each list.

A more general method involves a description of the set property: $A = \{x \mid x$ has the property $P\}$ designates "the set A of all objects x, such that x has the property P". Thus the sets described in the preceding paragraph would become: $A = \{x \mid x$ is a vowel of the English alphabet$\}$, $B = \{x \mid x$ is the square of a non-zero integer, and $x < 50\}$, while $S = T = \{x \mid x$ is one of the first four letters of the English alphabet$\}$. This method of designating sets is especially useful for very large sets.

I-4 RELATIONS BETWEEN SETS

Every set contains subsets. In the set of all horses there is a subset whose members are white horses, another subset whose members are stallions, another consisting of race horses, etc. If A and B are sets which are so related that every element of A is also an element of B, then A is called a *subset* of B, or A is said to be *contained* in B, and we write $A \subset B$; we may also state that B *contains* A, and write $B \supset A$.

If $A \subset B$, and there is at least one member of B which is *not* in A, then A is called a *proper* subset of B. If $A \subset B$ and there is *no* element of B which is not also a member of A, then sets A and B are *identical* since they then consist of exactly the same elements. Thus two sets A and B are *identical* (or *equal*) in case each is a subset of the other and we write $A = B$.

Two sets are said to be *disjoint* when no element of one set is also a member of the other. The set of all white horses and the set of all black horses are disjoint sets; the set of all airplanes and the set of all rabbits are disjoint sets.

Two sets are said to *meet* or *intersect* each other when at least one element of one set is also a member of the other. To illustrate, the set of all black horses and the set of all race horses intersect each other since some race horses are black.

It is of course possible to characterize a set by a property that would permit no objects to be in the set. Consider, for example, the set of "all women who have served as President of the United States" or the set of "all real roots of the polynomial $x^2 + 1 = 0$". The set which has no members is designated by the symbol $\varnothing$, and is called the *empty set* or *null set*. The null set is a subset of *every* set.

In many discussions all the sets are subsets of one particular set. This set is called the *universal set* (or *universe of discourse*) for that discussion. The universal set is often designated by the symbol $\mathscr{U}$, a script capital letter U. The set of all real numbers is the universal set for some mathematical discussions. Since the universal set may change from one discussion to another, it is well to avoid misunderstanding by stating specifically what the universal set will be. For example, the statement "there is no number whose square is ten" is valid if the discussion is limited to the set of integers or even to the set of rationals; but it is invalid if the universal set is the real numbers or the complex numbers.

A set is called *finite* if it is conceptually possible to identify a separate positive integer with each element of the set (i.e., count the elements) and verify that there is a largest number in the collection of identified integers.* The following sets are finite: the collection of books in the college library, the senior class, the set of all trees, the letters of the English alphabet. A set is *infinite* if it is not finite. The following sets are infinite: the set of all rational numbers, the integers themselves, the points on a line. A more rigorous definition of the words "finite" and "infinite" will be provided later in the text.

1-5   OPERATIONS ON SETS

Two binary operations† on sets have many of the algebraic properties of ordinary addition and multiplication of numbers, although conceptually they are quite different from these operations on numbers.

The *union* (*logical sum*) of two sets A and B is a new set consisting of precisely those elements that belong to either A or B or both A and B. In symbols, $A \cup B = \{x \mid x$ belongs to A or B or both$\}$. For simplicity, agreement will be made at this point that the word "or" shall be used in the inclusive sense; that is, the possibility of x belonging to both A and B is implied in the use of the word "or". In symbols, we need only write $A \cup B = \{x \mid x \in A$ or $x \in B\}$

The *intersection* (*logical product*) of two sets A and B is the new set consisting of those elements each of which belongs to both A and B. In symbols, $A \cap B = \{x \mid x \in A$ and $x \in B\}$.

These two operations may be extended to apply to more than two sets.

---

* The null set is also regarded as finite.

† A binary operation defined on sets is a rule affecting every two sets A and B which states the manner in which a third set C is to be derived from A and B. The set C is usually (but not always) different from A and B.

If $A_1, A_2, A_3, \ldots, A_n$ denote sets, $\bigcup_{i=1}^{n} A_i = \{x \mid x$ belongs to at least one set $A_i\}$, and $\bigcap_{i=1}^{n} A_i = \{x \mid x$ belongs to all sets $A_i\}$. Similarly, for an infinite collection $\{A_\alpha\}$ of sets A_α, we define $\bigcup_\alpha A_\alpha = \{x \mid x$ belongs to at least one set $A_\alpha\}$ and $\bigcap_\alpha A_\alpha = \{x \mid x$ belongs to all sets $A_\alpha\}$.

The symbol $A - B$, called the *complement of B in A*, is defined as the set of all elements in A which are *not* also in B. Thus, $A - B = \{x \mid x \in A$ and $x \notin B\}$. When dealing with a subset A of a universal set $\mathscr{U}$ it is natural to think of the set of all elements of $\mathscr{U}$ which are not in A. This set would be correctly designated as $\mathscr{U} - A$, but it is customary to use the symbol A' instead, and to call A' the *complement of A*. Hence, if $\mathscr{U}$ is the set of all people and A is the set of all blonds, then A' is the set of all people who are not blond. Note that the complement of a set depends very strongly on the universe of discourse.

EXAMPLES: Let $\mathscr{U} = \{1, 2, 3, 4, 5, 6, 7, 8, 9, 10\}$; $A = \{1, 2, 3, 4, 5, 6\}$; $B = \{5, 6, 7, 8\}$; and $C = \{1, 2, 9, 10\}$. Then $A \cup B = \{1, 2, 3, 4, 5, 6, 7, 8\}$; $A \cap B = \{5, 6\}$; $B \cup C = \{1, 2, 5, 6, 7, 8, 9, 10\}$; $B \cap C = \varnothing$; $A' = \{7, 8, 9, 10\}$; $A - B = \{1, 2, 3, 4\}$.

I-6 VENN DIAGRAMS*

Venn diagrams permit graphical illustration of the aforementioned relationships and operations. Sets are represented by use of closed figures, often circles. The points enclosed by the curve are regarded as representing the elements of the set. Several diagrams, together with their interpretations, are shown here:

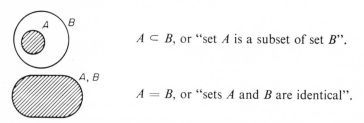

$A \subset B$, or "set A is a subset of set B".

$A = B$, or "sets A and B are identical".

* Leonard Euler (1707–1783) first introduced the use of circles to illustrate class statements. John Venn (1834–1923) presented an improved system which overcame severe limitations of Euler's method. To conform with current usage, we use the term "Venn Diagrams" to include all figures shown here even though several were presented first by Euler. Venn published his method in an article, "On the Diagrammatic and Mechanical Representation of Propositions and Reasonings", *Philosophical Magazine*, July, 1880.

Sets A and B are disjoint; they have no members or elements in common. In symbols, $A \cap B = \emptyset$.

Sets A and B meet each other. In this illustration the shaded area represents the intersection $A \cap B$ of A and B.

The shaded area represents the union $A \cup B$.

The shaded area represents $A - B$, the complement of B in A.

The shaded area represents $\bigcap\limits_{i=1}^{3} A_i$.

1-7 THEOREMS BASED ON THE SET OPERATIONS

Just as one can state and prove many theorems about numbers and their operations, so one can state many theorems about sets and their operations. Many of these theorems are similar, but because the postulates of sets differ somewhat from those of numbers, different theorems will also result.

To prove that a given set is contained in another, e.g., $A \subset B$, one approach is to let x (or some other letter) represent an arbitrarily chosen element of A and prove that x is also in B.

In order to verify that $A = B$, it is necessary to show that $A \subset B$ *and* $B \subset A$. Thus the proof has two parts.

EXAMPLE 1-7.1: Prove that $A \cap (B - C) \subset A - (B \cap C)$.

Proof:	*Reason:*	
1. Let $x \in A \cap (B - C)$	Arbitrary choice	
2. $x \in A$ and $x \in B - C$	Definition of $\cap$	(1)
3. $x \in B$ and $x \notin C$	Definition of $-$	(2)
4. $x \notin B \cap C$	Definition of $\cap$	(3)
5. $x \in A - (B \cap C)$	Definition of $-$	(2,4) ∎

[Be sure to list separately each use of a definition (do not skip steps) and in parentheses state which previous lines of the proof the definition applies to.]

In order to establish that $A \cap (B - C)$ is sometimes a proper subset of $A - (B \cap C)$, we shall construct an example specifying the elements of A, B, and C such that the two sets $A \cap (B - C)$ and $A - (B \cap C)$ are not equal. If we let $A = \{1, 4, 5, 7\}$, $B = \{2, 4, 6, 7\}$, and $C = \{3, 5, 6, 7\}$, then $A \cap (B - C) = \{4\}$ and $A - (B \cap C) = \{1, 4\ 5\}$.

EXAMPLE 1-7.2: Prove that $A \cap (B \cup C) = (A \cap B) \cup (A \cap C)$.

Part I: To show that $A \cap (B \cup C) \subset (A \cap B) \cup (A \cap C)$.

Proof:	*Reason:*	
1. Let $x \in A \cap (B \cup C)$	Arbitrary choice	
2. $x \in A$ and $x \in B \cup C$	Definition of $\cap$	(1)
3. $x \in B$ or $x \in C$	Definition of $\cup$	(2)
4. $x \in A \cap B$ or $x \in A \cap C$	Definition of $\cap$	(2,3)
5. $x \in (A \cap B) \cup (A \cap C)$	Definition of $\cup$	(4)

Part II: To show that $(A \cap B) \cup (A \cap C) \subset A \cap (B \cup C)$.

Proof:	*Reason:*	
1. Let $x \in (A \cap B) \cup (A \cap C)$	Arbitrary choice	
2. $x \in A \cap B$ or $x \in A \cap C$	Definition of $\cup$	(1)
*3. $x \in A$	Definition of $\cap$	(2)
*4. $x \in B$ or $x \in C$	Definition of $\cap$	(2)
5. $x \in B \cup C$	Definition of $\cup$	(4)
6. $x \in A \cap (B \cup C)$	Definition of $\cap$	(3,5)

Having established both parts, the proof is complete and the equation is therefore valid. **❙**

Example 1-7.2 is the counterpart in set-algebra of the familiar distributive law of multiplication over addition of real numbers, $a(b + c) = ab + ac$. Exercise 1-7.18 at the end of this chapter relates to the distributive law of union over intersection which is valid in set-algebra; but its counterpart with respect to real numbers, $a + b \cdot c = (a + b) \cdot (a + c)$, is not valid.

When facility in establishing set relations is achieved, the reader may choose to omit formally writing out the *Reason* column. Moreover, a liberty that is sometimes permitted in exercises relating to set equality is to observe, whenever possible, that the first part read in reverse order is a satisfactory proof for the second part. (Consider similarities and differences in Parts I and II of Example 1-7.2.) It should be emphasized that the shorter

---

* It is often wise to separate steps in order to avoid an ambiguous statement like "$x \in A$ and $x \in B$ or $x \in C$". Sometimes the proof is clearer if it is divided into two separate cases. For example, step 3 would read: "Case 1: $x \in A$ and $x \in B$; Case 2: $x \in A$ and $x \in C$".

form of proof does not excuse the student from a complete mental verification of all the details shown in the longer form of proof. Omissions in the
Proof column are not permitted.

EXAMPLE 1-7.3: Prove that $B - \bigcup\limits_{i=1}^{n} A_i = \bigcap\limits_{i=1}^{n} (B - A_i)$.

Part I: To show that $B - \bigcup\limits_{i=1}^{n} A_i \subset \bigcap\limits_{i=1}^{n} (B - A_i)$.

Proof:

1. Let $x \in B - \bigcup\limits_{i=1}^{n} A_i$

2. $x \in B$ and $x \notin \bigcup\limits_{i=1}^{n} A_i$

3. $x \in B$ and x does not belong to any A_i
4. x belongs to all $B - A_i$

5. $x \in \bigcap\limits_{i=1}^{n} (B - A_i)$

Part II: To show that $\bigcap\limits_{i=1}^{n} (B - A_i) \subset B - \bigcup\limits_{i=1}^{n} A_i$.

Read the above proof in reverse order to prove Part II. ▌

The Venn diagrams are useful in suggesting or illustrating the statement
of a theorem. Example 1-7.1 could be represented by the following two
diagrams, which show the relation-
ship of the sets described. Notice
that all points in the shaded area of
the first diagram are also in the
shaded area of the second.

$A \cap (B - C)$

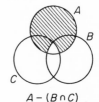

$A - (B \cap C)$

It is sometimes convenient to
number the areas determined by a
Venn diagram and associate with
each set the numbers of the areas
inside it. Compare the latter part of Example 1-7.1 with the numbered
figure given below.

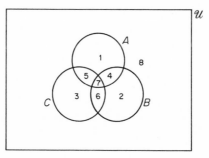

The use of Venn diagrams is limited to the role of illustration. Diagrams are not regarded as adequate proof of relationships. Illustrations often become very complicated when operations relate to more than four sets.

EXERCISES

1-7.1. Let $\mathscr{U} = \{a, b, c, d, e, f, g\}$, $R = \{a, b, c, d\}$, $S = \{c, d, e, f\}$, and $T = \{a, b, g\}$. Find R', S', T', $R - S$, $S - R$, $R \cap S$, $S \cup T$, $S \cap T$, $R' - T$, and $R' \cap T'$.

1-7.2. Tabulate the elements of the following sets:
$A = \{x \mid x$ is a root of the polynomial $x^2 + 5x + 6 = 0\}$.
$B = \{x \mid x$ is a prime number and $x < 27\}$.
$C = \{x \mid x$ is a letter in the word "Mississippi"$\}$.
(Note: when tabulating elements, each member of the set need only be listed once.)

1-7.3. Find all of the subsets for each of the following sets: $S_1 = \{1\}$; $S_2 = \{1, 2\}$; $S_3 = \{1, 2, 3\}$; $S_4 = \{1, 2, 3, 4\}$. Using this information, determine the number of subsets of a set having n elements. (A plausible guess is acceptable here.)

1-7.4. Draw a Venn diagram of the form illustrated for each of the following sets, and shade in the given areas:
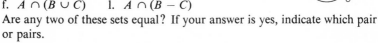

a. $(A \cup B) \cap C$ g. $(A - B) \cup C$
b. $A \cup (B \cap C)$ h. $A - (B \cup C)$
c. $(A - B) \cap C$ i. $(A \cup B) - C$
d. $A - (B \cap C)$ j. $A \cup (B - C)$
e. $(A \cap B) \cup C$ k. $(A \cap B) - C$
f. $A \cap (B \cup C)$ l. $A \cap (B - C)$

Are any two of these sets equal? If your answer is yes, indicate which pair or pairs.

Before beginning Exercises 1-7.5 through 1-7.21, the student should know the definitions of set operations $\cup$, $\cap$, and $-$ well enough to clearly understand that these definitions imply the following:
$x \notin A \cup B$ means that $x \notin A$ and $x \notin B$;
$x \notin A \cap B$ means that $x \notin A$ or $x \notin B$;
$x \notin A - B$ means that either $x \notin A$ or x belongs to both A and B;
$x \notin \bigcup\limits_{i=1}^{n} A_i$ means that x does not belong to any A_i;
$x \notin \bigcap\limits_{i=1}^{n} A_i$ means that x does not belong to at least one A_i.

1-7.5. Prove that $(A - B) \cap C \subset A - (B \cap C)$, and construct a specific example showing that $(A - B) \cap C \neq A - (B \cap C)$. (See Example 1-7.1, which illustrates the type of work expected.)

Exercises 1-7.6 through 1-7.11 are to be completed in the same way as Exercise 1-7.5.

1-7.6. $(A - B) \cap (C - D) \subseteq (A \cap C) - (B \cap D)$

1-7.7. $(A - B) \cap (A - C) \subseteq A - (B \cap C)$

1-7.8. $(A \cup B) - C \subseteq A \cup (B - C)$

1-7.9. $A \cap (B \cup C) \subseteq (A \cap B) \cup C$

1-7.10. $(A \cup B) - (C \cup D) \subseteq (A - C) \cup (B - D)$

1-7.11. $(A - C) \cup (B - D) \subseteq (A \cup B) - (C \cap D)$

For Exercises 1-7.12 through 1-7.21, prove the set equalities given, following the general pattern illustrated in Example 1-7.2.

1-7.12. $A - (B \cup C) = (A - B) - C$

1-7.13. $(A \cap B) - C = A \cap (B - C)$

1-7.14. $(A \cap C) - (B \cup D) = (A - B) \cap (C - D)$

1-7.15. $(A \cap B) - (A \cap C) = A \cap (B - C)$

1-7.16. $A - (B \cap C) = (A - B) \cup (A - C)$

1-7.17. $A - (B \cup C) = (A - B) \cap (A - C)$

1-7.18. $A \cup (B \cap C) = (A \cup B) \cap (A \cup C)$

1-7.19. $B - \bigcap_{i=1}^{n} A_i = \bigcup_{i=1}^{n} (B - A_i)$

For Exercises 1-7.20 and 1-7.21 assume that infinitely many sets A_α are involved.

1-7.20. $B - \bigcup_{\alpha} A_\alpha = \bigcap_{\alpha} (B - A_\alpha)$

1-7.21. $B - \bigcap_{\alpha} A_\alpha = \bigcup_{\alpha} (B - A_\alpha)$

2

The
Real
Number
System

2-1 INTRODUCTION

An understanding of the real number system is basic to a thorough understanding of analysis. Undoubtedly, the reader already has a working knowledge of some properties of real numbers; however, this chapter presents the real numbers as a logical system, with properties established by rigorous mathematical proof from a set of basic assumptions.

There are several ways in which this study could be presented. One way would be to start with the numbers 1, 2, 3, $\cdots$ (the "counting" numbers, or "positive integers"), proceed to the set of all integers (positive, negative, and zero), and then construct the larger system of rational numbers; finally, the real number system could be constructed from the rationals. At each successive step it would be necessary to show that the basic operations of addition and multiplication are defined and are consistent with the same operations of the preceding set of numbers, now viewed as a subset of the set newly constructed. Other characteristics and properties would also have to be verified and proved consistent at each step of such a development.

We shall, however, choose to start far out in this process and describe the real number system itself by means of a few fundamental properties or *axioms*. In general, axioms are basic assumptions which are not proved; it is only necessary that they be consistent. If one or more of the axioms should be changed, a different mathematical system might result. The conclusions obtained from the axioms by logical reasoning are called *theorems*. Because the theorems in this text will become increasingly difficult, it is well to start this chapter with a section on logic.

2-2 ELEMENTARY LOGIC

To communicate ideas in speech or writing, we use sentences. Sentences which have the property of being either true or false are called *statements*, and are illustrated by examples like "this desk is green", "the clock has stopped", and "two plus five equals seven". Of course, since statements can be false, "two plus two equals eight" is also an example of a statement. It must be remembered that the truth or falsity of a statement often depends upon which element of the universe of discourse is being considered—e.g., which desk, or which clock.

Let the letter A and the letter B denote statements. The statement "A and B" is called the *conjunction* of A and B. An *alternation* (sometimes called *disjunction*) is a statement of the form "A or B". The composition of several declarative sentences into one statement can be described by means of a *truth table*. Letting T and F denote "true" and "false", respectively, the truth tables for conjunction and alternation read as follows:

	Conjunction			Alternation	
A	B	A and B	A	B	A or B
T	T	T	T	T	T
T	F	F	T	F	T
F	T	F	F	T	T
F	F	F	F	F	F

Notice that all possible combinations of truth values (that is, T and F) are associated with A and B. Note that the conjunction is true only when A and B are true, while the alternation is true for all cases except where A and B are both false.

To deny a statement is to affirm another statement known as the *negation* of the first. For example, the negation of "this desk is green" could be stated "this desk is not green", or "it is not true that this desk is green", or "it is false that this desk is green". The truth table for negation is very simple:

Negation

A	not A
T	F
F	T

An *implication* is a statement of the form "if H, then C" (sometimes symbolized $H \to C$, and read "H implies C"). The statement H associated with the word "if" is called the *hypothesis*, and the statement C associated with the word "then" is called the *conclusion*. The statement "if two given triangles are congruent then their areas are equal" is an implication. An implication is false only if the hypothesis is true and the conclusion is false; hence the truth table for implications is constructed as follows:

Implication

H	C	if H, then C
T	T	T
T	F	F
F	T	T
F	F	T

At first thought one might suppose that it would be best to omit the last two lines of this truth table. However, in order to regard $H \to C$ as a statement for every pair of statements H and C, the implication must be completely defined. Mathematicians have decided to define $H \to C$ in this way.

There are several classical variations of the implication "if H, then C". If we exchange the two statements and write "if C, then H", we have a new sentence, called the *converse* of the original one. Two further useful implications can be formed: the *inverse*, "if not H, then not C", and the *contrapositive*, "if not C, then not H". It is important to construct a truth table for each of these statements in order to compare them. The following table is constructed from the information already given in the negation and implication tables. Extra columns are included for comparison and ease of computation:

H	C	Original Implication: if H, then C	Converse: if C, then H	not H	not C	Inverse: if not H, then not C	Contrapositive: if not C, then not H
T	T	T	T	F	F	T	T
T	F	F	T	F	T	T	F
F	T	T	F	T	F	F	T
F	F	T	T	T	T	T	T

From this analysis, it is clear that (1) the validity of the original proposition and the contrapositive always agree—that is, if one is true, so is the other; or if one is false, so is the other; (2) the validity of the converse and the inverse always agree. Sometimes a theorem can be more readily established by stating and proving its contrapositive, thus proving the original theorem.

Implications often appear as simple statements such as "base angles of an isosceles triangle are congruent" or "all books are heavy". These statements can be restated in if-then form by proper utilization of the definitions of the terms involved. The first example could be written, "if a triangle is isosceles, then the base angles are congruent," and the second example takes the form, "if an object is a book, then it is heavy".

Frequently, a theorem with a valid converse will be presented in such a way that both are included in a single sentence, as "base angles of an isosceles triangle are congruent, *and conversely*". Two other ways of expressing this same thing, often found in mathematics, are "two angles of a given triangle are congruent *if and only if* two sides of the triangle are equal" and "*a necessary and sufficient condition* that two angles of a triangle be congruent is that two sides of the triangle are equal". No matter which of these three ways is used, the student must clearly state the implication and its converse, and then furnish two complete proofs, one for the implication, and one for the converse.

Let us now construct the truth table for the statement "A if and only if B", sometimes written $A \leftrightarrow B$ and read "A is equivalent to B". Since $A \leftrightarrow B$ is defined by the conjunction $A \rightarrow B$ and $B \rightarrow A$, it is possible to derive the truth table for $\leftrightarrow$ from the truth tables of conjunction and implication. Extra columns have been used to indicate the successive steps used in this computation (see table at top of next page). Column (5) is obtained from columns (3) and (4) by use of the conjunction table. It is seen that if $A \leftrightarrow B$ is a true statement, then A and B have the same truth values—either both are true, or both are false.

Equivalence

(1) A	(2) B	(3) $A \to B$	(4) $B \to A$	(5) $A \leftrightarrow B$
T	T	T	T	T
T	F	F	T	F
F	T	T	F	F
F	F	T	T	T

EXERCISES

2-2.1. Which of the following sentences are statements:
   a. Kangaroos are not suitable for pets.
   b. What time is it?
   c. Walk right in.
   d. The quick brown fox jumped over the lazy dog.
   e. Just because my eyes are closed, don't think I am asleep.
   f. Now is the time for all good men to come to the aid of the party.

2-2.2. Construct truth tables for each of the following: (Parentheses are used to avoid ambiguity.)
   a. A or (not B)   h. if A, then (not B)
   b. (not A) or B i. if (not A), then B
   c. not (A or B)   j. not (if A, then B)
   d. (not A) or (not B) k. if (not A), then (not B)
   e. A and (not B)   l. $A \leftrightarrow$ not B
   f. not (A and B)   m. not ($A \leftrightarrow B$)
   g. (not A) and (not B) n. (not A) $\leftrightarrow$ (not B)
   Indicate which of the above statements have the same truth table. Special attention should be given to the comparison of statements c and g, and statements d and f.

2-2.3. Give the negation of each of the following statements:
   a. Some horses are white.
   b. No horse is white.
   c. All horses are white.
   d. The owl and the pussycat went to sea.
   e. I'll pass this course or I'll know the reason why.

2-2.4. Restate the following implications in if-then form, and give the converse, the inverse, and the contrapositive:
   a. All philosophers are wise.
   b. No philosopher is wicked.

2-3 THE FIELD AXIOMS
AND RELATED THEOREMS

In the following sections a single element may be represented by more than one symbol. We shall write $a = b$ if, and only if, the symbols a and b represent the same element of a given set.

Two of the operations in the real number system are *addition* and *multiplication*. They are often called binary operations because they serve to combine *two* elements (numbers) in prescribed ways. The familiar operations subtraction and division are defined in terms of addition and multiplication respectively. We shall start with eleven axioms, five of which (A-1 through A-5) describe addition, a similar five (M-1 through M-5) which describe multiplication, and one (labeled D) which interrelates the two operations in a particular way. Let R designate the set of real numbers. We have:

A-1. Every pair of numbers a and b in R have a unique sum $a + b$, which is also in R. (The *closure law* for addition.)

A-2. For a and b in R, $a + b = b + a$. (The *commutative law* for addition.)

A-3. For a, b, and c in R, $a + (b + c) = (a + b) + c$. (The *associative law* for addition.)

A-4. There is a number in R, symbolized by 0 and called "zero", such that for each a in R, $a + 0 = a$. (The existence of an *additive identity* or *zero element* in R.)

A-5. For every a in R, there exists a number in R, symbolized by $-a$, such that $a + (-a) = 0$. (The existence of an *additive inverse* or *negative* for each real number a.)

The *difference* between a and b is defined as $a + (-b)$, and the indicated operation is called *subtraction*. Often, $a - b$ is used as an abbreviation for $a + (-b)$. (Caution: the reader should not make the mistake of calling the symbol "$-a$" a negative number. As we shall see later, this symbol may stand for a positive number, a negative number, or even zero, depending upon a itself. The symbol $-a$ should be called "the additive inverse of a" or simply the "negative of a".)

M-1. Every pair of numbers a and b in R have a unique product ab, which is also in R. (The *closure law* for multiplication.)

M-2. For a and b in R, $ab = ba$. (The *commutative law* for multiplication.)

M-3. For a, b, and c in R, $a(bc) = (ab)c$. (The *associative law* for multiplication.)

M-4. There exists a number in R, symbolized by 1, where $1 \neq 0$, such that for each a in R, $a \cdot 1 = a$. (The existence of a *multiplicative identity* or *unit element* in R.)

M-5. For every $a \neq 0$ in R, there exists a number, symbolized by a^{-1}, such that $a \cdot a^{-1} = 1$. (The existence of a *multiplicative inverse* for each real number a other than 0; the term *reciprocal* is also used.)

The *quotient* of a and b, $(b \neq 0)$, is defined as $a \cdot b^{-1}$, or equivalently, $b^{-1}a$, and the indicated operation is called *division*. A common way of designating the quotient is a/b.

D. For a, b, and c in R, $a(b + c) = ab + ac$. (The *distributive law* of multiplication over addition.)

Note that if $b = c$ is given, then $a + b = a + c$ and $ab = ac$ for any number $a \in R$, since, by axioms A-1 and M-1, the sum and product are *uniquely* defined, and hence certainly do not depend on the symbols used to represent the numbers involved. For the same reasons, if $a = b$ and $c = d$, then $a + c = b + d$ and $ac = bd$.

These eleven axioms are called the *field axioms*, and any algebraic structure which satisfies the field axioms is called a *field*.

The real number system requires other axioms in addition to these for its complete description, but before presenting further axioms, we shall prove some theorems concerning real numbers, based only upon the axioms already stated.

THEOREM 2-3.1: *The Cancellation Law for Addition:* $b + a = c + a$ implies that $b = c$.

Proof:	*Reason:*
1. $b + a = c + a$	Hypothesis
2. $(b + a) + (-a) = (c + a) + (-a)$	A-1
3. $b + (a + (-a)) = c + (a + (-a))$	A-3
4. $b + 0 = c + 0$	A-5
5. $b = c$	A-4 ∎

THEOREM 2-3.2: If $a + a = a$, then $a = 0$.

Proof:	*Reason:*
1. $a + a = a$	Hypothesis
2. $a + 0 = a$	A-4
3. $a + a = a + 0$	Equality of (1) and (2)
4. $a = 0$	A-2, Theorem 2-3.1 ∎

It is often a good idea to restate a theorem into the form of an implication in order to make the proof more understandable. Be sure that the restatement is equivalent to the original theorem.

THEOREM 2-3.3: The additive inverse of a number is unique.

RESTATEMENT: If a number b has the property $a + b = 0$, then $b = -a$.

Proof:	Reason:
1. $a + b = 0$	Hypothesis
2. $a + (-a) = 0$	A-5
3. $a + b = a + (-a)$	Equality of (1) and (2)
4. $b + a = (-a) + a$	A-2
5. $b = -a$	Theorem 2-3.1 ▮

THEOREM 2-3.4: The additive inverse of $a - b$ is $b - a$; i.e., $-(a - b) = b - a$.

Proof:	Reason:
1. $a + (-a) = 0$	A-5
2. $b + (-b) = 0$	A-5
3. $[a + (-a)] + [b + (-b)] = 0$	A-1, A-4
4. $[a + (-b)] + [b + (-a)] = 0$	A-2, A-3
5. $(a - b) + (b - a) = 0$	Abbreviation
6. $(a - b) + [-(a - b)] = 0$	A-5
7. $-(a - b) = b - a$	Theorem 2-3.3 ▮

EXERCISES

Each of the following statements about real numbers is a theorem derivable from the eleven field axioms. Prove each one in a manner similar to the proofs of the preceding theorems.

2-3.1. The additive identity is unique. [*Hint*: Consider the restatement "if an element b has the property $a + b = a$ for all real numbers a, then $b = 0$".]

2-3.2. The additive inverse of the additive inverse of a number b is b itself; i.e., $-(-b) = b$.

2-3.3. The negative of zero is zero itself; i.e., $-0 = 0$

2-3.4. The *cancellation law for multiplication* holds; i.e., $ba = ca$, and $a \neq 0$ imply $b = c$.

2-3.5. The multiplicative inverse of a non-zero number is unique.

2-3.6. The multiplicative identity is unique.

2-3.7. $1^{-1} = 1$

2-3.8. $(c - b) + (b - a) = c - a$

2-3.9. The additive inverse of $a + b$ is $-a - b$; i.e., $-(a + b) = -a - b$. [Note that $-a - b$ is the abbreviation for $(-a) + (-b)$.]

2-3.10. $(c + a) - (c + b) = a - b$

2-4 SOME FURTHER THEOREMS

Up to this point, zero has not been mentioned except in connection with addition. We now see what happens when zero is involved in the operation of multiplication.

THEOREM 2-4.1: $a \cdot 0 = 0$, where a is any real number.

Proof: *Reason:*
1. $0 + 0 = 0$ A-4
2. $a \cdot (0 + 0) = a \cdot 0$ M-1
3. $a(0 + 0) = a \cdot 0 + a \cdot 0$ D
4. $a \cdot 0 + a \cdot 0 = a \cdot 0$ Equality of (2) and (3)
5. $a \cdot 0 = 0$ Theorem 2-3.2 ▌

A *corollary* is a statement which can be established from a theorem with very little additional proof.

COROLLARY 2-4.1: Zero has no reciprocal.

Proof: If there exists a number 0^{-1} such that $0^{-1} \cdot 0 = 1$, then Theorem 2-4.1 would be false. ▌

COROLLARY 2-4.2: If $a \neq 0$, then $a^{-1} \neq 0$.

Proof: If $a^{-1} = 0$, then $a \cdot a^{-1} = 0$, by Theorem 2-4.1; but this contradicts M-5. Hence a^{-1} cannot be 0. ▌

Corollaries 2-4.1 and 2-4.2 demonstrate the so-called *indirect proof.* One shows that if the conclusion is false then a contradiction with previous valid statements will exist.

THEOREM 2-4.2: If $ab = 0$, then either $a = 0$ or $b = 0$.

RESTATEMENT: If $ab = 0$ and $a \neq 0$, then $b = 0$.

Proof:	Reason:
1. $ab = 0$	Hypothesis
2. $a^{-1}(ab) = 0$	M-1, Theorem 2-4.1
3. $(a^{-1}a)b = 0$	M-3
4. $1 \cdot b = 0$	M-2, M-5
5. $b = 0$	M-2, M-4 ❙

EXERCISES

In some of the following theorems, which the reader is asked to prove as exercises, zero occurs in conjunction with multiplication.

2-4.1. If $a \neq 0$, then $(a^{-1})^{-1} = a$

2-4.2. $a/b = 0$ (where $b \neq 0$) if and only if $a = 0$

2-4.3. If $a \neq 0$, then $1/a = a^{-1}$; that is, "unity divided by a is the multiplicative inverse or reciprocal of a".

2-4.4. If $a \neq 0$ and $b \neq 0$, then $(ab)^{-1} = a^{-1}b^{-1}$ or $1/ab = (1/a)(1/b)$.

2-4.5. If $b \neq 0$ and $d \neq 0$, then $a/b = ad/bd$. [*Hint:* Use the notation of multiplicative inverses and convert to reciprocal form on the last step.]

2-4.6. If $b \neq 0$ and $d \neq 0$, then $(a/b)(c/d) = ac/bd$.

2-4.7. If $b \neq 0$ and $d \neq 0$, then $a/b + c/d = (ad + bc)/(bd)$. [*Hint:* Consider $(bd)^{-1}(ad + bc)$ and use the distributive law.]

2-5 THEOREMS INVOLVING MULTIPLICATION OF ADDITIVE INVERSES

The following theorems and exercises describe the additive inverse in relation to the operation multiplication, and help to lay the groundwork for the familiar rules governing multiplication of signed numbers. At this stage of the development of the real number system, we have not yet discussed positive and negative numbers. The statement $(-a)(-b) = ab$, which appears in the exercises, should not be read "the product of two negative numbers is positive", but instead "the product of the additive inverses of two numbers equals the product of the numbers themselves".

THEOREM 2-5.1: $(-1)(-1) = 1$

Proof: *Reason:*
1. $(-1) \cdot 0 = 0$ Theorem 2-4.1
2. $(-1)[1 + (-1)] = 1 + (-1)$ A-5
3. $(-1) \cdot 1 + (-1)(-1) = 1 + (-1)$ D (left member of (2))
4. $(-1) + (-1)(-1) = 1 + (-1)$ M-4
5. $(-1)(-1) = 1$ A-2, Theorem 2-3.1 ∎

EXERCISES

2-5.1. $(-1) \cdot a = -a$. [*Hint:* Start with $1 + (-1) = 0$ and multiply by a.]

2-5.2. $(-a)(-b) = ab$

2-5.3. $(-a) \cdot b = -(ab)$

2-5.4. $a(-b) = -(ab)$

2-5.5. $(-a)/b = -(a/b), b \neq 0$

2-5.6. $a/(-b) = -(a/b), b \neq 0$

2-5.7. $a(b - c) = ab - ac$. (This is the *distributive law of multiplication over subtraction*.)

2-5.8. Prove that the *general linear equation*, $ax + b = 0$, $a \neq 0$, has the unique solution $x = -(b/a)$.

2-6 THE AXIOMS OF ORDER

In addition to the field axioms, the real numbers have an *order relation*, which is based on the following axioms. The axioms of order relate to the abstract property of *positiveness*. We do not define positiveness, but accept it as a primitive concept.

O-1. Some numbers are positive.

O-2. For any number a, one and only one of the following statements is true: $a = 0$; a is positive; $-a$ is positive.

O-3. The sum of two positive numbers is positive.

O-4. The product of two positive numbers is positive.

By definition, the number a is *negative* if and only if $-a$ is positive. The following definitions pertain to the order relation:

1. The symbol $<$ (is less than) and the symbol $>$ (is greater than) are

defined by the statements "$x < y$ if and only if $y - x$ is positive"; "$x > y$ if and only if $x - y$ is positive".

2. The symbols $\leq$ (is less than or equal to) and $\geq$ (is greater than or equal to) are defined by "$x \leq y$ if and only if either $x < y$ or $x = y$"; "$x \geq y$ if and only if either $x > y$ or $x = y$".

It should be noted that $x < y$ and $y > x$ express the same order relation or inequality and hence are equivalent statements. The two statements $x \leq y$ and $y \geq x$ are also equivalent. The simultaneous inequalities $x < y$ and $y < z$ are usually written as the single statement $x < y < z$, and a similar explanation applies to $x \leq y \leq z$.

The axioms of order, together with the earlier axioms and theorems, now permit the proof of many new theorems which express additional properties of the real numbers. The style of proof in the theorems which follow is less formal, though not less rigorous, than our previous proofs. This "paragraph style" of proof is almost universally used in the more advanced works on mathematics.

THEOREM 2-6.1: $a > 0$ if and only if a is positive.

Part I: If a is positive, then $a > 0$. *Proof:* $a - 0 = a + (-0) = a + 0 = a$, and a is given as positive. By the definition of the symbol $>$ we may now write $a > 0$.

Part II: If $a > 0$, then a is positive. *Proof:* $a > 0$ implies that $a - 0$ is positive. But $a - 0 = a$, as seen in Part I. Thus a itself is positive. |

THEOREM 2-6.2: (*The transitive law for order relations*). If $a < b$ and $b < c$, then $a < c$. (Also, $a > b$ and $b > c$ imply $a > c$.)

Proof: $a < b$ means that $b - a$ is positive; $b < c$ means that $c - b$ is positive. By O-3, $(c - b) + (b - a)$ is positive. But $(c - b) + (b - a) = c - a$; thus $c - a$ is positive, and $a < c$. |

EXERCISES

Each of the following exercises involves the order axioms. Prove each statement. (*Note:* By definition, $a^2 = a \cdot a$; $a^3 = a \cdot a \cdot a$; etc.)

2-6.1. The *law of trichotomy:* For any a and b in R, one and only one of the following is true: $a < b$; $a = b$; or $a > b$.

2-6.2. *Additivity:* If $a > b$, and c is any real number, then $c + a > c + b$ and $a + c > b + c$.

2-6.3. *Multiplicativity:* If $a > b$, and $c > 0$, then $ca > cb$ and $ac > bc$.

2-6.4. The product of two negative numbers is positive.

2-6.5. The product of a positive number and a negative number is negative.

2-6.6. $a^2 > 0$ for any real number $a \neq 0$. [*Note:* this proves $1 > 0$.]

2-6.7. The equation $x^2 + 1 = 0$ has no real solution.

2-6.8. If $a > b$ and $c < 0$, then $ca < cb$ and $ac < bc$. [Multiplication of an inequality by a negative number reverses (the sense of) the order relation.]

2-6.9. If a is positive, then a^{-1} is positive, and if a is negative, then a^{-1} is negative.

2-6.10. If $0 < a < b$, then $0 < 1/b < 1/a$

2-6.11. If $a > b$ and $c > d$, then $a + c > b + d$, and $a - d > b - c$

2-6.12. If $a > b > 0$ and $c > d > 0$, then $ac > bd$ and $a/d > b/c$

2-6.13. If $a > 0$ and $b > 0$, then $a^2 > b^2$ if and only if $a > b$. [*Hint:* Consider $a^2 - b^2 = (a - b)(a + b)$.]

2-6.14. There is no largest real number. [*Hint:* Consider $x + 1 > x$.]

2-7   ABSOLUTE VALUE

Let x denote any real number. The *absolute value of x*, written $|x|$, is defined by

$$|x| = \begin{cases} x, & \text{if } x \geq 0, \\ -x, & \text{if } x < 0. \end{cases}$$

It is clear that $|x|$ is never negative; that is, $|x| \geq 0$.

THEOREM 2-7.1: $|x| \geq x$ and $|x| \geq -x$.

Proof: Case I. Suppose $x \geq 0$. By definition of absolute value, $|x| = x$. Moreover, $-x \leq 0$ (multiply $x \geq 0$ by -1), so $|x| \geq 0 \geq -x$.

Case II. Suppose $x < 0$. Then $|x| = -x$, and $|x| \geq 0 > x$. Thus, for all real numbers x, the theorem holds. ∎

THEOREM 2-7.2: For any real numbers x and y, $|x| + |y| \geq |x + y|$.

Proof: (1) $|x| \geq x$ and $|y| \geq y$ imply $|x| + |y| \geq x + y$;
(2) $|x| \geq -x$ and $|y| \geq -y$ imply $|x| + |y| \geq -x - y = -(x + y)$;
(3) By definition of absolute value, $|x + y|$ equals either $x + y$ or $-(x + y)$.
(4) In either case, $|x| + |y| \geq |x + y|$ by lines (1) and (2). ∎

THEOREM 2-7.3: If a denotes a positive real number, then $a > |x|$ if and only if $a > x > -a$.

Part I: If $a > |x|$, $a > 0$, then $a > x > -a$. *Proof:* By hypothesis and Theorem 2-7.1, $a > |x| \geq x$ and $a > |x| \geq -x$. Thus $a > x$ and $a > -x$. Multiply the second inequality by -1 to obtain $-a < x$; hence $a > x > -a$.

Part II: If $a > x > -a$, $a > 0$, then $a > |x|$. *Proof:* If $x \geq 0$, then $a > x = |x|$ by hypothesis and the definition of absolute value. If $x < 0$, then $|x| = -x$. Now, $-a < x$ is equivalent to $a > -x$ (multiply $-a < x$ by -1), so $a > |x|$. ▊

EXAMPLE 2-7.1: Find the values of x which satisfy the inequality $|x - 3| < 5$.

By Theorem 2-7.3, $-5 < x - 3 < 5$; adding 3, we get $-2 < x < 8$.

EXERCISES

In Exercises 2-7.1 through 2-7.6, find the values of x which satisfy the given inequalities*:

2-7.1. $|x + 4| < 2$ 2-7.2. $|4 - 5x| \leq 6$

2-7.3. $|3x - 2| < 7$ 2-7.4. $|x + 1| < |x|$

2-7.5. $|3x - 2| > 5$ 2-7.6. $|4x + 2| \geq 4$

[*Hint:* In Exercise 2-7.5, solve $|3x - 2| \leq 5$; the solution set for $|3x - 2| > 5$ is the complement in R of the solution set for $|3x - 2| \leq 5$. In Exercise 2-7.6, solve $|4x + 2| < 4$.]

In Exercises 2-7.7 through 2-7.12, prove the indicated properties:

2-7.7. $|xy| = |x| \cdot |y|$ [*Hint:* consider all possible cases of sign for x and y.]

2-7.8. $|x/y| = |x|/|y|$, where $y \neq 0$

2-7.9. $|x| = |-x|$ [*Note:* this proves that $|x - y| = |y - x|$, since $-(x - y) = y - x$.]

2-7.10. $|x - y| + |y - z| \geq |x - z|$

2-7.11. $|x| + |y| \geq |x - y|$

2-7.12. $|x| - |y| \leq |x - y|$

---

* For the definitions of the symbols 2, 3, 4, etc., see the first paragraph of Section 2-8.

2-8 NATURAL NUMBERS, INTEGERS, AND RATIONAL NUMBERS

Any field which has properties O-1, O-2, O-3, and O-4 is called an *ordered field*. A field must contain the element 1, and $1 \neq 0$, by M-4. By A-1, it must also contain the sum of *any* two elements in the field. In particular, it contains the element $1 + 1$, denoted by the symbol 2. Similarly, 3 denotes $2 + 1 = 1 + 1 + 1$; 4 denotes $3 + 1 = 1 + 1 + 1 + 1$; 5 denotes $4 + 1$; etc. The absence of parentheses in these expressions causes no ambiguity because of the associative axiom. Since $n + 1 > n$ for all numbers n in an ordered field, it follows that $1 < 2 < 3 < 4 < \ldots$.

The *natural number system* is the subset of the real numbers consisting of the numbers 0, 1, and all numbers that can be obtained by repeated addition using the number 1 only. We will assume that the sum of two natural numbers is also a natural number, and the product of two natural numbers is again a natural number.

The system of *integers* is the set of natural numbers together with their negatives. An integer which can be written in the form $2n$, where n is itself an integer is called *even*; an integer which is not even is called *odd*, and takes the form $2n + 1$. A natural number p other than 0 and 1 is called *prime* if there exists no factorization of p in the set of integers other than the two trivial factorizations $p = 1 \cdot p$ and $p = (-1)(-p)$. Two integers p and q are said to be *relatively prime* if $p = ac$ and $q = bc$, where a, b, and c are integers, implies that $|c| = 1$; in other words, two integers are relatively prime when they share no common integral factor other than 1 and -1.

The *rational number system* consists of all real numbers of the form a/b, where a and b are integers and $b \neq 0$. It can be shown that *any* ordered field must contain a subsystem algebraically similar to the rational numbers*; moreover, the rational numbers themselves constitute an ordered field.

However, the rational number system is quite limited. Often, the distance between points in Euclidean Space cannot be represented by any rational number. Consider the right triangle with height and base of length *one*. By the Pythagorean Theorem, the hypotenuse is of length $\sqrt{2}$. The square root of 2 is not rational. In order to prove this, we first establish the following lemma. (A *lemma* is a statement introduced to aid in the proof of a theorem.)

---

* Algebraic similarity is defined and studied in any standard course in Modern Algebra. (cf. Birkhoff and MacLane, *A Survey of Modern Algebra.* Topic: Isomorphic fields. The Macmillian Company, New York, 1953.)

LEMMA 2-8.1: If a^2 is even, then a is even.

RESTATEMENT (contrapositive): If a is odd, then a^2 is odd.

Proof: Let $a = 2n + 1$, where n is an integer. Then $a^2 = 4n^2 + 4n + 1 = 2(2n^2 + 2n) + 1 = 2m + 1$, where $m = 2n^2 + 2n$. Hence, a^2 is odd. ∎

THEOREM 2-8.1: $\sqrt{2}$ is not a rational number.

We shall use an indirect proof.

RESTATEMENT: "If $\sqrt{2}$ is rational, then we are led to a contradiction".

Proof:

Any rational number can be written in the form p/q, where p and q are relatively prime integers, because of the property $ac/bc = a/b$. Assume $p/q = \sqrt{2}$, $q \neq 0$, and p and q are relatively prime. Then $p^2/q^2 = 2$, or $p^2 = 2q^2$, so p^2 is even. By the preceding lemma, p must therefore be even, and hence representable in the form $p = 2n$, where n is an integer. Thus, $p^2 = (2n)^2 = 4n^2 = 2q^2$, or $2n^2 = q^2$. Hence q^2 is even, and by the lemma, q must also be even. But this means that p and q have a common factor of 2 and contradicts the assumption that p and q are relatively prime. ∎

All real numbers which are not rational are called *irrational*. Common examples of irrational numbers are $\sqrt{p}$, where p is a prime number; π, the ratio of the circumference of any given circle to its diameter; and e, the base of the natural logarithms.

In order to fully characterize the real number system, one additional property, called the *completeness axiom*, is needed. This will be discussed in the next section.

EXERCISES

2-8.1. Prove that: (a) The sum of two even integers is even; (b) The sum of two odd integers is even; (c) The sum of an even and an odd integer is odd; (d) The product ab of two integers a and b is odd if and only if both a and b are odd.

2-8.2. Given any two rational numbers a and b, where $a < b$. Prove that there exists a rational number x such that $a < x < b$. [*Hint:* Prove that $a < (a + b)/2 < b$.]

2-8.3. Prove that if a is rational and b is irrational, then $a + b$ is irrational. [*Hint:* Use an indirect proof.]

2-9 COMPLETENESS

Let S denote any non-empty set of real numbers. A real number b, where b is not necessarily in S, is called an *upper bound* for S if $x \leq b$ for every x in S.

EXAMPLE 2-9.1: Let $S = \{1, 3, 5, 7\}$. By the above definition, 10 is an upper bound, and so are 53, $\sqrt{1000}$, and 3π. The upper bound is not unique, since 7 or any number greater than 7 will serve as an upper bound.

Not all subsets of the real numbers have upper bounds.

EXAMPLE 2-9.2: The set $S = \{x \mid x$ is positive$\}$ does not have an upper bound. This fact is established by the following indirect proof: Suppose b is an upper bound for S; then $0 < 1 \leq b$, since $1 \in S$. Now $b + 1 > b > 0$, so $b + 1$ is positive, and therefore in S, and $b + 1$ is greater than the proposed upper bound b. This contradicts the definition of upper bound. $\blacksquare$

Sets which have an upper bound are said to be *bounded above*.

EXAMPLE 2-9.3: Let $S = \{x \mid x = n/(n + 1)$, where n is a positive integer$\}$. S is an infinite set with elements 1/2, 2/3, 3/4, 4/5, etc. Since $n + 1 > n$, we have $n/(n + 1) < 1$, obtained by multiplying the first inequality by the reciprocal of $n + 1$. The number 1 is an upper bound for S.

A real number c is called the *least upper bound* (abbreviated *l.u.b.*)* of a set S if (1) c is an upper bound for S, and (2) for any upper bound b other than c, $b > c$. The notation $c = $ l.u.b. S will mean that c is the least upper bound of the set S. The least upper bound of the set of Example 2-9.1 is 7. We will show later that the l.u.b. of the set of Example 2-9.3 is 1. Note that the l.u.b. need not belong to S; for instance, $1 \notin S$ in Example 2-9.3.

The least upper bound of a set S bounded above is unique. For suppose that b and c are upper bounds for S. If $b \neq c$, then $b < c$ or $c < b$, by Exercise 2-6.1, the law of trichotomy for order relations. Consequently b and c could not both be *least* upper bounds.

We now state the final axiom needed to describe the real number system R, called the *Axiom of Completeness*:

C: If S is any non-empty set of real numbers which has an upper bound in R, then S has a least upper bound in R.

The real number system can be precisely described as a *complete ordered field*.

---

* The word *supremum* (abbreviated *sup*) is often used in place of "least upper bound".

Some important theorems which are usually associated with the axiom of completeness follow.

THEOREM 2-9.1: (*The Archimedean Principle*) If b and c are real numbers and if $c > 0$, then there exists a natural number n such that $nc > b$.

Proof: (Indirect) Suppose there exist real numbers b and c where $c > 0$ and $nc \leq b$ for every natural number n. Then b is an upper bound for the set $S = \{x \mid x = nc$ where n is a natural number$\}$. By the Axiom of Completeness, there exists a real number a where $a = $ l.u.b. S. Since $a - c < a$, it must be true that $a - c$ is *not* an upper bound for S, and hence there exists an element $nc \in S$ such that $nc > a - c$. But this implies $(n + 1)c > a$. Now, since $(n + 1)c$ also belongs to S, this last inequality contradicts the assumption that a is an upper bound for S. ∎

COROLLARY 2-9.1: For every real number b, there exists a positive integer n such that $n > b$. (Note: This is equivalent to the statement: "The set of natural numbers is unbounded above.")

Proof: Let $c = 1$ in Theorem 2-9.1. ∎

COROLLARY 2-9.2: For every real number b, there exists an integer m such that $m < b$.

Proof: By Corollary 2-9.1, there exists an integer n such that $n > -b$; hence $-n < b$; let $m = -n$. ∎

COROLLARY 2-9.3: For every positive real number b, there exists a natural number n such that $1/n < b$.

Proof: By Corollary 2-9.1, there exists a natural number n such that $n > 1/b$. Multiplying both sides of this inequality by $n^{-1}b$, it becomes $1/n < b$. ∎

THEOREM 2-9.2: Given any real number x, there exists an integer k such that $x - 1 \leq k < x$.

Proof: By Corollaries 2-9.1 and 2-9.2, there exist integers m and n such that $m < x < n$. Choose the largest integer k from the finite collection $m,\ m + 1,\ m + 2, \ldots, n$, such that $k < x$. Thus $k + 1 \geq x$. Consequently, $k \geq x - 1$. This proves the theorem. ∎

THEOREM 2-9.3: (*The Rational Density Theorem*) If a and b are any two real numbers with $a < b$, then there exists a rational number r such that $a < r < b$.

Proof: By Corollary 2-9.3, there exists a natural number n such that $1/n < b - a$, or equivalently, $a < b - 1/n$. By Theorem 2-9.2, there exists an integer k such that $nb - 1 \leq k < nb$; hence $b - 1/n \leq k/n < b$. Combining the appropriate inequalities we obtain $a < b - 1/n \leq k/n < b$. Let $r = k/n$; then $a < r < b$. ∎

Theorem 2-9.3 establishes the fact that any real number b can be approximated as closely as we wish by a rational number. More precisely, given any positive number ε, there exists a rational number r such that $b - \varepsilon < r < b$.

THEOREM 2-9.4: Let b denote any real number and let $S = \{x \mid x$ is a rational number and $x < b\}$; then $b = $ l.u.b. S.

Proof: Obviously, b is *an* upper bound for S. Let $c = $ l.u.b. S; if $c < b$ then, by Theorem 2-9.3, there exists a rational number r such that $c < r < b$. But $r < b$ implies that $r \in S$ and contradicts the assumption that c is an upper bound for S. Therefore $c = b$. ∎

THEOREM 2-9.5: If a and b are real numbers and $a > 1$, then there exists a natural number n such that $a^n > b$. (Compare this statement with Theorem 2-9.1.)

Proof: (Indirect) Suppose $a^n \leq b$ for all natural numbers n. Then the set $S = \{x \mid x = a^n$ where n is a natural number$\}$ is bounded above. By the completeness axiom, there exists a real number $c = $ l.u.b. S. Now $c < ac$, or equivalently, $c/a < c$, since $a > 1$. Also, there must be an element a^n in S such that $a^n > c/a$, since c/a is less than the l.u.b. S. Hence $a^{n+1} > c$. But $a^{n+1} \in S$; this contradicts the assumption that c is an upper bound. The assumption that $a^n \leq b$ must be abandoned, and the theorem holds. ∎

The following corollary is useful in a discussion of decimal representation of real numbers:

COROLLARY 2-9.4: The powers of 10, that is, the set $S = \{x \mid x = 10^n$ where n is a natural number$\}$, is unbounded above.

Proof: This statement is a special case of Theorem 2-9.5, where $a = 10$. ∎

Lower bounds and greatest lower bounds are defined in a manner similar to their counterparts, the upper bounds and least upper bounds. Let S denote any non-empty set of real numbers. A real number b, where b is not necessarily in S, is called a *lower bound* for S if $x \geq b$ for every $x \in S$. A real number c is called the *greatest lower bound* of S (abbreviated g.l.b. and written $c = $ g.l.b. $S)^*$ if (1) c is a lower bound for S and (2) for any lower bound b other than c, $b < c$.

A set S is said to be *bounded* if there exists an upper bound and a lower bound for S.

We now return to Example 2-9.3 of this section and consider the set $S = \{x \mid x = n/(n+1)$ where n is a positive integer$\}$. As was observed, 1 is an upper bound for S.

Claim: $1 = $ l.u.b. S.

Proof: (Indirect) Suppose that $c = $ l.u.b. S and $c < 1$. Then there exists a natural number k such that $1/k < 1 - c$, by Corollary 2-9.3. Hence $c < 1 - 1/k = (k-1)/k$. But this means that c is less than an element of S. (If $k = 1$, then c is less than all elements of S.) This contradicts the assumption that c is an upper bound of S. Thus $c = 1$. ▍

EXERCISES

2-9.1. Give several real numbers which serve as upper bounds, and also several lower bounds, for each of the following sets:
a. $S = \{2, 7, -3, 0, 8\}$.
b. $S = \{x \mid x = n^2 + 2$ where n is a natural number less than 4$\}$.
c. $S = \{x \mid x^2 < 9/4\}$.

2-9.2. Let a and b denote real numbers. Prove that if $0 \le a - b < \varepsilon$ for every positive real number ε, then $a = b$.

2-9.3. Prove that if $c > 0$ and $d > 0$, then there exists a natural number n such that $c/n < d$. [See Corollary 2-9.3.]

2-9.4. If x denotes any real number, prove that there exists a unique integer n such that $n \le x < n + 1$. [*Hint:* Follow the general pattern of the proof of Theorem 2-9.2.]

2-9.5. If S is a non-empty set of real numbers with a lower bound, prove that there exists a greatest lower bound of S. [Outline: Let $T = \{x \mid -x \in S\}$. Prove that if b is a lower bound for S, then $-b$ is an upper bound for T. Use the Axiom of Completeness to obtain a number $c = $ l.u.b. T. Then prove that $-c = $ g.l.b. S.]

2-9.6. Prove that the greatest lower bound of a given set S bounded below is unique.

2-9.7. Prove that if $c = $ g.l.b. S and $d > c$, then there exists an element $x \in S$ such that $x < d$.

---

* The word *infimum* (abbreviated *inf*) is often used in place of "greatest lower bound".

2-9.8.   Let $S = \{x \mid x = (3n + 2)/n$ where n is a positive integer$\}$. Prove that (a) $5 = $ l.u.b. S, and (b) $3 = $ g.l.b. S.

2-9.9.   If a and b are any two real numbers where $a < b$, prove that there exists an irrational number c such that $a < c < b$. (Irrational Density Theorem.) [*Hint:* By Exercise 2-8.3 and Theorem 2-8.1, all real numbers of the form $\sqrt{2} + r$ are irrational if r is rational. Use Theorem 2-9.3 to prove that $a < \sqrt{2} + r < b$ for some rational number r.]

2-9.10. Let b denote a positive real number. Prove that there exists a natural number n such that $1/10^n < b$. [*Hint:* This follows easily from Corollary 2-9.4.]

2-9.11. Prove that for any two real numbers a and b, where $a < b$, there exists a rational number $k/10^n$ where k is an integer and n is a natural number, such that $a < k/10^n < b$. [*Hint:* Use Problem 2-9.10 and Theorem 2-9.2. Follow a pattern of proof similar to Theorem 2-9.3, replacing n by 10^n.]

Remark: Rational numbers which take the form $k/10^n$ as described in Exercise 2-9.11 above are called *decimal fractions*. Exercise 2-9.11 stipulates that each real number c can be approximated as closely as we wish by a decimal fraction; that is, given any positive number ε, there exists a decimal fraction $k/10^n$ such that $c - \varepsilon < k/10^n < c$.

2-10 CONSTRUCTION OF DECIMAL APPROXIMATIONS FOR REAL NUMBERS

Consider a positive rational number of the form

$$x = b_n(10)^n + b_{n-1}(10)^{n-1} + \cdots + b_1(10) + b_0 + \frac{a_1}{10} + \frac{a_2}{10^2} + \cdots + \frac{a_m}{10^m}$$

where n, m, a_i, b_i are natural numbers, and $0 \le a_i \le 9, 0 \le b_i \le 9$ for all i. A number of this type is most commonly written $x = b_n b_{n-1} \cdots b_1 b_0 . a_1 a_2 \cdots a_m$, and this expression is called a *terminating decimal.**

EXAMPLES:

$$524 = 5(10)^2 + 2(10) + 4;$$

$$20.004 = 2(10) + \frac{4}{10^3};$$

$$3.215 = 3 + \frac{2}{10} + \frac{1}{10^2} + \frac{5}{10^3}.$$

* The positive decimal fractions can be represented in this form.

We will now show how to construct a terminating decimal approximation for any given positive real number c.

There exists an integer b such that $b \leq c < b + 1$ (cf. Exercise 2-9.4). Since

$$b < b + 1/10 < b + 2/10 < \ldots < b + 9/10 < b + 1,$$

there exists an integer a_1, where $0 \leq a_1 \leq 9$, such that

$$b + \frac{a_1}{10} \leq c < b + \frac{(a_1 + 1)}{10}.$$

Since

$$b + \frac{a_1}{10} < b + \frac{a_1}{10} + \frac{1}{10^2} < b + \frac{a_1}{10} + \frac{2}{10^2} < \cdots$$

$$< b + \frac{a_1}{10} + \frac{9}{10^2} < b + \frac{a_1 + 1}{10},$$

there exists an integer a_2, where $0 \leq a_2 \leq 9$, such that

$$b + \frac{a_1}{10} + \frac{a_2}{10^2} \leq c < b + \frac{a_1}{10} + \frac{a_2 + 1}{10^2}.$$

Repeating this process k times, we obtain

$$b + \frac{a_1}{10} + \frac{a_2}{10^2} + \cdots + \frac{a_k}{10^k} \leq c < b + \frac{a_1}{10} + \frac{a_2}{10^2} + \cdots + \frac{a_{k+1} + 1}{10^k}.$$

Therefore

$$0 \leq c - \left(b + \frac{a_1}{10} + \frac{a_2}{10^2} + \cdots + \frac{a_k}{10^k} \right) < 1/10^k.$$

Any desired degree of accuracy can be obtained by taking k large enough.

Since it is conceptually possible to continue the above process indefinitely, we may consider the infinite set

$$S_c = \{ b, \ b.a_1, \ b.a_1a_2, \ b.a_1a_2a_3, \ \cdots \}.$$

THEOREM 2-10.1: $c = $ l.u.b. S_c.

Proof: c is an upper bound for S_c since, by construction, $b.a_1a_2a_3 \cdots a_k \leq c$ for all k. Let d be any real number less than c. There exists a natural number n such that $1/10^n < c - d$. (Cf. Exercise 2-9.10.) Also, by construction,

$$c - (b.a_1a_2 \cdots a_n) < 1/10^n.$$

Combining the last two inequalities, we have $c - d > c - (b.a_1a_2 \cdots a_n)$ or $d < b.a_1a_2 \cdots a_n$. Hence d is not an upper bound for S_c. ∎

The statement "*c* equals the *unending decimal* (or *non-terminating decimal*) $b.a_1a_2a_3 \cdots$" is defined to mean $c = $ l.u.b. S_c. Thus, Theorem 2-10.1 can be restated: "Every real number $c > 0$ can be expressed as an unending decimal." Conversely, every such unending decimal must represent a real number since $b.a_1a_2a_3 \cdots$ is bounded above by $b + 1$ and hence, by the completeness axiom, there exists a least upper bound of the set $\{b, b.a_1, b.a_1a_2, b.a_1a_2a_3, \cdots\}$.

To represent a negative real number d by a decimal expansion, we note that $-d > 0$. Hence $-d$ can be expressed in the form $b.a_1a_2a_3 \cdots$; we therefore write $d = -(b.a_1a_2a_3 \cdots)$.

EXERCISE

2-10.1. Prove that the first four elements of $S_{\sqrt{2}}$ are 1, 1.4, 1.41, 1.414. [*Hint:* Verify that $1 < \sqrt{2} < 2$, $1.4 < \sqrt{2} < 1.5$, etc., using Exercise 2-6.13.]

2-11 REPEATING DECIMALS

Some decimal expansions eventually establish a pattern of repetition, such as 4.3333 ... or 13.1250000 ... or .215215 .... In this section we will show that all such repeating decimals represent rational numbers.

The sum $a + ar + ar^2 + \ldots + ar^n$, where a and r are real numbers and n is a natural number, is called a geometric series.

THEOREM 2-11.1: If $r \neq 1$, then

$$a + ar + ar^2 + \cdots + ar^n = \frac{a(1 - r^{n+1})}{1 - r}.$$

Proof: Let $x = a + ar + ar^2 + \ldots + ar^n$; then

$$xr = ar + ar^2 + ar^3 + \ldots + ar^{n+1}.$$

Subtract the second expression from the first to obtain

$$x - xr = a - ar^{n+1};$$

hence

$$x(1 - r) = a(1 - r^{n+1}) \quad \text{or} \quad x = \frac{a(1 - r^{n+1})}{1 - r}. \quad \blacksquare$$

THEOREM 2-11.2: If $a > 0$ and $0 < r < 1$, then

$$\frac{a}{1 - r} = \text{l.u.b.} \left\{ x \,\middle|\, x = \frac{a(1 - r^{n+1})}{(1 - r)} \quad \text{where } n \text{ is a natural number} \right\}.$$

Proof:

$$\frac{a(1 - r^{n+1})}{1 - r} = \frac{a}{1 - r} - \frac{ar^{n+1}}{1 - r}.$$

Since

$$\frac{ar^{n+1}}{1 - r} > 0,$$

the rational number

$$\frac{a}{1 - r}$$

is an upper bound. Let d be any real number such that

$$d < \frac{a}{1 - r} \ ;$$

then $a - d(1 - r) > 0$. Since

$$\frac{1}{r} > 1,$$

there exists a natural number n such that

$$\frac{1}{r^n} > \frac{ar}{a - d(1 - r)}, \qquad \text{(Theorem 2-9.5)}.$$

It follows that

$$r^{n+1} < \frac{a - d(1 - r)}{a} = 1 - d\left(\frac{1 - r}{a}\right).$$

Consequently,

$$d\left(\frac{1 - r}{a}\right) < 1 - r^{n+1} \quad \text{or} \quad d < \frac{a(1 - r^{n+1})}{1 - r}.$$

Hence any number d less than $a/(1 - r)$ is not an upper bound. ∎

Theorem 2-11.2 is often stated as follows: "If $a > 0$ and $0 < r < 1$, then $a/(1 - r) = a + ar + ar^2 + \ldots$". It should be noted, however, that we do not claim to be able to find the sum of infinitely many numbers, but only to find the least upper bound for all finite sums of the form

$$a + ar + ar^2 + \ldots + ar^n$$

for any given positive real numbers a and $r < 1$.

EXAMPLE 2-11.1: The unending decimal 3.3333 ... may be written in the form $3 + 3/10 + 3/10^2 + 3/10^3 + \ldots$. But this is a geometric series with $a = 3$, and $r = 1/10$. Hence

$$3.3333 \ldots = \frac{3}{1 - 1/10} = \frac{30}{9}.$$

EXAMPLE 2-11.2: The unending decimal 5.7141414 . . . may be written

$$5 + .7 + .014 + .00014 + .0000014 + \ldots$$
$$= 5 + 7/10 + 14/10^3 + 14/10^5 + 14/10^7 + \ldots.$$

Ignoring for the moment $5 + 7/10$, we have a geometric series with $a = 14/10^3$ and $r = 1/10^2$. Hence

$$5.7141414 \ldots = 5 + \frac{7}{10} + \frac{14/10^3}{1 - 1/10^2} = 5657/990.$$

Since every repeating decimal expansion represents a rational number, the irrational numbers must be represented by unending decimals which do not establish a fixed pattern of repetition.

Note: In many areas of modern mathematical theory and application it is essential to consider random digits or random numbers. A succession of random digits could be generated by a ten-sided die, with faces numbered from 0 through 9, each of the faces having an equal chance of being uppermost on any roll of the die. It has been shown that the unending decimal expansions of certain irrational numbers meet the usual (imperfect) tests for successions of random digits. In such expansions, no single digit can be predicted from those that precede it. Successive digit pairs, digit triples, etc., are also random.

EXERCISES

2-11.1. Find the rational number represented by each of the following repeating decimals:

   a. 4.444 . . .   d. .00757575 . . .
   b. 32.121212 . . .   e. .125000000 . . .
   c. .603603603 . . .   f. 2.99999 . . .

   [Note that the decimal in the part f is not obtainable by the construction given; nevertheless, the set $S = \{2, 2.9, 2.99, \ldots\}$ has a least upper bound.]

2-11.2. Find decimal expansions for each of the following rational numbers:

   a. 3/7   c. 16/3   e. 17/99
   b. $15\frac{1}{2}$ d. 2/9   f. 3/16

2-11.3. Prove that every real number has a unique decimal expansion not ending in all zeros.

2-12 GEOMETRIC REPRESENTATION OF THE REAL NUMBERS

It is customary to identify the real numbers with the points on a line L by the following technique: select any point on L as the *origin* or *zero-point* and any other (nearby) point as the point "1". The unit of measure is given by the line segment from 0 to 1. With each real number x we identify a point on L of distance $|x|$ from the origin, such that the point is on the same side of the origin as 1 if $x > 0$ and on the opposite side if $x < 0$.

From the axioms of Euclidean Geometry, it is possible to prove that each real number corresponds to precisely one point, and conversely, each point corresponds to exactly one real number. Because of this, the words "real number" and "point" are often used interchangeably and the line with this identification is called the *real line*, or *real number line*, or *real axis*.

Given any two points a and b of the real line, where $a < b$. The set of all points between a and b is called an *interval from a to b*; a and b are called the *endpoints* of the interval. An interval may or may not contain the endpoints. We define

$$[a,b] = \{x \mid a \leq x \leq b\}$$
$$(a,b) = \{x \mid a < x < b\}$$
$$[a,b) = \{x \mid a \leq x < b\}$$
$$(a,b] = \{x \mid a < x \leq b\}$$

The set $[a,b]$ is called a *closed interval*; the set (a,b) is called an *open interval*; the remaining sets are sometimes called *half-open intervals*. General definitions of closed set and open set will be provided later.

3

Functions
and
Relations

This chapter deals primarily with the concept of function. Before introducing this concept, several preliminary ideas must be developed.

3-1 CARTESIAN PRODUCTS

Let A and B denote any two non-empty sets. The *cartesian product* of A and B, written $A \times B$, is the set of all ordered pairs (x,y) where $x \in A$ and $y \in B$. In symbols, $A \times B = \{(x,y) \mid x \in A \text{ and } y \in B\}$. The symbol x is called the *first element* of the pair, and y is called the *second element*; the first element must belong to A and the second element must belong to B.

EXAMPLE 3-1.1: If $A = \{a, b, c, d\}$ and $B = \{1, 2, 3\}$, then $A \times B$ consists of the twelve elements $(a,1)$, $(a,2)$, $(a,3)$, $(b,1)$, $(b,2)$, $(b,3)$, $(c,1)$, $(c,2)$, $(c,3)$, $(d,1)$, $(d,2)$, and $(d,3)$. Here, $(a,1) \in A \times B$, but $(1,a) \notin A \times B$.

3-2 RELATIONS

Any non-empty subset R of a cartesian product $A \times B$ is called a *relation from A to B*. If $(x,y) \in R$, we often write xRy and state "x is related to y".

36

A relation from A to A, that is, a given subset of $A \times A$, is called a *relation on A*.

EXAMPLE 3-2.1: Let $A = \{1, 2, 3\}$ and $B = \{1, 2, 3, 4\}$. Define $R = \{(x,y) \mid x > y\}$. Then $R = \{(2,1), (3,1), (3,2)\}$.

EXAMPLE 3-2.2: Let $A = \{1, 2, 3, 4\}$ and $B = \{1, 2, 3, 4, 5\}$. Define $R = \{(x,y) \mid$ the quotient $(5x + 1)/(2y + 1)$ is an integer.}. Then $R = \{(1,1), (2,5), (4,1), (4,3)\}$.

EXAMPLE 3-2.3: Let A denote the set of all real numbers. Define $R = \{(x,y) \mid 4x^2 + 9y^2 \le 36\}$. R is a *relation on A*.

Like any other set, a relation is defined by a property. Relations which have only a few elements are often tabulated; in this case, the tabulation itself is regarded as a defining property.

Some relations can be conveniently illustrated by diagrams. We shall show two methods of accomplishing this.

Method I: If sets A and B have a small number of elements, we tabulate A and B in vertical columns and connect related elements by line segments. Example 3-2.2 above is illustrated by the diagram in Figure 3-2.1.

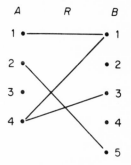

Figure 3-2.1

Method II: (Plane Analytic Geometry) If R is a relation from A to B, where A and B denote subsets of real numbers, then each element (x,y) of R is identified with a point in the plane, as illustrated in Figure 3-2.2. The *graph of R* is the totality of all points identified with elements (x,y) in R. The graph of the relation given in Example 3-2.3 is an ellipse centered at the origin, together with all points inside the ellipse (Figure 3-2.3).

The *domain* of a relation R is the set of all first elements (or first coordinates) of the pairs (x,y) which belong to R. The *range* of R is the set of

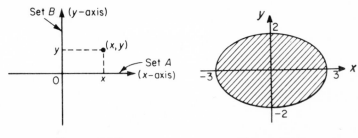

Figure 3-2.2   Figure 3-2.3

all second coordinates. Formally, Domain $R = \{x \mid \text{for some } y, (x,y) \in R\}$, and Range $R = \{y \mid \text{for some } x, (x,y) \in R\}$. In Example 3-2.1, Domain $R = \{2, 3\}$ and Range $R = \{1, 2\}$; in Example 3-2.2, Domain $R = \{1, 2, 4\}$, and Range $R = \{1, 3, 5\}$; and in Example 3-2.3, Domain $R = \{x \mid -3 \leq x \leq 3\}$, and Range $R = \{y \mid -2 \leq y \leq 2\}$.

3-3 FUNCTIONS

A refinement of the general concept of relation is the notion of function. A relation from A to B is called a *function* if (1) Domain $R = A$ and (2) whenever $(x,y) \in R$ and $(x,z) \in R$, then $y = z$. An equivalent definition is: "A function from A to B is a relation which associates *each element* of A with *one and only one element* of B."

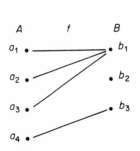

Figure 3-3.1

The letters f, g, h, F, G, and H, instead of R, are usually reserved to denote functions. The notation $f: A \to B$ means f is a function from A to B.

EXAMPLE 3-3.1: Consider sets $A = \{a_1, a_2, a_3, a_4\}$ and $B = \{b_1, b_2, b_3\}$. Let $f = \{(a_1,b_1), (a_2,b_1), (a_3,b_1), (a_4,b_3)\}$. The relation f is a function, since every element of A is related to exactly one element of B (Figure 3-3.1).

EXAMPLE 3-3.2: Using the same sets A and B as in Example 3-3.1, the relation R depicted in Figure 3-3.2 is not a function from A to B since a_3 is not related to any element of B; hence Domain $R \neq A$.

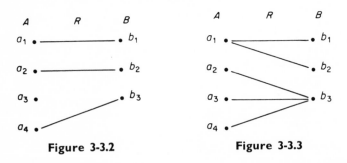

Figure 3-3.2   Figure 3-3.3

EXAMPLE 3-3.3: Again using sets A and B from Example 3-3.1, the relation R in Figure 3-3.3 is not a function from A to B since the element a_1 of A is related to more than one element of B; that is, $(a_1,b_1) \in R$ and $(a_1,b_2) \in R$ but $b_1 \neq b_2$.

EXAMPLE 3-3.4: Let A and B denote the set of all real numbers. The relation $R = \{(x,y) \mid x^2 + y^2 = 1\}$ is not a function from A to B for two reasons: each element of A in the open interval $(-1,1)$ is related to two elements in B; and those elements x in A for which $|x| > 1$ have no corresponding y value at all (Figure 3-3.4).

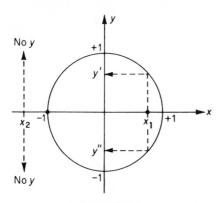

Figure 3-3.4

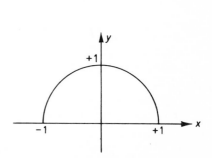

Figure 3-3.5

EXAMPLE 3-3.5: Let $A = \{x \mid x$ is a real number and $-1 \le x \le 1\}$, and let B denote all real numbers. The relation $f = \{(x,y) \mid y = \sqrt{1 - x^2}\}$ (where the symbol $\sqrt[n]{a}$ means the principal nth root of a, in this case the positive square root) is a function from A to B (Figure 3-3.5). Note that the entire set B need not be the range of f. (See also Example 3-3.1.)

EXAMPLE 3-3.6: Given any polynomial $a_0 + a_1 x + a_2 x^2 + \ldots + a_n x^n$, where $a_0, a_1, a_2, \ldots, a_n$ are real numbers. The relation $f = \{(x,y) \mid y = a_0 + a_1 x + a_2 x^2 + \ldots + a_n x^n\}$ is a function from the real line to the real line since every real number x is related to precisely one real number y.

EXAMPLE 3-3.7: Let A be the Euclidean plane. The elements of A can be represented in the form (x,y) where both x and y are real numbers. (We often state "xy-plane" to indicate that this representation will be used.) Let B denote the set of all real numbers, the z-axis in this illustration (Figure 3-3.6). The relation

$$f = \{[(x,y),z] \mid z = 4 - x^2 - y^2\}$$

is a function from A to B since every

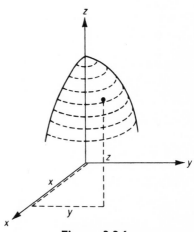

Figure 3-3.6

element (x,y) of A is related to exactly one element of B. The graph of f is a surface, and the diagram requires the three dimensions of Solid Analytic Geometry. This relation is an example of a *function of two variables*.

EXAMPLE 3-3.8: Let A be the xy-plane and let B be the uv-plane. The relation $f = \{[(x,y),(u,v)] \mid u = x - y \text{ and } v = x + y - 1\}$ is a function from plane A to plane B. The graph of such a function would require four dimensions.

3-4 FUNCTIONAL NOTATION

Given any function $f: A \to B$. The notation $f(x) = y$ means that $(x,y) \in f$. The symbol $f(x)$ used by itself designates the element of B that x is related to. In Examples 3-3.7 and 3-3.8, we write $f(x,y) = z$ and $f(x,y) = (u,v)$, respectively. In Example 3-3.5, $f(1/2) = \sqrt{3/4}$; in Example 3-3.7, $f(2,1) = -1$; in Example 3-3.8, $f(4,3) = (1,6)$, etc.

Like any other type of relation, a function need not be defined by a formula; a statement can suffice. However, if a formula (or several formulae) constitutes the defining property, then it is customary to identify the function by the formula only, rather than by the use of set notation. In Examples 3-3.5, 3-3.7, and 3-3.8, we would write $f(x) = \sqrt{1 - x^2}, f(x,y) = 4 - x^2 - y^2$ and $f(x,y) = (x - y, x + y - 1)$, respectively.

3-5 IMAGES

Let $f: S \to T$ be any function, and let A be a subset of S. Define $f(A) = \{y \mid \text{for some } x \text{ in } A, (x,y) \in f\}$, or equivalently, $f(A) = \{y \mid \text{for some } x \text{ in } A, f(x) = y\}$.* We call $f(A)$ the *image* of A in T (Figure 3-5.1).

Suppose now that D is a subset of T. Define $f^{-1}(D) = \{x \mid \text{for some } y \text{ in } D, (x,y) \in f\}$. (Here again, $(x,y) \in f$ is often replaced by $f(x) = y$.)† We call $f^{-1}(D)$ the *inverse image* of D in S (Figure 3-5.2).

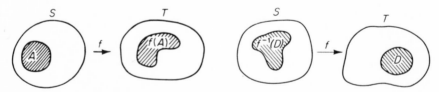

Figure 3-5.1   Figure 3-5.2

EXAMPLE 3-5.1: Let $S = \{s_1, s_2, s_3, s_4\}$ and $T = \{t_1, t_2, t_3\}$. Define $f: S \to T$ by $f(s_1) = t_1$, $f(s_2) = t_1$, $f(s_3) = t_1$, $f(s_4) = t_3$. Then the following

---

* $f(A)$ can also be defined by $f(A) = \{f(x) \mid x \in A\}$.
† $f^{-1}(D)$ can also be defined by $f^{-1}(D) = \{x \mid f(x) \in D\}$.

are true:

If $A = \{s_1, s_2\}$, then $f(A) = \{t_1\}$
If $A = \{s_3, s_4\}$, then $f(A) = \{t_1, t_3\}$
If $D = \{t_1, t_2\}$, then $f^{-1}(D) = \{s_1, s_2, s_3\}$
If $D = \{t_1\}$,   then $f^{-1}(D) = \{s_1, s_2, s_3\}$
If $D = T$,   then $f^{-1}(D) = S$
If $D = \{t_2\}$,   then $f^{-1}(D) = \varnothing$, the null set.

It is evident from these statements that f^{-1} cannot be regarded as a function.

EXAMPLE 3-5.2: Let S and T each be the set of all real numbers. Consider the images of several intervals with respect to the function $f(x) = 6x - x^2$ (Figure 3-5.3). If $A = [0,1]$, then $f(A) =$ [0,5]; if $A = (1,4)$, then $f(A) = (5,9)$; if $D = [0,5]$, then $f^{-1}(D) = [0,1] \cup [5,6]$; and if $D = (5,9]$, then $f^{-1}(D) = (1,5)$.

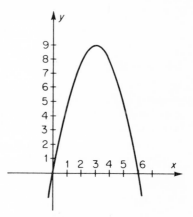

Returning to Example 3-3.8 of the preceding section, let us find the image of the line $x = 2$. It is necessary to substitute 2 for x in the given equations, and eliminate y from the result: $u = 2 - y$, $v = 2 + y - 1$; and adding, $u + v = 3$. Thus, if A is the line $x = 2$, then $f(A)$ is the line $u + v = 3$ (Figure 3-5.4).

Consider again Example 3-3.7. To find the inverse image of the interval [2,3] of the z-axis, we observe that $2 \leq z \leq 3$ and $z = 4 - x^2 - y^2$ together imply that

Figure 3-5.3

$2 \leq 4 - x^2 - y^2 \leq 3$, or, subtracting 4 and multiplying by -1, $2 \geq x^2 + y^2 \geq 1$. Thus, if D is the interval [2,3], then $f^{-1}(D)$ is the set consisting of the circles $x^2 + y^2 = 2$ and $x^2 + y^2 = 1$ and all points between these circles (Figure 3-5.5).

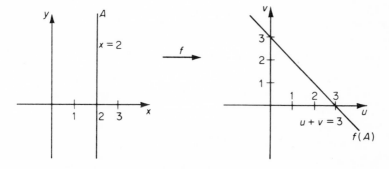

Figure 3-5.4

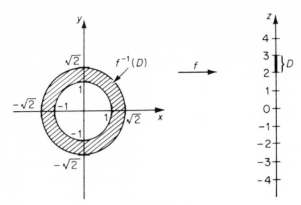

Figure 3-5.5

3-6 SOME BASIC THEOREMS

The following theorems relate to the general concept of function. Assume A and B are subsets of S, and let D and E be subsets of T; let $f: S \to T$ be any function.

THEOREM 3-6.1: $f(A \cap B) \subset f(A) \cap f(B)$.

Proof:	*Reason:*
1. Let $y \in f(A \cap B)$	Arbitrary choice
2. For some $x \in A \cap B$, $(x,y) \in f$	Definition of image
3. $x \in A$ and $x \in B$	Definition of $\cap$
4. $x \in A$ and $(x,y) \in f$ imply $y \in f(A)$	Definition of image
5. $x \in B$ and $(x,y) \in f$ imply $y \in f(B)$	Definition of image
6. $y \in f(A) \cap f(B)$	Definition of $\cap$ ∎

In order to show that in general $f(A \cap B) \neq f(A) \cap f(B)$, we need a specific example. Let $S = \{s_1, s_2, s_3\}$ and $T = \{t_1, t_2\}$; take $A = \{s_1, s_2\}$ and $B = \{s_2, s_3\}$. Define $f: S \to T$ by $f(s_1) = t_1$, $f(s_2) = t_2$, and $f(s_3) = t_1$. Then $f(A \cap B) = \{t_2\}$ while $f(A) \cap f(B) = \{t_1, t_2\}$.

THEOREM 3-6.2: $f^{-1}(D) \cup f^{-1}(E) = f^{-1}(D \cup E)$.

Proof: Part I: To show that $f^{-1}(D) \cup f^{-1}(E) \subset f^{-1}(D \cup E)$.

1. Let $x \in f^{-1}(D) \cup f^{-1}(E)$	Arbitrary choice
2. $x \in f^{-1}(D)$ or $x \in f^{-1}(E)$	Definition of $\cup$
3. For some y in D, $(x,y) \in f$ OR for some y in E, $(x,y) \in f$	Definition of inverse image
4. For some y in $D \cup E$, $(x,y) \in f$	Definition of $\cup$
5. $x \in f^{-1}(D \cup E)$	Definition of inverse image

Part II, to show that $f^{-1}(D \cup E) \subset f^{-1}(D) \cup f^{-1}(E)$, is left as an exercise (Ex. 3-6.8). ∎

THEOREM 3-6.3: $A \subset f^{-1}[f(A)]$.

Proof:	*Reason:*
1. Let $x \in A$	Arbitrary choice
2. For some y in T, $(x,y) \in f$	Definition of function; Domain $f = S$.
3. $x \in A$ and $(x,y) \in f$ imply $y \in f(A)$	Definition of image
4. $y \in f(A)$ and $(x,y) \in f$ imply $x \in f^{-1}[f(A)]$	Definition of inverse image ∎

In general, $A \neq f^{-1}[f(A)]$. Consider the sets $S = \{a_1, a_2, a_3, a_4\}$ and $T = \{b_1, b_2, b_3\}$. Define $f: S \to T$ by $f(a_1) = b_1$, $f(a_2) = b_1$, $f(a_3) = b_1$, and $f(a_4) = b_3$; let $A = \{a_1, a_2\}$; then $f(A) = \{b_1\}$, while $f^{-1}[f(A)] = f^{-1}(\{b_1\}) = \{a_1, a_2, a_3\} \neq A$.

EXERCISES

3-6.1. Tabulate the elements of the following relations from A to B:
   a. $A = \{1, 2, 3, 4\}$, $B = \{1, 2, 3, 4, 5, 6, 7\}$, and $R = \{(x, y) \mid y = x^2 - 3x + 3\}$
   b. $A = \{i, j, k, l, m, n\}$, $B = \{o, p, q, r, s, t\}$, and $R = \{(x, y) \mid "xy"$ is a word in the English language.$\}$
   c. $A = \{1, 2, 3\}$, $B = \{1, 2, 3, 4, 5\}$, and $R = \{(x, y) \mid 5x + 2y$ is a prime number.$\}$

3-6.2. Are any of the relations in Exercise 3-6.1 functions? Explain your answer in each case.

3-6.3. Each of the following formulae defines a relation on the real numbers. Which of them are functions from the x-axis to the y-axis? Explain.
   a. $y^2 + x = 0$ c . $|x| + y = 0$
   b. $y + x^2 = 0$ d. $x + |y| = 0$

3-6.4. Let $S = \{s_1, s_2, s_3, s_4\}$ and $\{t_1, t_2, t_3, t_4\}$. Define $f: S \to T$ by $f = \{(s_1, t_1), (s_2, t_1), (s_3, t_2), (s_4, t_4)\}$. Use Method I to illustrate f, and find the images of the following sets:
   a. $\{s_1, s_3\}$ b. $\{s_1, s_2\}$ c. $\{s_1, s_2, s_4\}$
   Find the inverse images of the following:
   d. $\{t_1\}$ e. $\{t_1, t_2, t_4\}$ f. $\{t_3\}$

3-6.5. Given the function $f(x) = x^2 - 4x + 4$ on the set of real numbers. Graph f (Method II) and find the images of the following intervals: a. [0,1]; b. (0,3);   c. [3,4). Find the inverse images of the following intervals: d. [0,1];   e. (1,2);   f. [−1,0).

In Exercises 3-6.6 through 3-6.13, let $f: S \to T$ be a function; let A and B be subsets of S, and D and E be subsets of T. Prove the following theorems:

3-6.6.   If $A \subset B$, then $f(A) \subset f(B)$.

3-6.7.   If $D \subset E$, then $f^{-1}(D) \subset f^{-1}(E)$.

3-6.8.   Prove Part II of Theorem 3-6.2.

3-6.9. $f(A \cup B) = f(A) \cup f(B)$.

3-6.10. $f^{-1}(D) \cap f^{-1}(E) = f^{-1}(D \cap E)$ [*Hint:* In order to verify that $f^{-1}(D) \cap f^{-1}(E) \subset f^{-1}(D \cap E)$, it is necessary to use the fact that $(x,y) \in f$ and $(x,y') \in f$ imply $y = y'$.]

3-6.11. $f[f^{-1}(D)] \subset D$, and give an example in which $f[f^{-1}(D)] \neq D$. [*Hint:* Again use the fact that $(x,y) \in f$ and $(x,y') \in f$ imply $y = y'$.]

3-6.12. $f(A) - f(B) \subset f(A - B)$, and give an example in which $f(A) - f(B) \neq f(A - B)$. [*Hint:* $y \notin f(B)$ implies that if $(x,y) \in f$, then $x \notin B$ by the definition of image.]

3-6.13. $f^{-1}(D) - f^{-1}(E) = f^{-1}(D - E)$. [*Hint:* State clearly what is meant by $x \notin f^{-1}(E)$, using the definition of inverse image.]

3-6.14. Refer to Example 3-3.8; find the image of the set A illustrated here. [*Hint:* Find the image of the lines $x = 0$, $y = 0$, $x = 1$, and $y = 2$. Assume that the image of the boundary of A is the boundary of $f(A)$.]

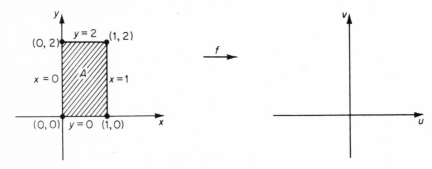

3-6.15. $f(x,y) = y^2 - x$ is a function from the xy-plane to the real line, represented by the z-axis; i.e., $z = y^2 - x$. Find the inverse image $f^{-1}(D)$, where D is the interval $[0,1]$ of the z-axis.

3-7 THE INVERSE OF A RELATION

Given any relation R from A to B, we define $R^{-1} = \{(y,x) \mid (x,y) \in R\}$. The relation R^{-1} from B to A is called the *inverse* of R. Note that $[R^{-1}]^{-1} = R$.

EXAMPLE 3-7.1: Let $A = \{1, 2, 3, 4\}$ and $B = \{4, 6, 9\}$. Define R as $\{(1,4), (2,4), (2,6), (4,6)\}$. Then $R^{-1} = \{(4,1), (4,2), (6,2), (6,4)\}$.

EXAMPLE 3-7.2: Let $R = \{(x,y) \mid x^2 = y\}$ be a relation from the real line to the real line, then $R^{-1} = \{(y,x) \mid x^2 = y\}$.

EXERCISE

3-7.1. Prove that Domain R^{-1} = Range R, and that Range R^{-1} = Domain R.

3-8 ONE-TO-ONE CORRESPONDENCE, CARDINALITY OF SETS

A child who is unable to count can nevertheless determine whether, for example, there are just as many blocks as marbles in his possession. He need only place one marble near one block, another marble near another block, and so on. If it is possible to establish a pairing of marbles and blocks which does not leave an excess of either blocks or marbles, then the pairing itself is called a *one-to-one correspondence*. It is intuitively evident that this is possible only when there are the same number of marbles as blocks.

More generally, let A and B denote any two (possibly infinite) sets. A relation R from A to B is called a *one-to-one* correspondence if (1) R is a function from A to B, and (2) R^{-1} is a function from B to A. Note that the following properties can be derived immediately from this definition: Domain $R = A$; Range $R = B$; if $(x,y) \in R$ and $(x,y') \in R$, then $y = y'$; and, if $(x,y) \in R$ and $(x',y) \in R$, then $x = x'$.

In Examples 3-8.1 and 3-8.2, let A and B be the set of all real numbers, represented by the x-axis and y-axis, respectively.

EXAMPLE 3-8.1: The function $f: A \rightarrow B$, given by $y = x^2$, is not a one-to-one correspondence for two reasons: (1) there are two elements x_1 and x_2 of A related to every $y_0 > 0$, and (2) there is no element of A related to any $y < 0$ in B (Figure 3-8.1).

EXAMPLE 3-8.2: The function $y = x^3$ is a one-to-one correspondence, since for every x there is exactly one y and for every y there is exactly one x satisfying the equation (Figure 3-8.2).

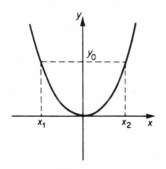

Figure 3-8.1

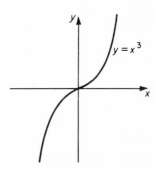

Figure 3-8.2

EXAMPLE 3-8.3: Let A denote the set of positive odd integers and B the set of positive even integers. Then the function $f: A \to B$ defined by $f(n) = n + 1$ is a one-to-one correspondence, since $f^{-1}: B \to A$, given by $f^{-1}(n) = n - 1$, is also a function (Figure 3-8.3).

A: 1   3   5   7   ...

B: 2   4   6   8   ...

Figure 3-8.3

Whenever there exists a one-to-one correspondence from set A to set B, we say that A is *equivalent* to B, and write $A \approx B$.

Properties:
(1) $A \approx A$ for any set A (the *reflexive* property)
(2) If $A \approx B$, then $B \approx A$ (the *symmetric* property)
(3) If $A \approx B$ and $B \approx C$, then $A \approx C$ (the *transitive* property)
Property 1 is evident since the identity function, $f(x) = x$, is a one-to-one correspondence from A to A. Property 2 is established by observing that if $f: A \to B$ is a one-to-one correspondence, then so is $f^{-1}: B \to A$. Property 3 will be assumed for the present. A simple proof will be given in the next section entitled "Composition of Functions" (Theorem 3-9.3).

The statements "A and B have the same *cardinality*" and "A and B have the same number of elements" are used interchangeably with "A is equivalent to B."

A non-empty set is finite if and only if it has the same cardinality as a bounded set $\{1, 2, 3, \ldots, n\}$ of natural numbers. The most basic of the infinite sets is the set of all positive integers, $I = \{1, 2, 3, 4, \ldots\}$. Other infinite sets are: the set of all primes, the set of all integers, the set of all real numbers, the set of all odd numbers, the set of all rational numbers, etc.

One might ask whether all infinite sets have the same cardinality—whether they share the "same degree of infinity", so to speak—or whether some infinite sets are "larger" than others. To answer this and other questions, we shall attempt to "count" the elements of such infinite sets by placing them, if possible, in one-to-one correspondence with the set I of positive integers. It is obvious that we cannot list all the elements of an infinite set and count them one by one, but it may be possible to find a function which relates the two sets in such a way that the function is a one-to-one correspondence. If such a one-to-one correspondence can be established between an infinite set A and the set I of all positive integers, then we shall say that the set A is *enumerable* or *enumerably infinite*.

EXAMPLE 3-8.4: The set B of all even integers is equivalent to I, since the function $f: I \to B$, defined by $f(n) = 2n$ is a one-to-one correspondence (Figure 3-8.4). Thus, when comparing infinite sets, a part may have "just as many" elements as the whole! This property is the basis of a story by David Hilbert (1862–1943), the famous German mathematician:

"Let us imagine a hotel with an infinite number of rooms, all occupied, and new guests who come in to ask for rooms. 'Certainly, gentlemen,' says the proprietor, 'just a minute.' He then moves the occupant of room N1 to N2, the occupant of N2 to N4, the occupant of N3 to N6, and so on. Now the odd-numbered rooms become free, and an infinity of new guests can be accommodated".

Many texts dealing with set theory give the following alternate definition of an infinite set: "A set S is infinite if, and only if, it can be placed in one-to-one correspondence with a proper subset of itself".

I: 1 2 3 4 ...
$\updownarrow$ $\updownarrow$ $\updownarrow$ $\updownarrow$
B: 2 4 6 8 ...

Figure 3-8.4

EXAMPLE 3-8.5: Let J be the set of all integers. Define $f: J \to I$ by $f(n) = 2n$ for all $n > 0$ and $f(n) = -2n + 1$ for $n \leq 0$. The function is a one-to-one correspondence from J to I (Figure 3-8.5).

I: 1 2   3 4   5 6   7 ...
$\updownarrow$ $\updownarrow$ $\updownarrow$ $\updownarrow$ $\updownarrow$ $\updownarrow$ $\updownarrow$
J: 0 1 -1 2 -2 3 -3 ...

Figure 3-8.5

Several theorems pertaining to infinite sets and their enumerability will now be proved. Some of them have been referred to already.

THEOREM 3-8.1: The number of primes is infinite.

Proof: (We assume that every natural number greater than one which is not prime can be represented as a product $P_1 \cdot P_2 \cdot P_3 \cdot \ldots \cdot P_n$ of prime integers P_i.) An indirect approach is needed, since we obviously cannot list all the primes if there really are infinitely many of them, and furthermore, there is no known formula which relates successive primes to successive integers. Assume that there is but a finite number of primes, and hence a last (largest) prime, P. Let N be the product of all primes; i.e., $N = 2 \cdot 3 \cdot 5 \cdot 7 \cdot 11 \cdot \ldots \cdot P$; now consider $N + 1 = (2 \cdot 3 \cdot 5 \cdot 7 \cdot 11 \cdot \ldots \cdot P) + 1$. Division of $N + 1$ by r, where r is one of the prime numbers 2, 3, 5, ..., P leaves a remainder of $1/r$. Therefore $N + 1$ itself must be a prime larger than P. This contradicts the assumption that P is the largest prime. ∎

The set of all primes can be placed in one-to-one correspondence with I as follows: Define $f: I \to \{x \mid x \text{ is a prime}\}$ by $f(1) = 2, f(2) = 3, f(3) = 5, f(4) = 7$, and in general $f(n) =$ the smallest prime greater than $f(n - 1)$.*

One of the unsolved problems in mathematics relates to "twin primes". Two primes are called *twin primes* if the absolute value of their difference is

---

* The natural number 1 is not regarded as a prime in many texts.

two; i.e., two primes, p and q, are twin primes in case $|p - q| = 2$. Examples: 3 and 5; 5 and 7; 11 and 13; 17 and 19; etc. Mathematicians have been unable either to prove or to disprove that there exist infinitely many twin primes.

THEOREM 3-8.2: There exists a one-to-one correspondence $f: I \to T$ from the positive integers to the set T of all positive rational numbers.

Proof: Since by definition every element of T can be written in the form a/b, where a and b are natural numbers, consider the following arrangement in which the nth row consists of all fractions with denominator n and numerators successively written 1, 2, 3, ..., and the mth column consists of all fractions with numerator m and denominators 1, 2, 3, ...:

$$1/1 \to 2/1 \quad 3/1 \to 4/1 \quad 5/1 \to 6/1 \quad 7/1 \to \ldots$$

$$1/2 \quad 2/2 \quad 3/2 \quad 4/2 \quad 5/2 \quad 6/2 \quad 7/2 \ldots$$

$$1/3 \quad 2/3 \quad 3/3 \quad 4/3 \quad 5/3 \quad 6/3 \quad 7/3 \ldots$$

$$1/4 \quad 2/4 \quad 3/4 \quad 4/4 \quad 5/4 \quad 6/4 \quad 7/4 \ldots$$

$$1/5 \quad 2/5 \quad 3/5 \quad 4/5 \quad 5/5 \quad 6/5 \quad 7/5 \ldots$$

$$1/6 \quad 2/6 \quad 3/6 \quad 4/6 \quad 5/6 \quad 6/6 \quad 7/6 \ldots$$

$$1/7 \quad 2/7 \quad 3/7 \quad 4/7 \quad 5/7 \quad 6/7 \quad 7/7 \ldots$$

By following the indicated path and omitting those fractions which have values already encountered along the path, we define the following function:

$$f(1) = 1, f(2) = 2, f(3) = 1/2, f(4) = 1/3,$$
$$f(5) = 3, f(6) = 4, f(7) = 3/2, f(8) = 2/3$$
$$f(9) = 1/4, f(10) = 1/5, \text{ etc.}$$

An arbitrary rational number a/b is located in the ath column and bth row of this arrangement, and therefore is reached after finitely many steps of the type listed above. This means that some positive integer n is associated with each rational number a/b. ∎

THEOREM 3-8.3: The set of all real numbers between zero and 1 is not enumerable.

Proof: (Indirect) Recalling that every real number can be represented as a non-terminating decimal, (some are repeating, others are non-repeating), let us assume that the real numbers between 0 and 1 constitute an enumerable set; that is, there exists a one-to-one correspondence $f: I \rightarrow \{x \mid x \text{ is real and } 0 < x < 1\}$. Symbolically,

$$f(1) = 0.a_{11}a_{12}a_{13}a_{14} \ldots$$
$$f(2) = 0.a_{21}a_{22}a_{23}a_{24} \ldots$$
$$f(3) = 0.a_{31}a_{32}a_{33}a_{34} \ldots$$
$$f(4) = 0.a_{41}a_{42}a_{43}a_{44} \ldots$$

$$\begin{array}{cc} \cdot & \cdot \\ \cdot & \cdot \\ \cdot & \cdot \end{array}$$

Each a_{ij} is an integer (a digit in the decimal expansion) so that $0 \leq a_{ij} \leq 9$. (NOTE: In cases where two representations are possible, such as $1/4 = .249999 \ldots = .250000 \ldots$ and $4/5 = .7999 \ldots = .8000 \ldots$, choose the repetition of 9's rather than 0's in each case. This establishes uniqueness of representation.) Such a list might look like

$$f(1) = 0.3582178423 \ldots$$
$$f(2) = 0.7210000392 \ldots$$
$$f(3) = 0.9090909090 \ldots$$
$$f(4) = 0.4734734734 \ldots$$
$$f(5) = 0.2613999999 \ldots$$

$$\begin{array}{cc} \cdot & \cdot \\ \cdot & \cdot \\ \cdot & \cdot \end{array}$$

In order to obtain the desired contradiction, we will show that there exists a real number c such that $0 < c < 1$, and $c \notin f(I)$. Consider $c = 0.c_1c_2c_3c_4 \ldots$, constructed as follows: let c_1 be any integer from 1 through 9 not equal to a_{11}; let c_2 be any integer from 1 through 9 not equal to a_{22}; in general, let c_i be any integer from 1 through 9 not equal to a_{ii}. By construction, c differs from $f(1)$ in the first decimal place; c differs from $f(2)$ in the second decimal place; and, in general, c differs from $f(i)$ in the ith decimal place. Hence, $f(I)$ fails to include c, and so we reject the assumption that the real numbers between 0 and 1 are enumerable. ∎

Because of the correspondence between real numbers and points on a line, Theorem 3-8.3 can be restated as follows: "The set of points in the open interval (0,1) of the real line is not enumerable".

For convenience, the symbol $\aleph_0$, read "aleph-null", is used to designate the cardinality of enumerably infinite sets. The symbol $\aleph_1$, read "aleph-one", designates the cardinality of the subset (0,1) of real numbers, as well as those infinite sets which can be put into one-to-one correspondence with $(0,1)$.

THEOREM 3-8.4: There exists a one-to-one correspondence from the open interval $(0,1)$ to the entire real line L.

Proof: Define $f: (0,1) \to L$ by $f(x) = (x - 1/2)/(x - x^2)$. (See Figure 3-8.6.) Note that if $0 < x_1 < x_2 < 1$, then $f(x_1) < f(x_2)$. ▌

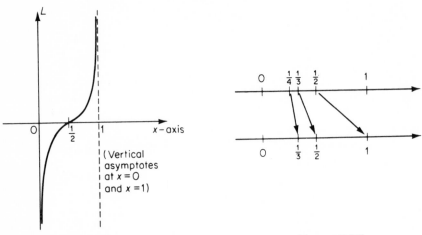

Figure 3-8.6   **Figure 3-8.7**

THEOREM 3-8.5: The intervals $(0,1)$ and $(0,1]$ have the same cardinality.

Proof: Let A represent the set of all fractions of the form $1/n$, where n is an integer greater than 1. Define $f: (0,1) \to (0,1]$ as follows: if $x \in (0,1) - A$, then $f(x) = x$; $f(1/2) = 1$, $f(1/3) = 1/2$, $f(1/4) = 1/3$; and in general, $f(1/n) = 1/(n - 1)$ for every integer $n > 1$. This is a one-to-one correspondence (see Figure 3-8.7). ▌

THEOREM 3-8.6: Let S be the subset of the xy-plane defined by $S = \{(x,y) \mid 0 < x \le 1 \text{ and } 0 < y \le 1\}$. There exists a one-to-one correspondence from S to the interval $(0,1]$ of the z-axis.

Proof: Represent each of the numbers x, y, and z by a non-terminating decimal. To insure the uniqueness of representation, use repetition of 9's rather than 0's whenever two representations are possible; e.g., use $1/2 = .4999\ldots$ instead of $.5000\ldots$. We now show how $f: S \to (0,1]$ is defined. Suppose $x = 0.34001207\ldots$ and $y = 0.02100996\ldots$. Write $x = 0.3\ 4\ 001\ 2\ 07\ldots$ and $y = 0.02\ 1\ 009\ 9\ 6\ldots$ and define

$$z = 0.3\ 02\ 4\ 1\ 001\ 009\ 2\ 9\ 07\ 6\ldots = 0.3024100100929076\ldots$$

In general, for every $(x,y) \in S$, mark off subsets of digits in the decimal expansions of x and y by going up to the next non-zero digit and then alternating these portions (starting with the first part of x) to obtain the decimal expansion for z. Thus $f: S \rightarrow (0,1]$ is a well-defined function. Conversely, if z is given, we can reconstruct x and y. Therefore f^{-1}: $(0,1] \rightarrow S$ is also a function. ∎

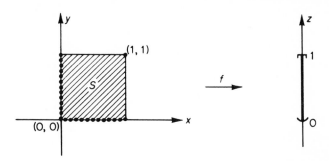

Attention is now given to the construction of sets with higher orders of cardinality than $\aleph_1$. The usual approach is to begin with a study of subsets. Given any set A, let $S(A)$ represent the collection of all subsets of A, and let $T(A)$ denote the set of all functions $f: A \rightarrow \{0, 1\}$—from A to the set consisting of the two elements 0 and 1.

THEOREM 3-8.7: $S(A)$ is equivalent to $T(A)$.

Proof: For each element $s \in S(A)$, let $f_s: A \rightarrow \{0, 1\}$ be defined as follows: $f_s(x) = 1$ if $x \in s$, $f_s(x) = 0$ if $x \notin s$. For example, if $A = \{a_1, a_2, a_3, a_4, a_5\}$ and $s = \{a_1, a_2, a_3\}$, then $f_s(a_1) = 1$, $f_s(a_2) = 1$, $f_s(a_3) = 1$, $f_s(a_4) = 0$, and $f_s(a_5) = 0$. By this correspondence, each subset s of A is related to exactly one function in $T(A)$. Conversely, each function $f: A \rightarrow \{0, 1\}$ has precisely one subset $s = \{x \mid x \in A$ and $f(x) = 1\}$ related to it. Thus, $H: S(A) \rightarrow T(A)$, defined by $H(s) = f_s$, is a one-to-one correspondence. ∎

COROLLARY 3-8.1: If A is a finite set with n elements, then the number of subsets of A is 2^n.

Proof: Consider the number of functions $f: A \rightarrow \{0, 1\}$. For each element $a \in A$ there are two possibilities: either $f(a) = 0$ or $f(a) = 1$. Therefore there are 2^n possible ways of defining a function from the n elements of A to $\{0, 1\}$. ∎

For any infinite set A, it is clear that there are at least as many subsets of A as elements in A; (consider the subsets consisting of only one element of A). The next theorem establishes the fact that $S(A)$ has a significantly larger number of elements than A.

THEOREM 3-8.8: For any set A, the set of all subsets $S(A)$ is *not* equivalent to A.

Proof: We will show that $T(A)$ is not equivalent to A. (cf. Theorem 3-8.7), using an indirect proof. Suppose there exists a one-to-one correspondence $H: A \to T(A)$. For each element $a \in A$, let f_a represent the corresponding element of $T(A)$; i.e., $H(a) = f_a$. We will obtain a contradiction by showing that there exists a function g in $T(A)$ which does not belong to the range of H. Consider $g: A \to \{0, 1\}$ constructed as follows: for each $a \in A$ let $g(a) = 0$ if $f_a(a) = 1$, $g(a) = 1$ if $f_a(a) = 0$. Thus, for any f_a in the range of H, g differs from f_a since $g(a) \neq f_a(a)$. The assumption that H is a one-to-one correspondence is therefore incorrect. ∎

Whenever two sets A and B have the properties (1) $A \subset B$ and (2) A is not equivalent to B, we say that the cardinality of B is of *higher order* than the cardinality of A.

COROLLARY 3-8.2: For any set A, there exists a set B with a higher order of cardinality than A.

Proof: Let B represent the set of all subsets of A where each subset $\{a\}$ containing only one element is replaced by the element a itself. (This substitution is necessary because a *set* containing one element should be distinguished from the *element*.) ∎

Corollary 3-8.2 states that there does not exist a *highest* order of cardinality. Mathematicians assume that it is legitimate to regard well-defined sets as elements of sets; however, such terms as "the set of all sets" are avoided since they lead to contradictions—with Corollary 3-8.2, for example.

EXERCISES

3-8.1.   For the function f in the proof of Theorem 3-8.6, find $f(1/4,1/3)$; $f(1/2,1)$; $f(1,1)$; $f(1/11,1/9)$; $f(.63072517008\ldots, .202130074091\ldots)$.

3-8.2.   Using the function f of Theorem 3-8.6, reconstruct x and y, given
 a. $z = 0.73221090034085502\ldots$;   b. $z = 0.12302102302102302\ldots$

3-8.3.   Consider the set $A = \{a_1, a_2, a_3\}$. List all subsets of A and tabulate the functions corresponding to each subset according to the rule given in the proof of Theorem 3-8.7.

3-8.4.   Show that the closed interval $[0,1]$ is equivalent to $(0,1)$ (cf. Theorem 3-8.5).

3-8.5.   Prove that the set of all points in the cube $C = \{(x,y,z) \mid 0 < x \leq 1, 0 < y \leq 1, 0 < z \leq 1\}$ is equivalent to the interval $(0,1]$ of real numbers. (Cf. Theorem 3-8.6.)

3-8.6. Find a one-to-one correspondence between the intervals
a. $(2,7)$ and $(0,1)$ b. $(-2,3)$ and $(0,1)$
c. (a,b) and $(0,1)$

3-8.7. Find a function $(u,v) = f(x,y)$ which is a one-to-one correspondence from the square $S = \{(x,y) \mid 0 \le x < 1, 0 \le y < 1\}$ of the xy-plane to the entire first quadrant $Q = \{(u,v) \mid 0 \le u, \ 0 \le v\}$ of the uv-plane. (Cf. Theorem 3-8.4, choosing u as a function of x and v as a function of y.)

3-8.8. Find a function which is a one-to-one correspondence from all real numbers to the positive real numbers. Sketch a graph of your function.

3-8.9. Referring to Theorem 3-8.6, show that simple alternation of the digits of the decimal expansion of x and y to obtain z does not define a one-to-one correspondence. [*Hint:* Consider $z_1 = 0.12909090\ldots$ and compare with $z_2 = 0.21090909\ldots.$]

3-8.10. Let $A \approx C$ and $B \approx D$. Prove that $A \times B \approx C \times D$. [*Hint:* Construct H: $A \times B \to C \times D$ from one-to-one correspondences $f: A \to C$ and $g: B \to D$. Note that H takes the form $H(x,y) = (u,v)$ where $x \in A$, $y \in B$, $u \in C$, and $v \in D$.]

3-8.11. Use Exercise 3-8.10 to prove that the following sets (squares) in the Euclidean plane are equivalent:
a. $(0,1) \times (0,1)$ b. $(0,1] \times (0,1]$
c. $[0,1] \times [0,1]$

3-9 COMPOSITION OF FUNCTIONS

Let $f: A \to B$ and $g: B \to C$ be any two functions. The *composite gf* of g with f is a function from A to C defined as follows: $(a,c) \in gf$ if and only if for some b, $(a,b) \in f$ and $(b,c) \in g$. Using functional notation, $gf(a) = c$ means that $f(a) = b$ and $g(b) = c$. We write g before f in order to allow the following convenient notation: $gf(a) = g[f(a)] = g(b) = c$. By virtue of this definition, the composite of two functions is sometimes referred to as a "function of a function". Schematically, the situation is illustrated in Figure 3-9.1.

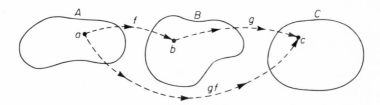

Figure 3-9.1

EXAMPLE 3-9.1: Let $f: A \to B$ and $g: B \to C$ be given as shown in Figure 3-9.2. Then

$$gf(a_1) = g[f(a_1)] = g(b_1) = c_1;$$
$$gf(a_2) = g[f(a_2)] = g(b_3) = c_1;$$
$$gf(a_4) = g[f(a_4)] = g(b_5) = c_3;$$
$$gf(A) = g[f(A)] = g[\{b_1, b_3, b_5\}] = \{c_1, c_3\}$$

and $gf(\{a_1, a_2\}) = g[\{b_1, b_3\}] = \{c_1\}.$

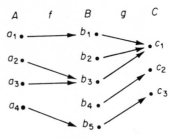

Figure 3-9.2

It should be clear that the operation of composition can be extended to more than two functions.

EXAMPLE 3-9.2: Let A, B, and C each denote the set of real numbers. Let $f: A \to B$ and $g: B \to C$ be defined by $f(x) = x^2 + 1$ and $g(x) = x^{20}$. Then $gf(x) = g[f(x)] = g[x^2 + 1] = (x^2 + 1)^{20}$. We may also form $fg(x) = f[g(x)] = f[x^{20}] = x^{40} + 1$. Note that $gf \neq fg$. In general, fg will not be considered unless $A = C$.

EXAMPLE 3-9.3: Let A be the xy-plane, B the set of all non-negative real numbers, and C the entire set of real numbers. Define $f: A \to B$ by $f(x,y) = x^2 + y^2$ and $g: B \to C$ by $g(x) = 3\sqrt{x}$. Then $gf: A \to C$ becomes $gf(x,y) = g[f(x,y)] = g[x^2 + y^2] = 3\sqrt{x^2 + y^2}$.

It is necessary to prove that gf is a function; this is done formally in the next theorem.

THEOREM 3-9.1: If $f: A \to B$ and $g: B \to C$ are functions, then $gf: A \to C$ is also a function.

Proof: Given any element a in A, there exists an element b in B such that $(a,b) \in f$, since Domain $f = A$. Moreover, for some element c in C, $(b,c) \in g$ since Domain $g = B$. By the definition of composition, $(a,c) \in gf$. This proves that Domain $gf = A$. Now suppose that $(a,c_1) \in gf$ and $(a,c_2) \in gf$. By the definition of composition, there exist elements b_1 and b_2 such that (1) $(a,b_1) \in f$ and $(b_1,c_1) \in g$, and (2) $(a,b_2) \in f$ and $(b_2,c_2) \in g$. From the first statements of (1) and (2), $b_1 = b_2$ since f is a function; it then follows that $c_1 = c_2$ from the second statements, since g is a function. Hence gf is also a function. ▌

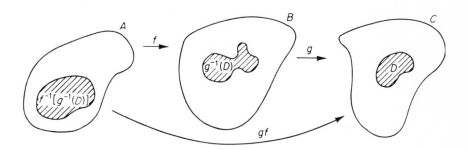

Figure 3-9.3

Let us again assume $f: A \to B$ and $g: B \to C$ are functions. Let D represent any subset of C. We use the customary definition of inverse image to obtain $[gf]^{-1}(D)$ in A; (i.e., the inverse image of D with respect to the function $gf: A \to C$). This set will be compared with $f^{-1}[g^{-1}(D)]$, involving two separate operations. See Figure 3-9.3.

THEOREM 3-9.2: $[gf]^{-1}(D) = f^{-1}[g^{-1}(D)]$.

Part I: To show that $[gf]^{-1}(D) \subseteq f^{-1}[g^{-1}(D)]$.

Proof:
1. Let $x \in [gf]^{-1}(D)$
2. For some z in D, $(x,z) \in gf$
3. For some y in B, $(x,y) \in f$ and $(y,z) \in g$
4. $y \in g^{-1}(D)$

5. $x \in f^{-1}[g^{-1}(D)]$

Reason:
Arbitrary choice
Definition of inverse image
Definition of composition

Definition of inverse image; ($z \in D$ from line 2)
Definition of inverse image.

Part II: To show that $f^{-1}[g^{-1}(D)] \subseteq [gf]^{-1}(D)$, is left as an exercise. (Ex. 3-9.2.) ▌

THEOREM 3-9.3: Let $f: A \to B$ and $g: B \to C$ be one-to-one correspondences. Then $gf: A \to C$ is also a one-to-one correspondence.

Proof: By hypothesis, each of the following relations are functions: (1) $f: A \to B$; (2) $f^{-1}: B \to A$; (3) $g: B \to C$; and (4) $g^{-1}: C \to B$. By Theorem 3-9.1, $gf: A \to C$ and $f^{-1}g^{-1}: C \to A$ are functions. Since $f^{-1}g^{-1} = [gf]^{-1}$. (Theorem 3-9.2), the proof is complete. ▌

EXERCISES

3-9.1. Let $A = \{a_1, a_2, a_3, a_4\}$, $B = \{b_1, b_2, b_3, b_4\}$, $C = \{c_1, c_2, c_3\}$, $f = \{(a_1,b_2),$ $(a_2,b_3), (a_3,b_3), (a_4,b_4)\}$, and $g = \{(b_1,c_2), (b_2,c_3), (b_3,c_3), (b_4,c_1)\}$. Note that $f: A \rightarrow B$ and $g: B \rightarrow C$. Tabulate the elements of $gf: A \rightarrow C$ and find Range gf.

3-9.2. Prove Part II of Theorem 3-9.2.

3-9.3. Let A, B, and C each represent the set of real numbers. Define $f: A \rightarrow B$ and $g: B \rightarrow C$ by $f(x) = 3x^2 + 2x$ and $g(x) = x - 1$. Find the formulas for $gf: A \rightarrow C$ and $fg: C \rightarrow A$.

3-9.4. Let A be the negative real numbers; let B and C represent the positive real numbers. Define $f: A \rightarrow B$ and $g: B \rightarrow C$ by $f(x) = 1/(2 - x)$ and $g(x) = 1/(1 + x)$. Find the formula for gf and also the range of gf.

3-9.5. Let A be the xy-plane; let B and C be the real numbers. Define $f: A \rightarrow B$ by $f(x,y) = 1/(x^2 + y^2 + 1)$, and define $g: B \rightarrow C$ by $g(x) = |x - 1/2|$. Find the formula for gf; also find the range of f, of g, and of gf.

3-10 MONOTONIC FUNCTIONS

Let S and T represent non-empty subsets of the real numbers. A function $f: S \rightarrow T$ is said to be *increasing* on a subset A of S if for every pair of points x_1, x_2 in A such that $x_1 < x_2$, it always follows that $f(x_1) \leq f(x_2)$. We say that f is *strictly increasing* if $x_1 < x_2$ implies $f(x_1) < f(x_2)$. Similarly, f is said to be *decreasing on A* if for x_1, x_2 in A, $x_1 < x_2$ implies $f(x_1) \geq f(x_2)$, and *strictly decreasing* if $x_1 < x_2$ implies $f(x_1) > f(x_2)$. The function f is called *monotonic on A* if it is increasing on A or if it is decreasing on A.

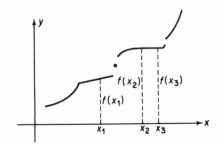

Figure 3-10.1

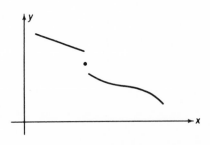

Figure 3-10.2

Illustrations: Figure 3-10.1 shows an increasing function. Figure 3-10.2 illustrates a strictly decreasing function. Note in Figure 3-10.1 that $x_1 <$ $x_2 < x_3$, and $f(x_1) < f(x_2)$, while $f(x_2) =$ $f(x_3)$. Both figures depict monotonic functions.

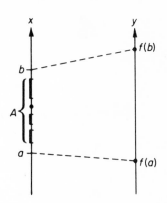

THEOREM 3-10.1: Let S and T be subsets of the real numbers, and let $f: S \rightarrow T$ be monotonic on S. Suppose A is a subset of S which is contained in the interval $[a,b]$, where a, b belong to S and $f(a) \neq f(b)$. Then $f(A)$ $\subset [f(a), f(b)]$, if f is increasing, and $f(A) \subset$ $[f(b), f(a)]$, if f is decreasing.

Proof: Suppose f is increasing on S. See Figure 3-10.3. For each $x \in A, a \leq x \leq b$ by hypothesis. Hence $f(a) \leq f(x) \leq f(b)$, or equivalently, $f(x) \in [f(a), f(b)]$, for all

Figure 3-10.3

$x \in A$, by the definition of an increasing function. This proves that $f(A)$ $\subset [f(a), f(b)]$. The second part of the proof is left as an exercise. $\blacksquare$

EXERCISES

3-10.1. Complete the proof of Theorem 3-10.1 by showing that $f(A) \subset [f(b), f(a)]$ if f is decreasing on S.

3-10.2. Prove that the function $f(x) = x^2 - 4x$ is strictly increasing for $\{x \mid x \geq 2\}$ and strictly decreasing for $\{x \mid x \leq 2\}$.

3-10.3. Prove that the function $f(x) = |x|/(1 + |x|)$ is strictly increasing for $\{x \mid x \geq 0\}$ and strictly decreasing for $\{x \mid x \leq 0\}$. Graph this function.

4

Metric
Sets
and
Limits

In this chapter the concept of a set with a distance function will be introduced. The notion of distance is used to establish the neighborhood system, which in turn is a most fundamental concept in the definition and discussion of the limit of a function and the limit of a sequence.

4-1 METRIC SETS

Let M be any set. We say that d is a *distance function* or *metric* with respect to M if and only if for every two elements p and q of M there is associated a real number $d(p,q)$, called the distance from p to q, satisfying the following properties:

1. $d(p,q) \geq 0$
2. $d(p,q) = 0$ if and only if $p = q$
3. $d(p,q) = d(q,p)$
4. $d(p,q) + d(q,r) \geq d(p,r)$ for all p, q, and r in M (the triangle inequality).

---

*d is a function from $M \times M$ to the real numbers.

These properties agree with intuitive concepts of distance.

A *metric set* is a pair (M,d) consisting of a set M and a metric d for M. The elements of M are usually called *points*.

EXAMPLE 4-1.1: Let $M = \{x \mid x \text{ is a real number}\}$. For every two points $p = x_1$ and $q = x_2$ in the set M, define $d(p,q) = |x_1 - x_2|$. Then the set M, together with the metric $d(p,q)$, constitutes the metric set which shall be symbolized by E^1, called Euclidean one-dimensional space. E^1 is represented geometrically by a straight line. The reader should verify that $d(p,q)$ is a metric—that it does satisfy the four properties required by the definition.

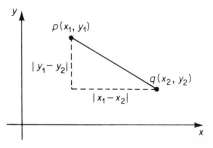

EXAMPLE 4-1.2: Let $M = \{(x,y) \mid x$ and y are real numbers$\}$. For every two points $p = (x_1,y_1)$ and $q = (x_2,y_2)$ in M, define

$$d(p,q) = \sqrt{(x_1 - x_2)^2 + (y_1 - y_2)^2}.$$

The resulting metric set shall be referred to as E^2, or Euclidean two-dimensional space. E^2 is represented by the plane. The reader should verify that $d(p,q)$ is a metric.

EXAMPLE 4-1.3: Let $M = \{(x,y,z) \mid x, y, \text{ and } z \text{ are real numbers}\}$. For every two points $p = (x_1,y_1,z_1)$ and $q = (x_2,y_2,z_2)$ in M define

$$d(p,q) = \sqrt{(x_1 - x_2)^2 + (y_1 - y_2)^2 + (z_1 - z_2)^2}.$$

The set M, together with the metric $d(p,q)$, is called Euclidean three-dimensional space, or more briefly, Euclidean 3-space, and symbolized by E^3. Geometrically, E^3 is our space of three dimensions.

EXAMPLE 4-1.4: Let $M = \{(x,y,z,w) \mid x, y, z, \text{ and } w \text{ are real numbers}\}$. For every two points $p = (x_1,y_1,z_1,w_1)$ and $q = (x_2,y_2,z_2,w_2)$, in set M, define

$$d(p,q) = \sqrt{(x_1 - x_2)^2 + (y_1 - y_2)^2 + (z_1 - z_2)^2 + (w_1 - w_2)^2}.$$

The set M, together with this metric, is referred to as E^4, or Euclidean 4-space, and is not representable geometrically.

This concept may be generalized to define Euclidean n-space for all positive integers n, even though no geometrical representation exists for $n > 3$.

The definition of a metric is sufficiently broad to allow for a large variety of distance functions. One distance function, which is different from the usual Euclidean distance, is presented in Example 4-1.5, and others occur in the next list of exercises.

EXAMPLE 4-1.5: Let M denote the set of all real numbers, with distance from $p = x_1$ to $q = x_2$ defined by

$$d(p, q) = \frac{|x_1 - x_2|}{1 + |x_1 - x_2|}$$

Here, $d(p,q)$ is always less than 1.

EXERCISES

4-1.1. Prove that the metrics of Examples 4-1.1, 4-1.2, and 4-1.5 obey the four properties required by the definition of a metric. *Hint:* For Example 4-1.5, prove that

$$\frac{|x_1 - x_2|}{1 + |x_1 - x_2|} + \frac{|x_2 - x_3|}{1 + |x_2 - x_3|} \geq \frac{|x_1 - x_2|}{1 + |x_1 - x_2| + |x_2 - x_3|} +$$

$$\frac{|x_2 - x_3|}{1 + |x_1 - x_2| + |x_2 - x_3|} \geq \frac{|x_1 - x_3|}{1 + |x_1 - x_3|}.$$

4-1.2. Let A be any set; let $d(p,q)$ be defined as follows: $d(p,q) = 0$ if $p = q$, and $d(p,q) = 1$ if $p \neq q$, for every pair of elements p and q in A. Prove that (A,d) is a metric set.

4-1.3. Let A denote the set of all real numbers. For every two points $p = x_1$ and $q = x_2$ in A, define
   a. $d_1(p,q) = |x_1^2 - x_2^2|$
   b. $d_2(p,q) = 2 |x_1 - x_2|$
   c. $d_3(p,q) = $ g.l.b. $\{2, |x_1 - x_2|\}$
   Is d_1, d_2, or d_3 a metric for A? Explain your answer in each case.

4-1.4. Let (M,d) be any metric set. Let A be a subset of M. Define $d_A(p,q) = d(p,q)$ for all $p, q \in A$—i.e., d_A is d restricted to pairs of elements of A. Prove that (A,d_A) is a metric set.

4-1.5. Let (A,d_A) and (B,d_B) represent any two metric sets. Given any two elements $p = (x_1,y_1)$ and $q = (x_2,y_2)$ in $A \times B$, where x_1 and x_2 belong to A, y_1 and y_2 belong to B; define $d(p,q) = \sqrt{[d_A(x_1,x_2)]^2 + [d_B(y_1,y_2)]^2}$ and prove that $d(p,q)$ is a metric for $A \times B$. Use this result to establish that $d(p,q)$ in Examples 4-1.2, 4-1.3, and 4-1.4 are metrics.

4-2 NEIGHBORHOODS

Let (M,d) be any metric set. Let p be a fixed point in M, and let ε be any positive real number. We define a *neighborhood* $N(p,\varepsilon)$ of p, with radius ε as follows: $N(p,\varepsilon) = \{q \mid q \in M \text{ and } d(p,q) < \varepsilon\}.$*

---

* Our use of the word "neighborhood" is limited here to metric sets; a neighborhood is determined by the point p and the radius ε.

EXAMPLE 4-2.1: In E^1, $N(p,\varepsilon)$ is the open interval $(p - \varepsilon, p + \varepsilon)$; equivalently, $N(p,\varepsilon)$ is $\{x \,|\, p - \varepsilon < x < p + \varepsilon\}$ or $\{x \,|\, |x - p| < \varepsilon\}$. The two points $p - \varepsilon$ and $p + \varepsilon$ do not belong to the neighborhood (Figure 4-2.1).

$$\begin{array}{ccc} p-\varepsilon & p & p+\varepsilon \end{array}$$

$$\leftarrow\varepsilon\rightarrow\!\bullet\!\leftarrow\varepsilon\rightarrow$$

Figure 4-2.1

EXAMPLE 4-2.2: In E^2, $N(p,\varepsilon)$ is the set of points inside the circle with center $p = (a,b)$ and radius ε, and is specifically described as $\{(x,y)\,|\,(x - a)^2 + (y - b)^2 < \varepsilon^2\}$. The circle $\{(x,y)\,|\,(x - a)^2 + (y - b)^2 = \varepsilon^2\}$ does not belong to the neighborhood (Figure 4-2.2).

EXAMPLE 4-2.3: In E^3, $N(p,\varepsilon)$ is the set of points inside the sphere with center at $p = (a,b,c)$ and radius ε. $N(p,\varepsilon) = \{(x,y,z)\,|\,(x - a)^2 + (y - b)^2 + (z - c)^2 < \varepsilon^2\}$. The spherical surface $\{(x,y,z)\,|\,(x - a)^2 + (y - b)^2 + (z - c)^2 = \varepsilon^2\}$ does not belong to $N(p,\varepsilon)$ (Figure 4-2.3).

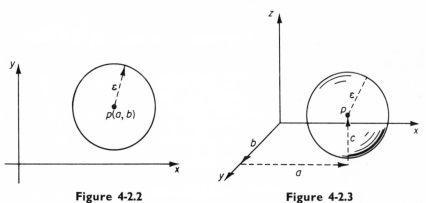

Figure 4-2.2   **Figure 4-2.3**

EXAMPLE 4-2.4: Let A be any set with metric defined by $d(p,q) = 0$ if $p = q$, and $d(p,q) = 1$ if $p \neq q$. Then $N(p,\varepsilon) = p$ if $\varepsilon \leq 1$ and $N(p,\varepsilon) = A$ if $\varepsilon > 1$.

A *deleted neighborhood* $N'(p,\varepsilon)$ is defined as follows: $N'(p,\varepsilon) = \{q \,|\, 0 < d(p,q) < \varepsilon\}$. Note that $N'(p,\varepsilon)$ has precisely one point less than $N(p,\varepsilon)$; that is, $N'(p,\varepsilon) = N(p,\varepsilon) - \{p\}$.

4-3 INTERIOR POINTS AND BOUNDARY POINTS OF A SET

For the remainder of this text, we will designate a metric set by the single letter previously associated with the set alone—for example, M instead of (M,d)—and indicate that a well defined metric is associated with M by use of the term "metric set M", instead of "set M".

Let A be any subset of a metric set M. A point p is called an *interior point* of A if there exists a neighborhood $N(p,\varepsilon)$ such that $N(p,\varepsilon) \subset A$. A point q is called an *exterior point* of A if there exists a neighborhood $N(q,\varepsilon)$ such that $N(q,\varepsilon) \subset M - A$. An exterior point of A is an interior point of $M - A$.

If every neighborhood $N(p,\varepsilon)$ contains a point of A and a point of $M - A$, then p is called a *boundary point* of A. Obviously, p is a boundary point of A if and only if it is a boundary point of $M - A$.

THEOREM 4-3.1: Let A be a subset of a metric set M. Every point p in M satisfies one and only one of the following conditions: (1) p is an interior point of A; (2) p is an exterior point of A; (3) p is a boundary point of A.

Proof: If p is neither an interior point of A nor of $M - A$, then every neighborhood $N(p,\varepsilon)$ must contain a point of A and a point of $M - A$ and so p is a boundary point of A. The reader should verify that no two of the three above conditions can exist simultaneously. ∎

The set of all interior points of A is called the *interior of A*, the set of all boundary points of A is called the *boundary of A*, and the set of all exterior points of A is called the *exterior of A*.

EXAMPLE 4-3.1: Let $M = E^1$ and $A = \{x \mid 0 < x \leq 1\}$. The interior of A is $(0,1)$; the boundary of A is $\{0, 1\}$, (two points); the exterior of A is $E^1 - [0,1] = \{x \mid x > 1\} \cup \{x \mid x < 0\}$ (Figure 4-3.1).

Figure 4-3.1

EXAMPLE 4-3.2: Let $M = E^2$ and $A = \{(x,y) \mid x^2 + y^2 \leq 4\}$. The interior of A is $\{(x,y) \mid x^2 + y^2 < 4\}$; the exterior of A is $\{(x,y) \mid x^2 + y^2 > 4\}$; the boundary of A is the circle $\{(x,y) \mid x^2 + y^2 = 4\}$ (Figure 4-3.2).

EXAMPLE 4-3.3: Let $M = E^2$ and $A = \{(x,y) \mid x^2 - y^2 > 1\}$. The interior of A is A itself, consisting of two disconnected portions; the exterior of A is

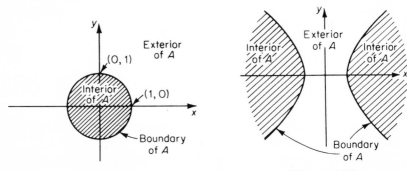

Figure 4-3.2   **Figure 4-3.3**

$\{(x,y) \mid x^2 - y^2 < 1\}$; the boundary of A is the hyperbola $\{(x,y) \mid x^2 - y^2 = 1\}$ (Figure 4-3.3).

4-4 OPEN SETS AND CLOSED SETS

Let A be a subset of a metric set M. A is called a *closed set* if and only if it contains all its boundary points. A is called an *open set* if and only if it does not contain any of its boundary points. Clearly A is an open set if every point in A is an interior point of A. Referring to the examples above, the set given in Example 4-3.1 is neither open nor closed; in Example 4-3.2, the set A is closed; while in Example 4-3.3, A is open.

THEOREM 4-4.1: The complement of an open set is closed, and the complement of a closed set is open.

Proof: Let A be an open set; since the boundary points of A are precisely the boundary points of $M - A$, and furthermore, since A contains none of these boundary points, $M - A$ must contain all of them; hence $M - A$ is closed. Now suppose A is closed; then all the boundary points belong to A and none belongs to $M - A$; therefore $M - A$ is open. ∎

4-5 LIMIT POINTS OF A SET

Let A be a subset of a metric set M, and let p be any point of M. We say that p is a *limit point of A* if every deleted neighborhood $N'(p,\varepsilon)$ contains a point of A. In other words, p is a limit point of A if every neighborhood $N(p,\varepsilon)$ contains a point of A other than p itself.

Consider again the examples of Section 4-3. The set of all limit points for the set given in Example 4-3.1 is $[0,1] = \{x \mid 0 \le x \le 1\}$; the set of all limit points of A in Example 4-3.2 is A itself; the set of all limit points of A in Example 4-3.3 is $\{(x,y) \mid x^2 - y^2 \ge 1\}$.

THEOREM 4-5.1: If p is a limit point of set A in a metric set M, then every neighborhood $N(p,\varepsilon)$ contains infinitely many points of A.

Proof: Suppose $N'(p,\varepsilon)$ contains only finitely many points $a_1, a_2, \ldots, a_n$ of set A. Let ε' equal the least of the n real numbers $d(p,a_1), d(p,a_2), \ldots, d(p,a_n)$. Note that $\varepsilon' > 0$. Now $N'(p,\varepsilon')$ does not contain any points of A, so p cannot be a limit point of A. ∎

THEOREM 4-5.2: A closed set contains all its limit points.

Proof: Let A be a closed set, and let p be a limit point of A. Since every neighborhood $N(p,\varepsilon)$ contains infinitely many points of A, the point p is not an interior point of $M - A$. By Theorem 4-3.1, p must belong to the interior or to the boundary of A. In either case, $p \in A$, by the definition of a closed set. **∎**

THEOREM 4-5.3: A set which contains all its limit points is closed.

Proof: Let A be a subset of a metric set M, which contains all its limit points. Let p be a boundary point of A. We must prove that $p \in A$.
Case I: If p is a limit point of A, then $p \in A$ by hypothesis.
Case II: If p is *not* a limit point of A, then there exists some deleted neighborhood $N'(p,\varepsilon)$ such that $N'(p,\varepsilon) \cap A = \varnothing$. Hence the only possible point in $N(p,\varepsilon)$ which could belong to A is p. Since p is a boundary point of A, every neighborhood $N(p,\varepsilon)$ must contain a point of A (as well as a point of $M - A$). Therefore $p \in A$. **∎**

Theorems 4-5.2 and 4-5.3 are converses of each other, so together they establish the following very useful *alternate definition of a closed set*: "A set is closed if and only if it contains all its limit points."

THEOREM 4-5.4: The union of any collection of open sets in a metric set M constitutes an open set in M.

Proof: Let $B = \bigcup_\alpha A_\alpha$ denote the union of (finitely or infinitely many) open sets A_α. Given any point $p \in B$; by the definition of union, p belongs to at least one set A_{α_1}. Since A_{α_1} is open (by hypothesis), there exists a neighborhood $N(p,\varepsilon)$ such that $N(p,\varepsilon) \subset A_{\alpha_1}$. Therefore $N(p,\varepsilon) \subset \bigcup_\alpha A_\alpha = B$. This proves that p is an interior point of B; hence B is open. **∎**

THEOREM 4-5.5: The intersection of any collection of closed sets in a metric set M constitutes a closed set in M.

Proof: Let $B = \bigcap_\alpha A_\alpha$, where each A_α is closed. Let p be a limit point of B. Since $B \subset A_\alpha$ for all A_α, it is easy to verify that p must also be a limit point of each A_α (Ex. 4-5.4). Since each A_α is closed, $p \in A_\alpha$ for all A_α. Therefore $p \in \bigcap_\alpha A_\alpha = B$. This proves that B contains all its limit points, and so B is closed. **∎**

We conclude this section by defining several concepts which will be needed later.

A set S in a metric set M is *bounded* if and only if there exists a neighborhood $N(p,r)$ of some point p in M such that $S \subset N(p,r)$. Note that p does not have to be in S.

Two sets A and B are *separated* if and only if $A \cap B = \varnothing$ and neither contains a limit point of the other.

A set S is *connected* if and only if it cannot be represented as the union of two non-empty separated sets.

The only non-empty connected sets in E^1 (other than E^1 itself) are of the following types: (a) a single point; (b) intervals (a,b), $[a,b)$, $(a,b]$, $[a,b]$; (c) rays $\{x \mid x < a\}$, $\{x \mid x \le a\}$, $\{x \mid x > b\}$, $\{x \mid x \ge b\}$.

EXERCISES

4-5.1. Let $M = E^2$ and $A = \{(x,y) \mid x^2 + 4y^2 < 4\}$. Find the interior of A, the exterior of A, the boundary of A, and the set of all limit points of A. Is A open? Is A closed? Draw a graph.

4-5.2. Let $M = E^1$ and $A = \{1, 2, 3, \ldots\}$ = the set of all positive integers. Prove that A has no limit points. Find the interior of A and the boundary of A. Is A open? Is A closed?

4-5.3. Consider the set in E^2 of points $\{(x,y) \mid (x,y) = (1/n, 1 - 1/n),$ where n is a positive integer$\}$. Find the limit points, interior points, and boundary points. Determine whether this set is open or closed.

4-5.4. Let A and B be subsets of a metric set M, where $B \subset A$. Show that if p is a limit point of B then p is also a limit point of A.

4-5.5. Determine whether the following sets in E^1 are separated; explain in each case:
a. The intervals $(0,1)$ and $(1,2)$
b. The intervals $(0,1]$ and $(1,2)$
c. The intervals $[0,1]$ and $[1,2]$
d. The set of rationals, and the set of irrationals.

4-5.6. Verify that the set $\{x \mid x = 0$ or x equals the reciprocal of a positive integer$\}$ is closed and bounded in E^1.

4-5.7. Prove that any finite set in a metric set M is closed in M.

4-5.8. Verify that the set D of all rational numbers in E^1 is neither open nor closed. Show also that D is not connected.

4-5.9. Verify that the empty set $\varnothing$ is both open and closed.

4-5.10. Let M be any set with distance defined as $d(p,q) = 0$ if $p = q$, $d(p,q) = 1$ if $p \ne q$. Let A be any subset of M. Is A open? Is A closed? Is A bounded? Under what condition(s) is A connected? Explain your answers.

4-5.11. Prove that the intersection of finitely many open sets in a metric set M is an open set in M. [*Hint:* Take $p \in \bigcap_{i=1}^{n} A_i$ where each A_i is open, and consider the finite number of neighborhoods $N(p,\varepsilon_1) \subset A_1$, $N(p,\varepsilon_2) \subset A_2, \ldots,$ $N(p,\varepsilon_n) \subset A_n$.]

4-5.12. Give an example in which the intersection of infinitely many open sets is not open.

4-5.13. Prove that the union of finitely many closed sets in a metric set M constitutes a closed set in M. [*Hint:* Use Theorem 4-4.1, Exercise 4-5.11 and the formula $M - \bigcup_{i=1}^{n} A_i = \bigcap_{i=1}^{n} (M - A_i)$ from Example 1-7.3.]

4-5.14. Give an example in which the union of infinitely many closed sets is not closed.

4-6   SEQUENCES

Let I designate the set of positive integers. A *sequence* in a set M is defined by a function $f: I \to M$. Each element $f(n)$ is called a *term* of the sequence. Although the terms of a sequence do constitute a set, the order in which the terms occur is important; a rearrangement of non-equal terms results in a different sequence.

EXAMPLE 4-6.1: Let $f: I \to E^1$ be defined by $f(n) = 1/n$. The resulting sequence $f(1), f(2), f(3), f(4), \ldots$ is: $1, 1/2, 1/3, 1/4, \ldots$.

EXAMPLE 4-6.2: Let $f: I \to E^1$ be given by $f(n) = (1 - 1/n)$. The resulting sequence $f(1), f(2), f(3), f(4), \ldots$ is: $0, 1/2, 2/3, 3/4, \ldots$.

EXAMPLE 4-6.3: Let $f: I \to E^1$ be defined by $f(n) = (-1)^{n+1}(1 - 1/n)$. The resulting sequence is: $0, -1/2, 2/3, -3/4, 4/5, \ldots$. This sequence is illustrated below:

EXAMPLE 4-6.4: Let $f: I \to E^2$ be defined by $f(n) = (1/n, 1 - 1/n)$; the resulting sequence is: $(1,0), (1/2,1/2), (1/3,2/3), (1/4,3/4), \ldots$. The graph of this function is shown in Figure 4-6.1.

EXAMPLE 4-6.5: Let $f: I \to E^2$ be defined by $f(n) = (2n,n)$. The resulting sequence is: $(2,1), (4,2), (6,3), (8,4), \ldots$.

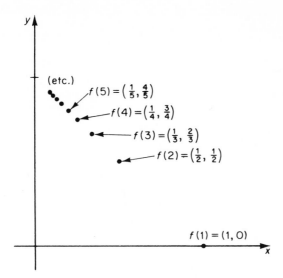

Figure 4-6.1

4-7 LIMIT OF A SEQUENCE

Let M denote a metric set. A neighborhood $N(b,\varepsilon)$ in M is said to *confine* a sequence $f: I \to M$ if there exists an integer J such that $f(n) \in N(b,\varepsilon)$ for every $n > J$. In other words, $N(b,\varepsilon)$ confines the sequence $f(1), f(2), f(3), \dots$ if all but a finite number of its terms lie inside $N(b,\varepsilon)$. If *every* neighborhood $N(b,\varepsilon)$ of b confines the sequence f, then we say *the sequence has the limit b*, and write $\lim_{n\to\infty} f(n) = b$. Note that $\lim_{n\to\infty} f(n) \neq b$ if there exists even one neighborhood $N(b,\varepsilon)$ of b which does not confine the sequence.

EXAMPLES: Consider the preceding examples. In Example 4-6.1, every neighborhood $N(0,\varepsilon)$ confines the sequence, and $\lim_{n\to\infty} f(n) = 0$. In Example 4-6.2, every neighborhood $N(1,\varepsilon)$ confines the sequence, and $\lim_{n\to\infty} f(n) = 1$. In Example 4-6.3, the sequence has no limit because there are infinitely many terms close to $+1$ and infinitely many terms close to -1; thus, no neighborhood $N(b,\varepsilon)$, where $\varepsilon = 1/2$, could confine this sequence, regardless of the choice of point b. In Example 4-6.4, every neighborhood $N[(0,1),\varepsilon]$ confines the sequence, and $\lim_{n\to\infty} f(n) = (0,1)$. Finally, in Example 4-6.5, infinitely many terms lie outside every neighborhood $N(b,\varepsilon)$ no matter how large ε may be, so no limit exists.

THEOREM 4-7.1: A sequence $f: I \to M$ can have at most one limit. That is, if $\lim_{n \to \infty} f(n) = b$ and $\lim_{n \to \infty} f(n) = c$, then $c = b$.

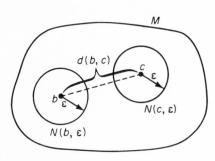

Proof: Assume $b \neq c$; let $\varepsilon = d(b,c)/3$; then not both $N(b,\varepsilon)$ and $N(c,\varepsilon)$ can confine the sequence, since $N(b,\varepsilon) \cap N(c,\varepsilon) = \varnothing$. Thus, the assumption $b \neq c$ is wrong. ∎

An alternate notation for a sequence in a metric set M is $a_1, a_2, a_3, \ldots$ or $\{a_n\}$ to designate the terms of the sequence as well as the sequence itself. In either case, we assume there exists a function $f: I \to M$ such that $f(n) = a_n$. Using this notation, $\lim_{n \to \infty} a_n = b$ means that the element b is the limit of the sequence $\{a_n\}$. A sequence which has a limit is called a *convergent sequence*; if no limit exists, the sequence is said to be *divergent*.

A *subsequence* of a sequence $\{a_n\}$ is a sequence whose terms are chosen from the terms of the sequence $\{a_n\}$ and arranged in the same order as their relative order in $\{a_n\}$. A subsequence of $\{a_n\}$ is often designated $\{a_{n_k}\}$ with terms $a_{n_1}, a_{n_2}, a_{n_3}, \ldots$.

EXAMPLE 4-7.1: The sequence $1/4, 1/9, 1/16, 1/25, \ldots$ is a subsequence of $1/2, 1/3, 1/4, \ldots, 1/n, \ldots$.

EXAMPLE 4-7.2: The sequence $(1/2,1/2), (1/5,4/5), (1/8,7/8), (1/11,10/11), \ldots$ is a subsequence of $\{(1/n, 1 - 1/n)\}$.

THEOREM 4-7.2: Given a function $f: A \to B$, where A and B are subsets of a metric set M; let $a_1, a_2, a_3, \ldots$ be a sequence in A; then $f(a_1), f(a_2), f(a_3), \ldots$ is a sequence in B.

Proof: Since $a_1, a_2, a_3, \ldots$ is a sequence, there exists a function $g: I \to A$ such that $g(n) = a_n$. Then $f(a_1), f(a_2), f(a_3), \ldots$ is the sequence defined by the composite function $fg: I \to B$ with terms $f[g(1)], f[g(2)], f[g(3)], \ldots$. ∎

EXERCISES

4-7.1. Find at least one simple rule $f(n)$ for obtaining all terms in each of the following sequences; write the next four terms in each sequence:
   a. $1/2, 1/4, 1/8, 1/16, \ldots$
   b. $1, -2/3, 3/7, -4/15, \ldots$

c. $-1/2, -2/5, -3/8, -4/11, \ldots$
d. $1, 0, 1, 0, \ldots$
e. $1/2, 1/3, 1/4, 1/9, 1/8, 1/27, \ldots$
f. $3, 2, 1, 3, 2, 1, 3, 2, 1, \ldots$
g. $1/4, 3/7, 1/2, 7/13, 9/16, \ldots$
h. $0, 2, 24, 324, \ldots$
i. $(1,1), (-1,1/2), (1,2/3), (-1,3/4), \ldots$
j. $(3/2,1/2), (7/4,3/4), (15/8,7/8), (31/16,15/16), \ldots$

4-7.2. Find the limit of each sequence in Exercise 4-7.1, if the limit exists. Justify each limit on the basis of the definition of a limit. Designate each sequence as convergent or divergent.

4-7.3. Given any convergent sequence $f: I \to M$; prove that $A = \{f(n) \mid n$ is a positive integer$\}$ is a bounded *set*.

4-7.4. Prove that any subsequence of a convergent sequence converges, and its limit is the same as the limit of the original sequence.

4-7.5. Give examples to show that a divergent sequence may have convergent subsequences.

4-8 MONOTONIC SEQUENCES IN E^1

A sequence $f: I \to E^1$ is called monotonic if f is a monotonic function. That is, the sequence $f: I \to E^1$ is *increasing* if for every pair of positive integers n_1 and n_2, $n_1 < n_2$ implies $f(n_1) \leq f(n_2)$. Similarly, if $n_1 < n_2$ implies $f(n_1) \geq f(n_2)$, then the sequence is *decreasing*.

A sequence $f: I \to E^1$ is said to be *bounded above* if there exists a real number b_1 such that $f(n) \leq b_1$ for all n. Similarly, if there exists a real number b_2 such that $b_2 \leq f(n)$ for all n, then we say that the sequence is *bounded below*.

THEOREM 4-8.1: If $f: I \to E^1$ is an increasing sequence which is bounded above, then f is convergent.

Proof: By the completeness property of the real numbers there exists a real number c such that $c = $ l.u.b. $\{f(n) \mid n \in I\}$. We shall show that $\lim_{n \to \infty} f(n) = c$. Given any positive number ε, there exists an integer J such that $f(J) > c - \varepsilon$, since $c - \varepsilon$ is less than the least upper bound. Now $c - \varepsilon < f(n) \leq c$ for all $n \geq J$, since f is increasing and c is an upper bound. Thus, $f(n) \in N(c,\varepsilon)$ for all $n \geq J$. In other words, the sequence $\{f(n)\}$ is confined by every neighborhood of c; hence $\lim_{n \to \infty} f(n) = c$. ∎

EXERCISES

4-8.1. Prove that if $f: I \to E^1$ is a decreasing sequence which is bounded below, then f is convergent.

4-8.2. State which of the sequences in Exercise 4-7.1, parts a through h, are monotonic. Which are bounded above? Which are bounded below?

4-9 CAUCHY SEQUENCES

A sequence $a_1, a_2, a_3, \ldots$ in a metric set M is called a *Cauchy sequence* if for every real number $\varepsilon > 0$ there exists a positive integer J such that $d(a_j, a_k) < \varepsilon$ whenever $j > J$ and $k > J$; that is, beyond the Jth term, the distance between *any two* terms of the sequence is less than ε.

THEOREM 4-9.1: Every convergent sequence is a Cauchy sequence.

Proof: Let $a_1, a_2, a_3, \ldots$ be any convergent sequence in M; then $\lim_{n \to \infty} a_n = p$, for some p in M. Given any $\varepsilon > 0$, there exists an integer J such that $d(a_k, p) < \varepsilon/2$ if $k > J$. Therefore if $j, k > J$, we have $d(a_j, a_k) \leq d(a_j, p) + d(p, a_k) < \varepsilon/2 + \varepsilon/2 = \varepsilon$. This is the Cauchy condition by the above definition. ∎

THEOREM 4-9.2: Every Cauchy sequence is bounded; i.e., the terms of a Cauchy sequence constitute a bounded set.

Proof: Let $\varepsilon = 1$; there exists an integer J such that $d(a_j, a_k) < 1$ if $j, k > J$. In particular, $d(a_{J+1}, a_k) < 1$ for $k > J$. Thus $N(a_{J+1}, 1)$ contains all but a finite number of terms of the sequence. Choose a real number $r \geq 1$ which is larger than the distances from a_{J+1} to all of the finitely many terms outside $N(a_{J+1}, 1)$. Now it is obvious that $N(a_{J+1}, r)$ contains the entire sequence; hence the sequence is bounded. ∎

We will show that the converse of Theorem 4-9.1 is valid if $M = E^n$. First consider E^1.

THEOREM 4-9.3: Every Cauchy sequence $\{a_n\}$ in E^1 converges.

Proof: Let c_1 and c_2 represent a lower and an upper bound, respectively, for the terms of the sequence $\{a_n\}$. (See Theorem 4-9.2.) Define the subset B of E^1 as follows: $B = \{x \mid x \leq a_n$ for infinitely many positive integers $n\}$. Obviously B is bounded above by c_2 (an upper bound for the sequence). Moreover, $B \neq \varnothing$ since $c_1 \in B$. By the completeness property of the real numbers, there exists a number p such that $p = $ l.u.b. B. It will be proved that p is the (sequential) limit of $\{a_n\}$.

Consider any neighborhood $N(p,\varepsilon)$. Since $p - \varepsilon/2 < p$, there exists an element b in B such that $p - \varepsilon/2 < b \le p$. This implies that infinitely many terms of the sequence are greater than $p - \varepsilon/2$. Since $p + \varepsilon/2 > p$, $p + \varepsilon/2 \notin B$; hence at most a finite number of terms of the sequence are greater than or equal to $p + \varepsilon/2$. Thus $N(p,\varepsilon/2)$ contains infinitely many terms of the sequence. By the Cauchy criterion, there exists an integer J such that $d(a_k,a_j) < \varepsilon/2$ if j, $k > J$. Choose a term a_{j_0} such that $a_{j_0} \in N(p,\varepsilon/2)$ and $j_0 > J$. Then for all $k > J$,

$$d(a_k,p) \le d(a_k,a_{j_0}) + d(a_{j_0},p) < \varepsilon/2 + \varepsilon/2 = \varepsilon.$$

This proves that $N(p,\varepsilon)$ confines the sequence; hence $\lim\limits_{n \to \infty} a_n = p$. $\blacksquare$

THEOREM 4-9.4: Every Cauchy sequence in E^n converges.

Proof: (The proof will be presented for E^2, but a similar proof may be given for Euclidean spaces of higher dimensions.) Let (a_1,b_1), (a_2,b_2), (a_3,b_3), ... be a Cauchy sequence in E^2. It will first be shown that a_1, a_2, a_3, ... is a Cauchy sequence in E^1. Given any positive real number ε, by the Cauchy criterion, there exists an integer J such that $d((a_j,b_j),(a_k,b_k)) < \varepsilon$ if j, $k > J$. By the definition of distance in E^2, $\sqrt{(a_j - a_k)^2 + (b_j - b_k)^2} < \varepsilon$ if j, $k > J$. Relating this to the metric $d(a_j,a_k)$ in E^1,

$$d(a_j,a_k) = |a_j - a_k| = \sqrt{(a_j - a_k)^2} \le \sqrt{(a_j - a_k)^2 + (b_j - b_k)^2} < \varepsilon,$$

whenever j, $k > J$. This proves that $\{a_n\}$ is a Cauchy sequence; hence $\lim\limits_{n \to \infty} a_n = p$ for some real number p. (See Theorem 4-9.3.) Similarly, $\{b_n\}$ is a Cauchy sequence in E^1, and $\lim\limits_{n \to \infty} b_n = q$ for some real number q.

We will now prove that the sequence (a_1,b_1), (a_2,b_2), (a_3,b_3), ... converges to (p,q). Consider any neighborhood $N((p,q),\varepsilon)$ of (p,q) in E^2. Since $\lim\limits_{n \to \infty} a_n = p$, there exists an integer K_1 such that $|a_n - p| < \varepsilon/2$ if $n > K_1$.

Since $\lim\limits_{n \to \infty} b_n = q$, there exists an integer K_2 such that $|b_n - q| < \varepsilon/2$ if $n > K_2$. Let K be the larger of the numbers K_1 and K_2. Then, if $n > K$,

$$d((a_n,b_n),(p,q)) = \sqrt{(a_n - p)^2 + (b_n - q)^2} < \sqrt{(\varepsilon/2)^2 + (\varepsilon/2)^2} < \varepsilon.$$

This proves that $N((p,q),\varepsilon)$ confines the sequence $\{(a_n,b_n)\}$; hence

$$\lim\limits_{n \to \infty} (a_n,b_n) = (p,q). \quad \blacksquare$$

From the theorems just proved, we see that there is a way of testing an arbitrary sequence in E^n for convergence without knowing in advance what its limit is. Intuitively, the terms of a sequence get arbitrarily near to some fixed value, for sufficiently large subscripts, if and only if they get arbitrarily close to each other, for sufficiently large subscripts (the Cauchy condition).

We are now ready to prove a basic theorem, called the "Bolzano-Weierstrass Theorem". The proof will again be presented for E^2, with the understanding that a similar proof may be given for Euclidean spaces of other dimensions.

THEOREM 4-9.5: (*Bolzano-Weierstrass Theorem*) Every bounded infinite set A in E^n has at least one (set) limit point.

Proof: Since A is bounded, it is possible to find a square closed region S which contains A. Subdivide S into four squares by joining midpoints

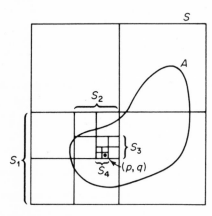

of its opposite sides. At least one of these smaller squares, together with its boundary, must contain infinitely many points of A, since A is infinite. Call this square S_1. Now subdivide S_1 into four squares in the same manner to obtain S_2 containing infinitely many points of A. By continuing this process we obtain a set of closed squares $S, S_1, S_2, \ldots,$ $S_n, \ldots$ such that: (1) each S_i contains infinitely many points of A; (2) $S \supset S_1 \supset S_2 \supset S_3 \supset \ldots$; (3) $\lim_{n \to \infty}$ (length of side of S_n) $= 0$. Form a Cauchy sequence from the elements of A as follows: choose a point (a_1,b_1) of A in S_1; select another point (a_2,b_2) of A in S_2 such that $(a_2,b_2) \neq (a_1,b_1)$. In general, for every positive integer n, let (a_n,b_n) be a point of A chosen from the points inside S_n such that $(a_n,b_n) \neq (a_k,b_k)$ for all $k < n$. The resulting sequence (a_1,b_1), (a_2,b_2), $(a_3,b_3), \ldots$ satisfies the Cauchy condition since $\lim_{n \to \infty}$ (length of the side of $S_n) = 0$. Hence there exists a point (p,q) in E^2 such that $\lim_{n \to \infty} (a_n,b_n) = (p,q)$, by Theorem 4-9.4. The point (p,q) must be a set limit point of A, since every neighborhood $N((p,q),\varepsilon)$ contains infinitely many distinct points (a_n,b_n) of A. ∎

Two types of limits have been discussed so far, the limit of a sequence and the limit of a set. The following examples illustrate the difference between these two concepts.

EXAMPLE 4-9.1: The sequence $f: I \to E^1$ defined by $f(n) = (-1)^n(1 - 1/n)$ has no (sequential) limit. However, the set A of all points in E^1 of the form $(-1)^n(1 - 1/n)$, where n is a positive integer, has two (set) limit points, -1 and $+1$.

EXAMPLE 4-9.2: The sequence $f: I \to E^1$ defined by $f(n) = 1$, called a "constant sequence" and having terms 1, 1, 1, 1, . . . , has the (sequential) limit point 1. However, the set A consisting of the point 1 alone, has no (set) limit point.

THEOREM 4-9.6: If p is a limit point of a set A in a metric set M, then there exists a sequence $a_1, a_2, a_3, \ldots$ of distinct points in A such that p is the (sequential) limit of the sequence; that is, $\lim_{n \to \infty} a_n = p$.

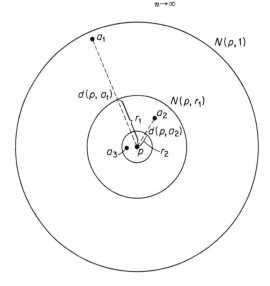

Proof: Since p is a limit point of A, there exists a point a_1 in A such that $a_1 \in N'(p,1)$. (Note that $a_1 \neq p$.) Let $r_1 = d(p,a_1)/2$, $(0 < r_1 < 1/2)$. For the same reason, there exists a point a_2 in A such that $a_2 \in N'(p,r_1)$; note that $a_2 \neq p$ and $a_2 \neq a_1$. Let $r_2 = d(p,a_2)/2$; then $0 < r_2 < r_1/2 < (1/2)^2$. There exists a point a_3 in A such that $a_3 \in N'(p,r_2)$; note that a_3 is different from p, a_1, and a_2. Let $r_3 = d(p,a_3)/2$; then $0 < r_3 < (1/2)^3$. Continue this process indefinitely to obtain a sequence $a_1, a_2, a_3, a_4, \ldots$ where $d(p,a_n)/2 = r_n < (1/2)^n$ or $d(p,a_n) = 2r_n < (1/2)^{n-1}$. Here, the distance $d(p,a_n)$ approaches zero as n gets large. Hence $\lim_{n \to \infty} a_n = p$. We have thus constructed a sequence in set A having p as its (sequential) limit. ∎

EXERCISES

4-9.1. Which of the sequences given in Exercise 4-7.1, are Cauchy sequences? Explain.

4-9.2. Let $\{a_n\}$ be the sequence in E^1 defined by $a_1 = 1$, $a_2 = 1 + 1/2$, $a_3 = 1 + 1/2 + 1/3$, and in general, $a_n = 1 + 1/2 + \ldots + 1/n$. Note that $\lim\limits_{n \to \infty} |a_{n+1} - a_n| = 0$. Prove that this sequence does not satisfy the Cauchy criterion.

4-9.3. Verify that every Cauchy sequence in E^3 converges by following the pattern of proof given in Theorem 4-9.4.

4-9.4. Prove that the Bolzano-Weierstrass Theorem is valid for E^1 and for E^3. Follow the pattern of proof given in Theorem 4-9.5.

4-10 NON-TERMINATING DECIMALS DEFINED AS CAUCHY SEQUENCES

Suppose we are given an unending decimal $m \cdot a_1 a_2 a_3 \ldots$ where $m \geq 0$ is an integer and each a_i is an integer such that $0 \leq a_i \leq 9$. Let $c_1, c_2, c_3, \ldots$ be the sequence of rational numbers defined by

$$c_1 = m + a_1/10$$
$$c_2 = m + a_1/10 + a_2/10^2$$
$$c_3 = m + a_1/10 + a_2/10^2 + a_3/10^3$$
$$\cdot$$
$$\cdot$$
$$\cdot$$
$$c_n = m + a_1/10 + a_2/10^2 + \ldots + a_n/10^n$$
$$\cdot$$
$$\cdot$$
$$\cdot$$

Then we can prove the following theorem:

THEOREM 4-10.1: The sequence $c_1, c_2, c_3, \ldots$ is a Cauchy sequence.

Proof: Given any $\varepsilon > 0$; there exists an integer J such that $1/10^J < \varepsilon$. If $j, k > J$, then $|c_j - c_k| < 1/10^J < \varepsilon$, which is the Cauchy criterion. ∎

Suppose we are given an unending decimal $m \cdot a_1 a_2 a_3 \ldots$ and wish to determine the corresponding point p on line E^1. We consider the related

Cauchy sequence $c_1, c_2, c_3, \ldots$ of rational numbers. Every Cauchy sequence in E^1 converges (Theorem 4-9.3) and we have $p = \lim\limits_{n\to\infty} c_n$.

4-11 THE LIMIT OF A FUNCTION

Given any two metric sets A and B, let a be a fixed point of A and b represent a fixed point of B. Let f denote a function either from A to B or from $A - \{a\}$ to B. (It is not required that the point a belong to the domain of f.) Assume that $N'(a, \delta) \neq \varnothing$ for every positive number δ.* We write

$$\lim_{x\to a} f(x) = b$$

if and only if, corresponding to *each* neighborhood $N(b,\varepsilon)$ in B there exists a neighborhood $N(a,\delta)$ in A such that

$$f[N'(a,\delta)] \subset N(b,\varepsilon).$$

In order to establish that a limit exists, we must provide a rule determining $\delta > 0$, the radius of $N(a,\delta)$, for every $\varepsilon > 0$, the radius of $N(b,\varepsilon)$.

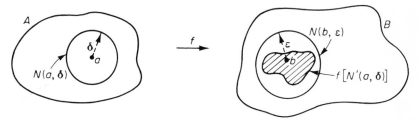

Figure 4-11.1

The equation $\lim\limits_{x\to a} f(x) = b$ is read "the limit of $f(x)$ as x approaches a is equal to b". It should be noted that the symbol x is a *variable*—that is, x is used to represent *any* element of A—whereas a and b are *constants*; each is a symbol used to designate precisely one element.

In less rigorous wording, $\lim\limits_{x\to a} f(x) = b$ means that "$f(x)$ approaches b as x approaches a". In the definition of limit, it is not necessary that $f(a) = b$, or even that $f(a)$ be defined at all; we are only interested in the values of x different from a. This is why the deleted neighborhood $N'(a,\delta)$, rather than $N(a,\delta)$ is used in the definition.

---

* We avoid the fruitless definition of limit at an isolated point a of the set A. If a is an isolated point of the domain of f, then for a small enough δ, $N'(a,\delta) = \varnothing$; hence $f[N'(a,\delta)] \subset N(b,\varepsilon)$ for every element b in the set B.

The "key formula" $f[N'(a,\delta)] \subset N(b,\varepsilon)$ can be written in the following equivalent ways:

1. $N'(a,\delta) \subset f^{-1}[N(b,\varepsilon)]$;
2. If $x \in N'(a,\delta)$, then $f(x) \in N(b,\varepsilon)$.

Of special interest is the case in which A and B are subsets of E^1. Statement 2 takes the form:

2'. If $x \in (a - \delta, \, a + \delta) - \{a\}$, then $f(x) \in (b - \varepsilon, \, b + \varepsilon)$; or, using absolute value notation, we have:

2". If $0 < |x - a| < \delta$, then $|f(x) - b| < \varepsilon$.

Consequently, if A and B are subsets of E^1, the following alternate definition of limit may be used:

$\lim\limits_{x \to a} f(x) = b$ means that, corresponding to every positive number ε,

there exists a positive number δ (depending on ε), such that if $0 < |x - a| < \delta$, then $|f(x) - b| < \varepsilon$.

The proof of the equivalence of the above statements is left as an exercise (Ex. 4-11.5).

EXAMPLE 4-11.1: Consider the function $f(x) = (2x^2 + x - 3)/(x - 1)$. In this case the domain of f is $E^1 - \{1\}$; that is, $f: E^1 - \{1\} \to E^1$. Here, $\lim\limits_{x \to 1} f(x) = 5$, since $f[N'(1,\delta)] \subset N(5,\varepsilon)$ whenever $\delta \le \varepsilon/2$, no matter how large or, more importantly, how small ε may be. Even though we define $f(1) = 0$, or $f(1) = 2$, etc., the value of the limit remains 5.

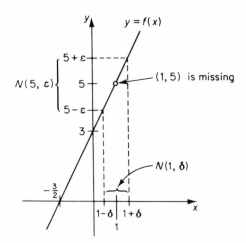

Figure 4-11.2

We shall verify that $\delta = \varepsilon/2$ is the maximum possible value for δ. First note that if $x \neq 1$, then

$$f(x) = \frac{2x^2 + x - 3}{x - 1} = \frac{(2x + 3)(x - 1)}{x - 1} = 2x + 3.*$$

Now search for a rule relating δ to ε such that

$$0 < |x - 1| < \delta \Rightarrow |f(x) - 5| = |(2x + 3) - 5| < \varepsilon.$$

This is easy to do for the given function, since

$$0 < |x - 1| < \delta \Rightarrow 2|x - 1| < 2\delta \Rightarrow$$
$$|2x - 2| < 2\delta \Rightarrow |(2x + 3) - 5| < 2\delta;$$

if δ is now set equal to $\varepsilon/2$, the limit is verified. (See Figure 4-11.2.)

Sometimes, in solving for δ in terms of ε, it is convenient to consider the x and y axes separated, rather than at right angles to each other in the conventional arrangement. Figure 4-11.3 is an illustration of Example 4-11.1 with the axes separated. In this figure, a value for δ less than the maximum possible value is used. This manner of representation suggests an alternate method of relating δ to ε. Consider the image $f[N'(1,\delta)]$. Since f is strictly increasing and $N(1,\delta)$ is bounded above by $1 + \delta$ and bounded below by $1 - \delta$, we observe that $f(1 - \delta) < f(x) < f(1 + \delta)$ for all $x \in N'(1,\delta)$, or equivalently,

$$f[N'(1,\delta)] \subset (f(1 - \delta), f(1 + \delta)),$$

an open interval. Now

$$f(1 - \delta) = 2(1 - \delta) + 3 = 5 - 2\delta,$$

and

$$f(1 + \delta) = 2(1 + \delta) + 3 = 5 + 2\delta;$$

hence

$$f[N'(1,\delta)] \subset (5 - 2\delta, 5 + 2\delta) = N(5,2\delta).$$

Thus it is clear that 2δ must be less than or equal to ε; $\delta = \varepsilon/2$ is the maximum value allowable for δ, and will of course suffice as a solution to this particular problem.

---

* The graph of $y = (2x^2 + x - 3)/(x - 1)$ has one point less than the graph of $y = 2x + 3$; the missing point is $(1,5)$.

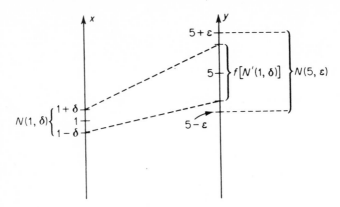

Figure 4-11.3

EXAMPLE 4-11.2: Let $f: E^1 \to E^1$ be defined by $f(x) = x^2$. To verify that $\lim_{x \to 2} f(x) = 4$, we must demonstrate that for each neighborhood $N(4,\varepsilon)$ there exists a neighborhood $N(2,\delta)$ such that $f[N'(2,\delta)] \subset N(4,\varepsilon)$. Figure 4-11.4 shows the traditional graph of this function. ε has been arbitrarily chosen, and the points $4 + \varepsilon$ and $4 - \varepsilon$ are shown on the y-axis. The positive values x_1 and x_2, for which $f(x_1) = 4 - \varepsilon$ and $f(x_2) = 4 + \varepsilon$, are also shown. Note $x_1 < 2 < x_2$, but $|2 - x_1| > |x_2 - 2|$. Intuitively we see that the length of the shorter of these two intervals is a maximum for all δ such that $f[N'(2,\delta)] \subset N(4,\varepsilon)$.

Figure 4-11.5 shows the function $f(x) = x^2$ with axes separated. Since f is strictly increasing for $\{x \mid x \geq 0\}$, $f[N'(2,\delta)] \subset (f(2 - \delta), f(2 + \delta))$, if $0 < \delta < 2$.

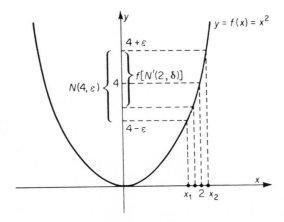

Figure 4-11.4

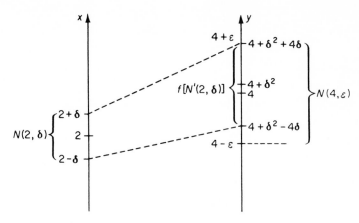

Figure 4-11.5

Now

$$f(2 - \delta) = (2 - \delta)^2 = 4 - 4\delta + \delta^2$$

and

$$f(2 + \delta) = (2 + \delta)^2 = 4 + 4\delta + \delta^2.$$

Therefore

$$f[N'(2,\delta)] \subset (4 - 4\delta + \delta^2, 4 + 4\delta + \delta^2) = N(4 + \delta^2, 4\delta).$$

It is clear that $N(4 + \delta^2, 4\delta) \subset N(4,\varepsilon)$ if $4 + \delta^2 + 4\delta = 4 + \varepsilon$—if the upper endpoints of these intervals coincide. Solving the quadratic equation $\delta^2 + 4\delta - \varepsilon = 0$ for δ, we obtain

$$\delta = \sqrt{4 + \varepsilon} - 2.$$

(The other root of the quadratic equation is a negative number, and is extraneous.) For this function, we do not investigate the coincidence of the lower endpoints of the intervals, since δ would then be so large that $f[N'(2,\delta)]$ would extend beyond $N(4,\varepsilon)$ at its upper endpoint.

From the preceding two examples it is clear that the verification of a limit involving a function f from a set of real numbers to E^1 is greatly simplified if f is strictly monotonic in an interval about the point a where the limit is considered. The procedure involves finding the image of the end points of $N(a,\delta)$ and noting that $f[N'(a,\delta)] \subset (f(a - \delta), f(a + \delta))$ for strictly increasing functions and $f[N'(a,\delta)] \subset (f(a + \delta), f(a - \delta))$ for strictly decreasing functions.

Functions defined on a metric set other than E^1 usually require a more careful analysis.

EXAMPLE 4-11.3: Let $f:E^2 \to E^1$ be defined by $f(x,y) = x^2 + y^2$. To verify that $\lim\limits_{(x,y)\to(1,2)} f(x,y) = 5$, first consider $f^{-1}[N(5,\varepsilon)]$, which is the ring-shaped area contained between the circles $x^2 + y^2 = 5 - \varepsilon$ and $x^2 + y^2 = 5 + \varepsilon$. (Figure 4-11.6.) The point $p = (2,1)$ is within this ring. To find δ such that $f[N'(p,\delta)] \subset N(5,\varepsilon)$, we must determine the radius of a circle that can be drawn entirely inside the shaded ring, with center at (2,1). The distance from the origin to (2,1) is $\sqrt{5}$; and since the point (2,1) is nearer the outer boundary of $f^{-1}[N(5,\varepsilon)]$, the maximum value for δ is $\sqrt{5 + \varepsilon} - \sqrt{5}$.

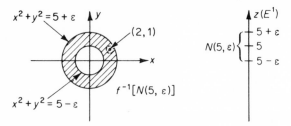

Figure 4-11.6

So far we have only studied examples for which the limit exists. It is also instructive to consider functions which have no limit at certain points.

EXAMPLE 4-11.4: Consider the function $f: E^1 \to E^1$ defined by $f(x) = |x|/x$ for $x \neq 0$, $f(0) = 0$. This function is sometimes called the signum function and written $f(x) = \operatorname{sgn} x$. We shall attempt to find $\lim\limits_{x\to 0} f(x)$. Let $N(0,\delta)$ be any neighborhood of the origin on the x-axis. Then $f[N'(0,\delta)] = \{-1, +1\}$, and so $f[N'(0,\delta)]$ could not be contained in any neighborhood $N(b,\varepsilon)$ when $\varepsilon < 1$, regardless of which point b is considered. Thus, $\lim\limits_{x\to 0} f(x)$ does not exist. (Figures 4-11.7 and 4-11.8.)

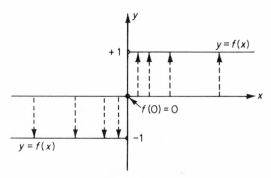

Figure 4-11.7

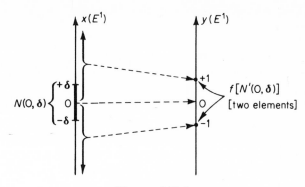

Figure 4-11.8

EXAMPLE 4-11.5: Let $f: E^1 \to E^1$ be defined by $f(x) = \sin(1/x)$ for $x \neq 0$, and $f(0) = 0$. The reader should verify that the graph in Figure 4-11.9 represents this function. Notice that as x approaches 0 from either direction this function oscillates more and more rapidly between -1 and $+1$. Let $N(0,\delta)$ be any neighborhood of $x = 0$. Then $f[N'(0,\delta)] = [-1,+1]$ no matter how large or how small δ is; hence $f[N'(0,\delta)]$ could not be contained in any neighborhood $N(b,\varepsilon)$ when $\varepsilon < 1$, regardless of which point b of

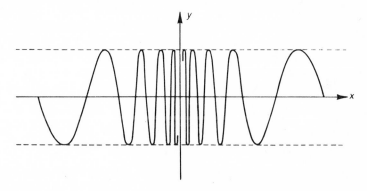

Figure 4-11.9

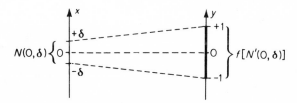

Figure 4-11.10

the y-axis is considered. (Figure 4-11.10.) Therefore, $\lim_{x \to 0} f(x)$ does not exist for this function.

EXAMPLE 4-11.6: Let $f: E^2 \to E^1$ be defined by $f(x,y) = 2xy/(x^2 + y^2)$ for $(x,y) \neq (0,0)$ and $f(0,0) = 0$. If $x = y \neq 0$, then $f(x,y) = 1$; if $x = -y \neq 0$, then $f(x,y) = -1$; and if $x = 0$ or $y = 0$, then $f(x,y) = 0$.

For all pairs of real numbers (x,y) it is true that $(x - y)^2 \geq 0$ or $x^2 - 2xy + y^2 \geq 0$, and so $x^2 + y^2 \geq 2xy$. Replace x by $|x|$ and y by $|y|$ to obtain $x^2 + y^2 \geq 2|xy|$; hence the absolute value of $f(x,y) = 2xy/(x^2 + y^2)$ will

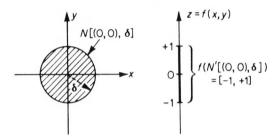

Figure 4-11.11

always be numerically less than or equal to 1. Let $N[(0,0),\delta]$ be any neighborhood of the origin in the xy-plane. Then $f(N'[(0,0),\delta]) = [-1,+1]$, a closed interval. No matter how small δ becomes, there are always points (x,y) in $N'[(0,0),\delta]$ for which $x = y$, $x = -y$, $x = 0$, $y = 0$, and infinitely many others. Thus $f(N'[(0,0),\delta])$ is not contained in any neighborhood $N(b,\varepsilon)$ for which $\varepsilon < 1$; hence $\lim_{(x,y) \to (0,0)} f(x,y)$ does not exist. (Figure 4-11.11).

THEOREM 4-11.1: Given any two metric sets S and T with $f: S \to T$. If $\lim_{x \to a} f(x) = b$ and $\lim_{x \to a} f(x) = c$, where $a \in S$, b and $c \in T$, then $b = c$. In other words, "If the limit exists, then it is unique".

Proof: (Indirect) Assume $b \neq c$. Let $\varepsilon = d(b,c)/3$. Since $\lim_{x \to a} f(x) = b$, there exists a neighborhood $N(a,\delta_1)$ such that $f[N'(a,\delta_1)] \subset N(b,\varepsilon)$; since

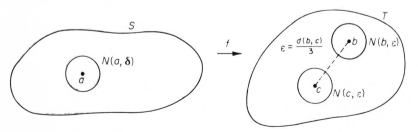

$\lim\limits_{x \to a} f(x) = c$, there exists a neighborhood $N(a,\delta_2)$ such that $f[N'(a,\delta_2)] \subset$
$N(c,\varepsilon)$. Let δ equal the lesser of the two values δ_1 and δ_2; then $f[N'(a,\delta)] \subset$
$N(b,\varepsilon)$ and $f[N'(a,\delta)] \subset N(c,\varepsilon)$. But this is impossible since $N(b,\varepsilon) \cap$
$N(c,\varepsilon) = \varnothing$, and $N'(a,\delta) \neq \varnothing$. (See definition of limit.) Hence the
assumption $b \neq c$ leads to a contradiction and must be abandoned. ▮

EXERCISES

4-11.1. Prove that $\lim\limits_{x \to 3} \dfrac{4x^2 - 17x + 15}{x - 3} = 7$. [Find δ in terms of ε.]

4-11.2. Prove that $\lim\limits_{x \to 1} \dfrac{5 - 8x + 3x^2}{1 - x} = 2$. [Find δ in terms of ε.]

4-11.3. Let $f: E^1 \to E^1$ be defined by $f(x) = x^2$. Find the largest δ such that:
a. $f[N'(2,\delta)] \subset N(4,1/2)$;   b. $f[N'(1,\delta)] \subset N(1,1/2)$;
c. $f[N'(3,\delta)] \subset N(9,1/2)$.
What conclusion can you draw regarding the size of δ for a fixed value of ε,
but at various values of x?

4-11.4. Using the function of Exercise 4-11.3,
a. Verify that $\lim\limits_{x \to 3} f(x) = 9$
b. Verify that $\lim\limits_{x \to a} f(x) = a^2$, for any real number a by proving that

$$f[N'(a,\delta)] \subset N(a^2,\varepsilon) \text{ if } \delta = \sqrt{a^2 + \varepsilon} - |a|.$$

4-11.5. Prove that $f[N'(a,\delta)] \subset N(b,\varepsilon)$ is equivalent to Statement 1 and to Statement
2 on page 76. Prove that Statement 2″ is also equivalent under the condi-
tions given. [cf. Theorem 3-6.3, and Exercises 3-6.6, 3-6.7, and 3-6.11.]

4-11.6. Let $f: E^1 - \{0\} \to E^1$ be defined by $f(x) = x \sin(1/x)$. Prove that

$$\lim\limits_{x \to 0} f(x) = 0$$

by showing $f[N'(0,\delta)] \subset N(0,\varepsilon)$ if $\delta = \varepsilon$.

4-11.7. Let $f: E^2 \to E^1$ be defined by $f(x,y) = x^2 + y^2$.
a. Verify that $\lim\limits_{(x,y) \to (1,1)} f(x,y) = 2$ by proving $f[N'((1,1),\delta)] \subset N(2,\varepsilon)$ if
$\delta = \sqrt{2 + \varepsilon} - \sqrt{2}$;
b. Verify that $\lim\limits_{(x,y) \to (a,b)} f(x,y) = a^2 + b^2$ for any point (a,b) of the plane, by
proving that $f(N'[(a,b),\delta) \subset N(a^2 + b^2,\varepsilon)$ if $\delta = \sqrt{a^2 + b^2 + \varepsilon} - \sqrt{a^2 + b^2}$.

4-12 PROPERTIES OF LIMITS

In order to understand how the basic operations of arithmetic relate to the limits of functions $f: M \to E^1$ from a metric set M to the real numbers, it is useful to first study arithmetic of sets in E^1.

Let A and B denote any two subsets of E^1. Using the usual symbols of operation from arithmetic, we define:

$$A + B = \{a + b \mid a \in A \text{ and } b \in B\};$$
$$A - B = \{a - b \mid a \in A \text{ and } b \in B\};$$
$$A \cdot B = \{a \cdot b \mid a \in A \text{ and } b \in B\}; \text{ and}$$
$$A \div B = \{a \div b \mid a \in A, b \in B, \text{ and } b \neq 0\}.$$

(The expression $A - B$ as defined here applies to the arithmetic of sets, and should not be confused with the earlier use of $A - B$ to designate the complement of set B in set A.)

The following lemmas are stated for E^1.

LEMMA 4-12.1:* $N(p,\varepsilon/2) + N(q,\varepsilon/2) \subset N(p + q, \varepsilon)$.

Proof: Suppose $r \in N(p,\varepsilon/2)$ and $s \in N(q,\varepsilon/2)$; then $|r - p| < \varepsilon/2$ and $|s - q| < \varepsilon/2$. By Theorem 2-7.2,

$$|(r + s) - (p + q)| = |(r - p) + (s - q)|$$
$$\leq |r - p| + |s - q| < \varepsilon/2 + \varepsilon/2 = \varepsilon.$$

Hence $r + s \in N(p + q,\varepsilon)$, and the lemma is proved. ∎

LEMMA 4-12.2:* $N(p,\varepsilon/2) - N(q,\varepsilon/2) \subset N(p - q, \varepsilon)$.
To be proved as an exercise. (Ex. 4-12.1.)

LEMMA 4-12.3: $N(p,\varepsilon') \cdot N(q,\varepsilon') \subset N(p \cdot q, \varepsilon)$, where $\varepsilon' \leq 1$ and $\varepsilon' \leq \varepsilon/(|p| + |q| + 1)$.

Proof: Let $r \in N(p,\varepsilon')$ and $s \in N(q,\varepsilon')$; then $|r - p| < \varepsilon'$ and $|s - q| < \varepsilon'$. Using Theorem 2-7.2, $|rs - pq| = |rs - rq + rq - pq| = |r(s - q) + (r - p)q| \leq |r| \cdot |s - q| + |r - p| \cdot |q| < |r| \varepsilon' + |q| \varepsilon' = (|r| + |q|)\varepsilon' < (|p| + 1 + |q|)\varepsilon' \leq \varepsilon$. Hence $rs \in N(pq,\varepsilon)$, and the lemma is established. (Note that $|r| < |p| + 1$, since $|r| - |p| \leq |r - p| < \varepsilon' \leq 1$. See Exercise 2-7.12.) ∎

---

* It is possible to show that equality, rather than simple inclusion, holds for the cases of addition and subtraction; however, inclusion will suffice for our purposes.

LEMMA 4-12.4: $N(p,\varepsilon') \div N(q,\varepsilon') \subset N(p/q,\varepsilon)$, where $q \neq 0$, $\varepsilon' \leq |q|/2$, and $\varepsilon' \leq q^2\varepsilon/2(|p| + |q|)$. To be proved as an exercise. (Ex. 4-12.2.)

EXAMPLES: By Lemma 4-12.1, $N(1,4) + N(2,4) \subset N(3,8)$, or equivalently, when expressed in open-interval terminology, $(-3,5) + (-2,6) \subset (-5,11)$. Here $\varepsilon = 8$, and $\varepsilon/2 = 4$.
By Lemma 4-12.2, $N(1,4) - N(2,4) \subset N(-1,8)$, or equivalently, $(-3,5) - (-2,6) \subset (-9,7)$. Again $\varepsilon = 8$ and $\varepsilon/2 = 4$. Note that the difference seems easier to compute when these subsets of E^1 are expressed as neighborhoods, rather than as open intervals.
By Lemma 4-12.3, $N(3,1/2) \cdot N(2,1/2) \subset N(6,4)$, or equivalently, $(5/2,7/2) \cdot (3/2,5/2) \subset (2,10)$. Here $p = 3$, $q = 2$, $\varepsilon = 4$, and $\varepsilon' = 1/2$, which is less than $\varepsilon/(|p| + |q| + 1) = 4/(3 + 2 + 1) = 2/3$. Note that in this example, ε' could have been as large as $2/3$ for $\varepsilon = 4$. The reader should verify that $N(3,2/3) \cdot N(2,2/3) \subset N(6,4)$.
By Lemma 4-12.4, $N(3,1/2) \div N(2,1/2) \subset N(3/2,5/4)$. Here $\varepsilon' = 1/2$ while $\varepsilon = 5/4$. The reader should carefully compare the details of this example with the provisions of Lemma 4-12.4.

Now let M be any metric set, and let $f: M \to E^1$ and $g: M \to E^1$ denote any two functions. Define:

$$f + g: M \to E^1 \text{ by } [f + g](x) = f(x) + g(x);$$
$$f - g: M \to E^1 \text{ by } [f - g](x) = f(x) - g(x);$$
$$f \cdot g: M \to E^1 \text{ by } [f \cdot g](x) = f(x) \cdot g(x); \text{ and}$$
$$f \div g: M^- \to E^1 \text{ by } [f \div g](x) = f(x) \div g(x), \text{ where}$$
$$M^- = M - \{x \,|\, g(x) = 0\}.$$

EXAMPLES: Let $f: E^1 \to E^1$ and $g: E^1 \to E^1$ be defined by $f(x) = 3x^2 + 5x + 2$ and $g(x) = x - 1$. Then

$$[f + g](x) = 3x^2 + 6x + 1;$$
$$[f - g](x) = 3x^2 + 4x + 3;$$
$$[f \cdot g](x) = 3x^3 + 2x^2 - 3x - 2;$$

and

$$[f \div g](x) = (3x^2 + 5x + 2)/(x - 1), x \neq 1.$$

THEOREM 4-12.1: Let A represent any subset of M; then

$$[f + g](A) \subset f(A) + g(A);$$
$$[f - g](A) \subset f(A) - g(A);$$
$$[f \cdot g](A) \subset f(A) \cdot g(A);$$

and if $A \subset M^-$, then

$$[f \div g](A) \subset f(A) \div g(A).$$

Proof: Part 1:	*Reason:*
1. Let $y \in [f + g](A)$	Arbitrary choice
2. $[f + g](x) = y$ for some x in A	Definition of image
3. $f(x) + g(x) = y$	Definition of $f + g$
4. $f(x) \in f(A)$ and $g(x) \in g(A)$	Definition of image; $x \in A$
5. $f(x) + g(x) \in f(A) + g(A)$	Definition of the sum of two sets
6. $y \in f(A) + g(A)$	Equality, lines 3 and 5.

The proof of the remaining three parts is left as an exercise. (Ex. 4-12.5.) It is easy to verify that inclusion, rather than equality, is all that can be proved here. Consider, for example, $f(x) = x$ and $g(x) = 1 - x$ defined on the real numbers. Let $A = (0,1)$; then $f(A) = (0,1)$ and $g(A) = (0,1)$; hence $f(A) + g(A) = (0,2)$. But $[f + g](x) = 1$, a constant function; therefore $[f + g](A) = \{1\}$, a single point. Thus $[f + g](A) \neq f(A) + g(A)$. ∎

In Theorems 4-12.2 through 4-12.5, let a be any point of M; assume $f: M \to E^1$, $\lim_{x \to a} f(x) = b$, and $\lim_{x \to a} g(x) = c$.

THEOREM 4-12.2: $\operatorname*{Lim}_{x \to a} [f + g](x) = b + c$.

Proof: Consider any neighborhood $N(b + c, \varepsilon)$ of $b + c$ in E^1; since $\lim_{x \to a} f(x) = b$, there exists a $\delta_1 > 0$ such that $f(N'(a,\delta_1)) \subset N(b,\varepsilon/2)$; and since $\lim_{x \to a} g(x) = c$, there exists a $\delta_2 > 0$ such that $g(N'(a,\delta_2)) \subset N(c,\varepsilon/2)$. Let $\delta > 0$ be the lesser of the two values δ_1 and δ_2. Then $[f + g](N'(a,\delta)) \subset f(N'(a,\delta)) + g(N'(a,\delta)) \subset f(N'(a,\delta_1)) + g(N'(a,\delta_2)) \subset N(b,\varepsilon/2) + N(c,\varepsilon/2) \subset N(b + c, \varepsilon)$, by Theorem 4-12.1 and Lemma 4-12.1. ∎

THEOREM 4-12.3: $\operatorname*{Lim}_{x \to a} [f - g](x) = b - c$.

To be proved as an exercise (Ex. 4-12.6); the proof is very like that of Theorem 4-12.2.

THEOREM 4-12.4: $\operatorname*{Lim}_{x \to a} [f \cdot g](x) = b \cdot c$.

Proof: Consider any neighborhood $N(bc,\varepsilon)$ of bc in E^1. Let $\varepsilon' > 0$ be chosen subject to the conditions $\varepsilon' \leq 1$ and $\varepsilon' \leq \varepsilon/(|b| + |c| + 1)$. Since $\lim_{x \to a} f(x) = b$, there exists a $\delta_1 > 0$ such that $f(N'(a,\delta_1)) \subset N(b,\varepsilon')$; and since $\lim_{x \to a} g(x) = c$, there exists a δ_2 such that $g(N'(a,\delta_2)) \subset N(c,\varepsilon')$. Let $\delta > 0$ be the lesser of the two values δ_1 and δ_2. Then $[f \cdot g](N'(a,\delta)) \subset f(N'(a,\delta)) \cdot g(N'(a,\delta)) \subset f(N'(a,\delta_1)) \cdot g(N'(a,\delta_2)) \subset N(b,\varepsilon') \cdot N(c,\varepsilon') \subset N(b \cdot c, \varepsilon)$, by Theorem 4-12.1 and Lemma 4-12.3. ∎

THEOREM 4-12.5: $\lim_{x \to a} [f \div g](x) = b/c$, if $c \neq 0$.

(To be proved as an exercise.)

The statements of Theorems 4-12.2 through 4-12.5 are frequently written in the form

$$\lim_{x \to a} [f(x) + g(x)] = \lim_{x \to a} f(x) + \lim_{x \to a} g(x);$$

$$\lim_{x \to a} [f(x) - g(x)] = \lim_{x \to a} f(x) - \lim_{x \to a} g(x);$$

$$\lim_{x \to a} [f(x) \cdot g(x)] = \lim_{x \to a} f(x) \cdot \lim_{x \to a} g(x); \text{ and}$$

$$\lim_{x \to a} f(x)/g(x) = \lim_{x \to a} f(x)/\lim_{x \to a} g(x), \text{ if } \lim_{x \to a} g(x) \neq 0.$$

The first statement is read "the limit of the sum of two functions is equal to the sum of the limits of the functions". The second statement is read "the limit of the difference of two functions is equal to the difference of the limits of the functions", etc. These statements are predicated on the assumption that both $\lim_{x \to a} f(x)$ and $\lim_{x \to a} g(x)$ exist.

EXERCISES

4-12.1 Prove Lemma 4-12.2.

4-12.2. Prove Lemma 4-12.4. [*Hint:* First show that if $s \in N(q, \varepsilon')$, then $|s| > |q|/2$; also use the equalities $|r/s - p/q| = (|rq - ps|)/|sq| = (|rq - pq + pq - ps|)/|s| \cdot |q|.$]

4-12.3. Use the Lemmas to verify that:
  a. $N(1,2) + N(4,2) \subset N(5,4)$
  b. $(3,5) + (1,3) \subset (4,8)$
  c. $N(1,3) - N(4,3) \subset N(-3,6)$
  d. $(3,7) - (1,5) \subset (-2,6)$
  e. $N(3,1) \cdot N(4,1) \subset N(12,8)$
  f. $(1,2) \cdot (2,3) \subset (5/4, 25/4)$
  g. $N(6,1) \div N(3,1) \subset N(2,2)$
  h. $(0,4) \div (2,6) \subset (0,2)$

4-12.4. Let $f(x) = 4x^3 - 3x + 3$ and $g(x) = x^2 + x - 2$. Give the formula for $[f + g](x)$; $[f - g](x)$; $[f \cdot g](x)$; $[f/g](x)$. Find the points for which f/g is not defined.

4-12.5. Complete the proof of Theorem 4-12.1.

4-12.6. Prove Theorem 4-12.3.

4-12.7. Prove Theorem 4-12.5.

4-12.8. Let k be any real number. If $\lim\limits_{x \to a} f(x) = b$, prove that $\lim\limits_{x \to a} k \cdot f(x) = kb$.

4-13 ONE-SIDED LIMITS

Let A and B represent subsets of the real numbers and $f: A \to B$ be any function. Let a be a real number such that some deleted neighborhood of a is contained in A. We say that "the limit of $f(x)$ as x approaches a from the left is equal to b," written $\lim\limits_{x \to a^-} f(x) = b$, if and only if, corresponding to every positive number ε, there exists a positive number δ such that $a - \delta < x < a$ and $x \in A$ imply $|f(x) - b| < \varepsilon$. We also say that "the limit of $f(x)$ as x approaches a from the right is equal to c", written $\lim\limits_{x \to a^+} f(x) = c$ if, and only if, corresponding to every positive number ε, there exists a positive number δ such that $a < x < a + \delta$ and $x \in A$ imply $|f(x) - c| < \varepsilon$.

It is easy to prove that $\lim\limits_{x \to a} f(x)$ exists whenever $\lim\limits_{x \to a^+} f(x)$ and $\lim\limits_{x \to a^-} f(x)$ both exist and are equal.

EXERCISES

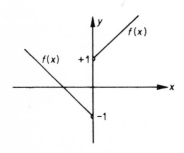

4-13.1. Consider the function $f: E^1 - \{0\} \to E^1$, defined by $f(x) = (x^2 + x)/|x|$. Note that if $x > 0$, then $f(x) = x + 1$, and if $x < 0$, then $f(x) = -x - 1$. Prove that $\lim\limits_{x \to 0^-} f(x) = -1$ and $\lim\limits_{x \to 0^+} f(x) = +1$. [Find δ in terms of ε in each case.]

4-13.2. Graph the functions (a) $f(x) = (|x|/x) + 5$ and (b) $g(x) = (|x - 1|/(x - 1)) + 2x + 1$. Find $\lim\limits_{x \to 0^-} f(x)$; $\lim\limits_{x \to 0^+} f(x)$; $\lim\limits_{x \to 1^-} g(x)$; $\lim\limits_{x \to 1^+} g(x)$. (A careful guess is acceptable for this exercise.)

4-13.3. Assume $\lim\limits_{x \to a^-} f(x) = b$ and $\lim\limits_{x \to a^+} f(x) = b$; that is, the left and right limits exist and are equal. Prove $\lim\limits_{x \to a} f(x) = b$.

4-13.4. Let $\lim\limits_{x \to a^-} f(x) = b$ and $\lim\limits_{x \to a^+} f(x) = c$, where $b \neq c$. Prove that $\lim\limits_{x \to a} f(x)$ does not exist. [*Hint:* Let $\varepsilon = d(b,c)/4$ and consider $N(b,\varepsilon)$ and $N(c,\varepsilon)$. Use an indirect proof.]

5

Continuity
and
Differentiation

5-1 THE DEFINITION OF CONTINUITY

Let A and B represent metric sets, and consider $f: A \to B$. The function f is said to be *continuous at point a* $(a \in A)$ if and only if $\lim_{x \to a} f(x) = f(a)$.*
Note that the continuity of a function f at a point a has three implications:

1. f is defined at a—i.e., $f(a)$ exists;
2. $\lim_{x \to a} f(x)$ exists;
3. $\lim_{x \to a} f(x)$ is equal to $f(a)$.

If any of these three conditions fails, then the function is *discontinuous* at a. We say that f is *continuous on a subset S* of A if and only if f is continuous at each point of S.

EXAMPLE 5-1.1: Refer to Example 4-11.1. The function

$$f(x) = (2x^2 + x - 3)/(x - 1)$$

---

* By the definition of limit, for each neighborhood $N(f(a),\varepsilon)$ there exists a neighborhood $N(a,\delta)$ such that $f[N(a,\delta)] \subset N(f(a),\varepsilon)$.

fails to be continuous at $x = 1$ since $f(1)$ is not defined. However, $\lim_{x \to 1} f(x) =$ 5. If we define $f(1) = 5$, then the function becomes continuous. This is an example of a function with a *removable discontinuity* at $x = 1$. In general, if a function is discontinuous at a point a, and if defining (or re-defining) $f(a)$ would make the function continuous at a, then we say that $f(x)$ has a removable discontinuity at $x = a$.

EXAMPLE 5-1.2: Consider $f: E^1 \to E^1$ defined by $f(x) = x^2$. (See Example 4-11.2 and Exercise 4-11.4b.) This function is continuous at each point a of E^1, since $\lim_{x \to a} f(x) = a^2$ and $f(a) = a^2$.

EXAMPLE 5-1.3: The function $f: E^2 \to E^1$ defined by $f(x) = x^2 + y^2$ (see Example 4-11.3 and Exercise 4-11.7b) is continuous at each point (a,b) of the plane E^2 since $\lim_{(x,y) \to (a,b)} f(x,y) = a^2 + b^2$ and $f(a,b) = a^2 + b^2$.

EXAMPLE 5-1.4: The function $f(x) = |x|/x$ for $x \neq 0$ and $f(0) = 0$ (see Example 4-11.4) is discontinuous at $x = 0$ since $\lim_{x \to 0} f(x)$ does not exist. However, $\lim_{x \to 0^-} f(x) = -1$ and $\lim_{x \to 0^+} f(x) = +1$. This is an example of a *jump discontinuity*. In general we say that a function defined on a subset of the real numbers has a jump discontinuity at $x = a$ if both $\lim_{x \to a^-} f(x)$ and $\lim_{x \to a^+} f(x)$ exist and are not equal. A jump discontinuity cannot be removed by redefining $f(a)$.

EXAMPLE 5-1.5: The function $f(x) = \sin(1/x)$ for $x \neq 0$, and $f(0) = 0$ (see Example 4-11.5) is not continuous at $x = 0$ since $\lim_{x \to 0} f(x)$ does not exist. This is neither a removable discontinuity nor a jump discontinuity.

EXAMPLE 5-1.6: The function $f(x,y) = 2xy/(x^2 + y^2)$ for $(x,y) \neq 0$, and $f(0,0) = 0$ (see Example 4-11.6) is not continuous at $(0,0)$ because $\lim_{(x,y) \to (0,0)} f(x,y)$ does not exist.

EXAMPLE 5-1.7: The "bracket function" or "step-function" $f: E^1 \to E^1$, symbolized by $f(x) = [x]$, and defined by "$f(x)$ is the largest integer less than or equal to x", has domain E^1 and range $\{y \mid y \text{ is an integer}\}$. It is continuous for all values of x except where x is an integer. The discontinuities are jump discontinuities (Figure 5-1.1).

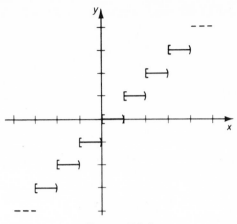

Figure 5-1.1

THEOREM 5-1.1: If functions $f: M \to E^1$ and $g: M \to E^1$ from a metric set M to E^1 are continuous at a point a in M, then the following functions are continuous at a: (1) $f + g$; (2) $f - g$; (3) $f \cdot g$; and (4) $f \div g$, if $g(a) \neq 0$.

Proof: By hypothesis, $\lim\limits_{x \to a} f(x) = f(a)$ and $\lim\limits_{x \to a} g(x) = g(a)$. Now,

(1) $\lim\limits_{x \to a} [f + g](x) = f(a) + g(a)$, by Theorem 4-12.2;

(2) $\lim\limits_{x \to a} [f - g](x) = f(a) - g(a)$, by Theorem 4-12.3;

(3) $\lim\limits_{x \to a} [f \cdot g](x) = f(a) \cdot g(a)$, by Theorem 4-12.4;

(4) $\lim\limits_{x \to a} [f \div g](x) = f(a) \div g(a)$, if $g(a) \neq 0$, by Theorem 4-12.5.

By the definitions of the sum, difference, product, and quotient of functions, $[f + g](a) = f(a) + g(a)$; $[f - g](a) = f(a) - g(a)$; $[f \cdot g](a) = f(a) \cdot g(a)$; and $[f \div g](a) = f(a) \div g(a)$, if $g(a) \neq 0$. This completes the proof. ∎

THEOREM 5-1.2: All polynomials $p(x) = c_0 + c_1 x + c_2 x^2 + \ldots + c_n x^n$, $p: E^1 \to E^1$, are continuous at each point of E^1.

Proof: It is easy to verify that $f(x) = c$, where c is a constant, and $g(x) = x$ are continuous on the entire line E^1. (Exercise 5-1.1.) By Part (3) of Theorem 5-1.1, $f \cdot g(x) = cx$ must also be continuous on E^1. By Part (1) of Theorem 5-1.1, $h(x) = c_1 x + c_0$ is also continuous (the sum of continuous functions is again continuous). By repeatedly using Theorem 5-1.1, we conclude that $p(x) = c_0 + c_1 x + c_2 x^2 + \ldots + c_n x^n$ is continuous on E^1. ∎

COROLLARY 5-1.1: Rational functions $h: E^1 \to E^1$, i.e., quotients of polynomials,

$$h(x) = \frac{a_0 + a_1 x + a_2 x^2 + \ldots + a_m x^m}{b_0 + b_1 x + b_2 x^2 + \ldots + b_n x^n},$$

are continuous for all x except at those points for which $b_0 + b_1 x + b_2 x^2 + \ldots + b_n x^n$ is zero.

Proof:
Theorem 5-1.2 and Part (4) of Theorem 5-1.1 establish this corollary. ∎

EXERCISES

5-1.1. Prove that $f(x) = c$ and $g(x) = x$ are continuous on E^1.

5-1.2. Discuss the continuity of $f(x) = (x^2 + x - 6)/(x - 2)$. Is it possible to define $f(2)$ so that $f(x)$ is continuous on E^1? Graph the function.

5-1.3. Discuss the continuity of $f(x) = x/(x - 2)$. Is it possible to define $f(2)$ so that $f(x)$ is continuous on E^1? Draw a graph.

5-1.4. Prove that $f(x) = |x|$ is continuous at each point of E^1. [*Hint:* Consider separately the cases $x > 0$, $x < 0$, $x = 0$.]

5-1.5. Graph the function $f(x) = |x^2 - x - 12|/(x^2 - x - 12)$ for $x \neq -3$, and $x \neq 4, f(-3) = f(4) = 0$. What type of discontinuity does this function have?

5-1.6. Prove that $f(x) = x \cos(1/x)$ has a removable discontinuity at $x = 0$.

5-1.7. Let $f: E^1 \to \{0, 1\}$ be defined by $f(x) = 1$ if x is rational and $f(x) = 0$ if x is irrational. Prove that $f(x)$ is discontinuous for every x in E^1. [*Hint:* Use the fact that for every two real numbers a and b, $a < b$, there exists a rational number x_1 and an irrational number x_2 such that x_1 and x_2 belong to (a,b).]

5-2 SOME PROPERTIES OF CONTINUOUS FUNCTIONS

THEOREM 5-2.1: Let A, B, and C represent metric sets. If $f: A \to B$ is continuous on A, and $g: B \to C$ is continuous on B, then $gf: A \to C$ is continuous on A.

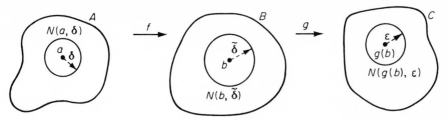

Proof: Let a be any point of A and let $b = f(a)$. Given any neighborhood $N(g(b),\varepsilon)$, there exists a neighborhood $N(b,\tilde{\delta})$ such that

(1) $$g[N(b,\tilde{\delta})] \subset N(g(b),\varepsilon) = N(gf(a),\varepsilon),$$

since g is continuous at b. Now, since f is continuous at a, there exists a neighborhood $N(a,\delta)$ such that

(2) $$f[N(a,\delta)] \subset N(f(a),\tilde{\delta}) = N(b,\tilde{\delta}).$$

From lines (1) and (2),

$$gf[N(a,\delta)] \subset g[N(b,\tilde{\delta})] \subset N(gf(a),\varepsilon).$$

Therefore gf is continuous at a. ∎

For the remainder of this section the letters S and T will denote metric sets.

THEOREM 5-2.2: Let $\{a_n\}$ be any sequence in S. If $\lim_{n\to\infty} a_n = p$ and $f: S \to T$ is continuous at p, then $\lim_{n\to\infty} f(a_n) = f(p)$. ("Continuity preserves sequential limits".)

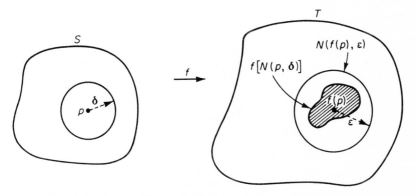

Proof: Consider any neighborhood $N(f(p),\varepsilon)$ in T. Since $f: S \to T$ is continuous at p, there exists a neighborhood $N(p,\delta)$ such that $f[N(p,\delta)] \subset N(f(p),\varepsilon)$. Since $\lim_{n\to\infty} a_n = p$, there exists an integer J such that $a_n \in N(p,\delta)$

for all $n > J$. But this means that $f(a_n) \in f[N(p,\delta)] \subset N(f(p),\varepsilon)$ for all $n > J$; thus $N(f(p),\varepsilon)$ confines the sequence $f(a_1), f(a_2), f(a_3), \ldots$, and so $\lim\limits_{n\to\infty} f(a_n) = f(p)$. ∎

THEOREM 5-2.3: If $f: S \to T$ is continuous and D is an open set in T, then $f^{-1}(D)$ is open in S; (i.e., "the inverse image of an open set is open").

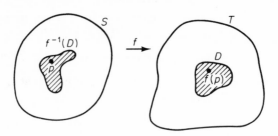

Proof: Let $p \in f^{-1}(D)$; then $f(p) \in D$. There exists a neighborhood $N(f(p),\varepsilon) \subset D$, since D is open. By continuity, there exists a neighborhood $N(p,\delta)$ such that $f(N(p,\delta)) \subset N(f(p),\varepsilon) \subset D$. Therefore $N(p,\delta) \subset f^{-1}(D)$, which proves that $f^{-1}(D)$ is open. ∎

THEOREM 5-2.4: If $f: S \to T$ is continuous and C is a closed set in T, then $f^{-1}(C)$ is closed in S; (i.e., "the inverse image of a closed set is closed").

Proof: Let $D = T - C$. Then D is open, since it is the complement of a closed set.

Now $f^{-1}(D) = f^{-1}(T - C) = f^{-1}(T) - f^{-1}(C) = S - f^{-1}(C)$ by Exercise 3-6.13. Moreover, $f^{-1}(D)$ is open by Theorem 5-2.3. Hence $f^{-1}(C)$ is closed (since $f^{-1}(C)$ is the complement of an open set). ∎

Several illustrations are in order here to show that the image of an open set need not be open, and the image of a closed set need not be closed.

EXAMPLE 5-2.1: Let $f: E^1 \to E^1$ be defined by $f(x) = 2$, a constant. Let $A \subset E^1$ be the open interval $(0,1)$. Now $f(A) = \{2\}$, a set consisting of exactly one point, is closed.

EXAMPLE 5-2.2: Let $f: E^1 \to E^1$ be defined by $f(x) = 1/(1 + x^2)$. Let A be the closed set $\{x \mid x \geq 0\}$; then $f(A) = \{x \mid 0 < x \leq 1\}$, which is not closed.

THEOREM 5-2.5: Let A be a closed and bounded subset of E^m, and let $f: A \to E^n$ be continuous; then $f(A)$ is also closed.

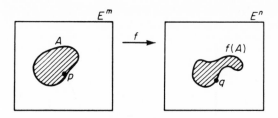

Proof: Let q be any limit point of the set $f(A)$. Every neighborhood $N'(q,1/n)$ contains a point of $f(A)$. Choose $a_n \in A$ such that $f(a_n) \in N'(q,1/n)$ for every positive integer n. The infinite bounded set $\{a_n\}$ has at least one limit point p by the Bolzano-Weierstrass Theorem. Since A is closed, $p \in A$. Choose a subsequence $a_1', a_2', a_3', \ldots$ in $\{a_n\}$ such that $\lim_{n \to \infty} a_n' = p$ (Theorem 4-9.6). By Theorem 5-2.2 $\lim_{n \to \infty} f(a_n') = f(p)$. By construction, $\lim_{n \to \infty} f(a_n') = q$; therefore $q = f(p) \in f(A)$. This proves that $f(A)$ contains all its limit points. $\blacksquare$

THEOREM 5-2.6: Let A be a closed and bounded subset of E^m, and let $f: A \to E^n$ be continuous. Then $f(A)$ is bounded.

Proof: Denote by 0 the origin in E^n. Suppose the theorem is false. Then for each integer n there exists a point $a_n \in A$ such that $d(f(a_n),0) > n$. The infinite bounded set $\{a_n\}$ in A has at least one limit point p, by the Bolzano-Weierstrass Theorem. Since A is closed, $p \in A$. Choose a subsequence $a_1', a_2', a_3', \ldots$ of $\{a_n\}$ such that $\lim_{n \to \infty} a_n' = p$. By continuity, $\lim_{n \to \infty} f(a_n') = f(p)$, and by construction, $\lim_{n \to \infty} f(a_n')$ does not exist. This contradiction arises from the assumption that the theorem is false. $\blacksquare$

COROLLARY 5-2.1: Let A be any closed and bounded subset of E^m, and let $f: A \to E^1$ be continuous. Then there exist two fixed points $u \in A$ and $v \in A$ such that for every point p in A, $f(u) \leq f(p) \leq f(v)$; (minimum and maximum values for f).

Proof: By Theorem 5-2.6, $f(A)$ is bounded. Let $M =$ l.u.b. $f(A)$ and let $m =$ g.l.b. $f(A)$. Thus, $M \geq f(p) \geq m$ for every point p in A. By Theorem 5-2.5, $f(A)$ is closed; hence M and m belong to $f(A)$. [The reader should verify that the l.u.b. and the g.l.b. of a closed set in E^1 belong to the set.] Choose u in A such that $f(u) = m$ and v in A such that $f(v) = M$. This establishes the corollary. $\blacksquare$

THEOREM 5-2.7: (*The Intermediate Value Theorem*) Let $[a,b]$ be any closed interval in E^1, and let $f: [a,b] \to E^1$ be continuous. If k is any real number between $f(a)$ and $f(b)$, then there exists a point $p \in [a,b]$ such that $f(p) = k$.

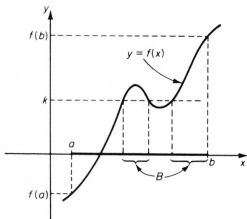

Proof: Suppose $f(a) < k < f(b)$. Let $A = \{x \mid x \in [a,b]$ and $f(x) < k\}$, and let $B = \{x \mid x \in [a,b]$ and $f(x) \geq k\}$. Then $a \in A$, $b \in B$, $A \cap B = \varnothing$, and $A \cup B = [a,b]$. Let $p = $ l.u.b. A; then $a \leq p \leq b$, and p is a boundary point of both A and B. (Every neighborhood $N(p,\delta)$ contains a point of A and a point of B.) Consider any neighborhood $N(f(p),\varepsilon)$;

$$f(N(p,\delta)) \subset N(f(p),\varepsilon)$$

for some δ. Therefore every neighborhood $N(f(p),\varepsilon)$ contains elements greater than or equal to k, as well as elements less than k; hence $f(p) = k$. (A similar proof can be given for $f(a) > k > f(b)$.) ∎

COROLLARY 5-2.2: Let $[a,b]$ be any closed interval in E^1, and let $f: [a,b] \to E^1$ be continuous. Then $f([a,b])$ is either a single point or a closed interval. (To be proved as an exercise.)

EXERCISES

5-2.1. Let C denote a closed and bounded set in E^1. Let $M = $ l.u.b. C and $m = $ g.l.b. C; prove that M and m belong to C.

5-2.2. Prove Corollary 5-2.2. [See Corollary 5-2.1 and Theorem 5-2.7.]

5-2.3. Assume that $f: [a,b] \to E^1$ is a continuous function such that $f(a)$ and $f(b)$ have opposite signs. Prove that there exists a root c of the equation $f(x) = 0$; i.e., $f(c) = 0$ for some number $c \in (a,b)$.

5-2.4. Use Theorem 5-2.7 and the function $f(x) = x^2$ defined on the interval $[1,2]$ to establish the existence of a real number c such that $c^2 = 2$.

5-3 UNIFORM CONTINUITY

Let S and T represent metric sets. Let A be a subset of S containing no isolated points of S^* and consider a function $f: S \to T$. By the definition of continuity and the definition of limit, f is continuous at a point a of A if and only if for every $\varepsilon > 0$ there exists a $\delta > 0$ such that $f[N(a,\delta)] \subset N(f(a),\varepsilon)$. It is important to note that the question of continuity relates to individual points. *Usually, δ not only depends on ε but also on the point a under consideration.*

The function $f: S \to T$ is said to be *uniformly continuous* on A if for every $\varepsilon > 0$ there exists a $\delta > 0$, *depending only on ε*, such that $f[N(a,\delta)] \subset N(f(a),\varepsilon)$ for every point a in A. The important aspect of this definition is that δ *depends only on ε*; that is, δ can be chosen so that it does not depend on individual points a of the set A. The following statement is an equivalent definition: $f: S \to T$ is uniformly continuous on A if for every $\varepsilon > 0$ there exists a $\delta > 0$, depending only on ε, such that $d(a_1,a_2) < \delta$ implies $d(f(a_1), f(a_2)) < \varepsilon$ for every pair of points a_1, a_2 in A.

Uniform continuity always relates to a set. Furthermore, uniform continuity on a set A always implies continuity at each point of A. However, the converse of this last statement is not true.

EXAMPLE 5-3.1: Consider $f: E^1 \to E^1$ defined by $f(x) = x^2$. Given any $\varepsilon > 0$, if $\delta = \sqrt{a^2 + \varepsilon} - |a|$, then $f[N(a,\delta)] \subset N(f(a),\varepsilon)$. (See Exercise 4-11.4b.) Hence f is continuous at each point a in E^1. Let S be any bounded subset of E^1; $S \subset N(0,r)$ for some real number r. We will show that f is uniformly continuous on S. For every $\varepsilon > 0$, choose $\delta = \sqrt{r^2 + \varepsilon} - r$.

Now, $|a| \le r$ implies $\sqrt{a^2 + \varepsilon} - |a| \ge \sqrt{r^2 + \varepsilon} - r$,

so $f[N(a,\delta)] \subset N(f(a),\varepsilon)$ for *every* point a in S — δ does not depend on a.

EXAMPLE 5-3.2: Consider $f: (0,4) \to E^1$ defined by $f(x) = 1/x$. This function is continuous at each point of the interval $(0,4)$. Given any $\varepsilon > 0$, the largest δ such that $f[N(a,\delta)] \subset N(f(a),\varepsilon)$ is given by the formula

$$1/(a - \delta) = 1/a + \varepsilon, \text{ or max } \delta = \varepsilon a^2/(\varepsilon a + 1).$$
$$\text{However, } \lim_{a \to 0} (\text{max } \delta) = \lim_{a \to 0} \varepsilon a^2/(\varepsilon a + 1) = 0.$$

This means that for any given $\varepsilon > 0$, there exists *no* $\delta > 0$ small enough such that $f[N(a,\delta)] \subset N(f(a),\varepsilon)$ for all $a \in (0,4)$. Hence, f is not uniformly continuous on the set $(0,4)$. See Figure 5-3.1.

---

* See footnote, page 75.

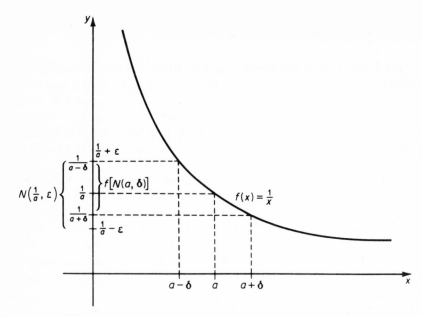

Figure 5-3.1

THEOREM 5-3.1: Let $f: A \to B$ denote a continuous function. If A is a closed and bounded subset of E^n, then f is uniformly continuous on A.

Proof: An indirect proof will be used. Assume that f is continuous but not uniformly continuous on a closed and bounded subset A of E^n. Since f, by our assumption, is not uniformly continuous on A, there exists an $\varepsilon > 0$ such that for every positive integer n, points p_n and q_n in A can be found where $d(p_n, q_n) < 1/n$ but $d(f(p_n), f(q_n)) \geq \varepsilon$. Consider the sequence $p_1, p_2, p_3, \ldots p_n, \ldots$ in A. By the Bolzano-Weierstrass Theorem, there exists at least one point a such that every neighborhood $N(a, \delta)$ contains infinitely many terms of the sequence. Since A is closed, $a \in A$. Choose a subsequence $p'_1, p'_2, p'_3, \ldots, p'_n, \ldots$ of $\{p_n\}$, which converges to a. Let $q'_1, q'_2, q'_3, \ldots, q'_n, \ldots$ be the related subsequence of $\{q_n\}$. Note that $d(p'_n, q'_n) < 1/n$ and $d[f(p'_n), f(q'_n)] \geq \varepsilon$ for each n; moreover, $\{q'_n\}$ must also converge to a. Since f is continuous at a, there exists a neighborhood $N(a, \delta)$ such that $f(N(a, \delta)) \subset N(f(a), \varepsilon/2)$. Now $N(a, \delta)$ confines both $\{p'_n\}$ and $\{q'_n\}$; thus there must exist a pair (p'_n, q'_n), with the same subscript, belonging to $N(a, \delta)$.

So $f(p'_n), f(q'_n) \in f(N(a, \delta)) \subset N(f(a), \varepsilon/2)$,

whence $d[f(p'_n), f(q'_n)] < \varepsilon$. This contradiction forces us to accept the theorem as stated. ∎

EXERCISES

5-3.1. Show that the function $f(x) = x^2$ is not uniformly continuous on E^1.

5-3.2. Prove that the function $f(x) = 1/x$ is uniformly continuous on $(1,4)$.

5-3.3. Prove that the function $f: E^2 \to E^1$ defined by $f(x,y) = x^2 + y^2$ is uniformly continuous on every bounded subset of E^2, but not uniformly continuous on the entire space E^2. (See Exercise 4-11.7b.)

5-4   THE DERIVATIVE

Let $f: E^1 \to E^1$ be any function. For each point $a \in E^1$, we define

$$f'(a) = \lim_{h \to 0} \frac{f(a + h) - f(a)}{h}.$$

If this limit exists, $f(x)$ is said to be differentiable at $x = a$, and $f'(a)$ is called *the derivative of f at a*. A geometric interpretation of this definition is shown in Figure 5-4.1. Here, $g(h) = [f(a + h) - f(a)]/h$ denotes the tangent of the angle of inclination α, or the slope of the line joining points $(a, f(a))$ and $((a + h), f(a + h))$. By definition, $f'(a) = \lim_{h \to 0} g(h)$. Hence $f'(a)$ is equal to the slope of the curve $y = f(x)$ at the point $(a, f(a))$. (The slope of a curve at a given point is defined to be the slope of the tangent line to the curve at that point.)

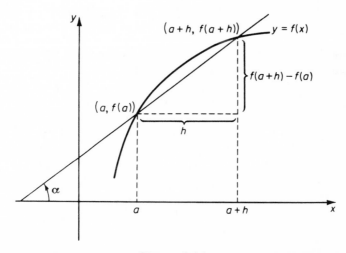

Figure 5-4.1

It should be noted that $g(h) = [f(a + h) - f(a)]/h$ is not defined at $h = 0$. However, this fact has no bearing on the $\lim_{h \to 0} g(h)$. (See definition of limit.)

The reader undoubtedly remembers this definition of the derivative from his work in elementary calculus. Some portions of the following work will be a review of this important concept.

EXAMPLE 5-4.1: Find the derivative of $f: E^1 \to E^1$ given by $f(x) = \sqrt{x}$, at $x = 1$ (Figure 5-4.2). By definition, $f'(1) = \lim_{h \to 0} \dfrac{\sqrt{1 + h} - 1}{h}$; rationalizing the numerator, this becomes

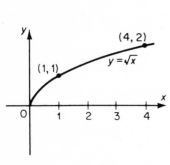

$$\lim_{h \to 0} \frac{\sqrt{1 + h} - 1}{h} \cdot \frac{\sqrt{1 + h} + 1}{\sqrt{1 + h} + 1}$$

$$= \lim_{h \to 0} \frac{1 + h - 1}{h(\sqrt{1 + h} + 1)}$$

$$= \lim_{h \to 0} \frac{1}{\sqrt{1 + h} + 1} = 1/2.$$

It is possible to replace $h/[h(\sqrt{1 + h} + 1)]$ by $1/(\sqrt{1 + h} + 1)$ since these two functions differ only at $h = 0$; consequently the limit as $h \to 0$ is not affected.

Figure 5-4.2

EXAMPLE 5-4.2: Given $f: E^1 \to E^1$ defined by $f(x) = |x|$. Find the derivative (if it exists) at $x = 0$ (Figure 5-4.3). By definition,

$$f'(0) = \lim_{h \to 0} \frac{|0 + h| - |0|}{h} = \lim_{h \to 0} \frac{|h|}{h}.$$

Study the function $g(h) = |h|/h$, graphed in Figure 5-4.4; $\lim_{h \to 0} g(h)$ does not exist (see Example 4-11.4); hence $f'(0)$ does not exist.

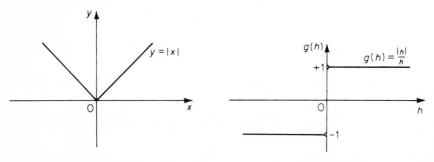

Figure 5-4.3   **Figure 5-4.4**

THEOREM 5-4.1: If $f: E^1 \to E^1$ and $f(x)$ is differentiable at $x = a$, then $f(x)$ is continuous at a.

Proof: Since $f(x)$ is differentiable at a, $f'(x) = \lim_{h \to 0} [f(a + h) - f(a)]/h$ exists. Now,

$$\lim_{h \to 0} [f(a + h) - f(a)] = \lim_{h \to 0} \frac{f(a + h) - f(a)}{h} \cdot h = [f'(a)] \cdot 0 = 0.$$

This means that $\lim_{h \to 0} f(a + h) = f(a)$. Let $x = a + h$; then $h \to 0$ implies $x \to a$, and we may write

$$\lim_{x \to a} f(x) = \lim_{h \to 0} f(a + h) = f(a).$$

This is the definition of continuity of f at the point a. ∎

The converse of Theorem 5-4.1 is not valid; that is, we cannot conclude that if a function is continuous at some point $x = a$ then it is necessarily differentiable there. The function $f(x) = |x|$, of Example 5-4.2 above, is continuous at $x = 0$, but not differentiable at $x = 0$.

The definition of the derivative is often written in the form

$$f'(x) = \lim_{h \to 0} \frac{f(x + h) - f(x)}{h} .$$

It is important to remember that x is held constant and h is the variable when evaluating this limit. Using this notation, $f'(x)$ is the slope of the curve $y = f(x)$ at the point $(x, f(x))$. The derivative is also denoted by symbols $D_x f(x), f', dy/dx, df(x)/dx, y'$, etc.

Often, the less precise notations Δx instead of h and Δy instead of $f(x + \Delta x) - f(x)$ are used. The symbol Δx is referred to as "a change in the variable x", and Δy is called "the corresponding change in y". The definition of the derivative is then written $dy/dx = \lim_{\Delta x \to 0} \Delta y/\Delta x$. (See Figure 5-4.5.)

EXAMPLE 5-4.3: Find $f'(x)$ for $f(x) = x^n$, where n is a positive integer. By definition,

$$f'(x) = \lim_{h \to 0} \frac{(x + h)^n - x^n}{h}$$

$$= \lim_{h \to 0} \frac{x^n + nx^{n-1}h + [n(n - 1)/2!]x^{n-2}h^2 + \cdots + nxh^{n-1} + h^n - x^n}{h}$$

(using the binomial formula to expand $(x + h)^n$).

Hence $f'(x) = \lim_{h \to 0} [nx^{n-1} + n(n - 1)x^{n-2}h/2!$

$$+ n(n - 1)(n - 2)x^{n-3}h^2/3! + \cdots + h^{n-1}] = nx^{n-1}.$$

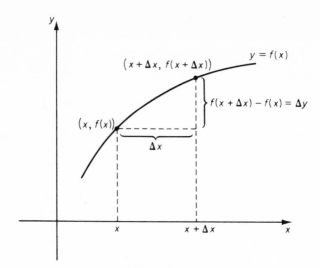

Figure 5-4.5

EXAMPLE 5-4.4: Given $f(x) = \sin x$; find $f'(x)$ at any point x. First it is necessary to evaluate two special limits:

$$(1) \quad \lim_{h \to 0} \frac{\sin h}{h} \quad \text{and} \quad (2) \quad \lim_{h \to 0} \frac{\cos h - 1}{h},$$

where h is measured in radians.

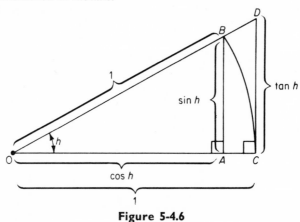

Figure 5-4.6

Part 1: Since $(\sin h)/h = [\sin(-h)]/-h$, we need only consider the case for which $h > 0$. Figure 5-4.6 illustrates the sector of a unit circle with center at O. The central angle AOB is equal to h, and the segments BA and DC are perpendicular to OC. The area of the right triangle OAB inside the sector is given by $(\sin h)(\cos h)/2$; the area of the sector OCB is given by $(h/2\pi)\pi$ or $h/2$; and the area of the right triangle OCD outside the sector is given by $(\tan h)/2$. Therefore, $(\sin h)(\cos h)/2 \leq h/2 \leq (\tan h)/2$. Dividing by $(\sin h)/2$, we have $\cos h \leq h/(\sin h) \leq 1/\cos h$, and since $\lim\limits_{h \to 0} \cos h =$

$$\lim_{h \to 0} \frac{1}{\cos h} = 1, \text{ we conclude that } \lim_{h \to 0} \frac{h}{\sin h} = 1, \text{ and consequently } \lim_{h \to 0} \frac{\sin h}{h} = 1.$$

Part 2: To prove that

$$\lim_{h \to 0} \frac{\cos h - 1}{h} = 0.$$

$$\lim_{h \to 0} \frac{\cos h - 1}{h} \cdot \frac{\cos h + 1}{\cos h + 1} = \lim_{h \to 0} \frac{\cos^2 h - 1}{h(\cos h + 1)}$$

$$= \lim_{h \to 0} \frac{-\sin^2 h}{h(\cos h + 1)}$$

$$= \lim_{h \to 0} \frac{\sin h}{h} \cdot \frac{-\sin h}{\cos h + 1}$$

$$= 1 \cdot 0 = 0.$$

Now we can easily find the derivative of $f(x) = \sin x$ by writing

$$f'(x) = \lim_{h \to 0} \frac{\sin (x + h) - \sin x}{h}$$

$$= \lim_{h \to 0} \frac{\sin x \cdot \cos h + \cos x \cdot \sin h - \sin x}{h}$$

$$= \lim_{h \to 0} \left[(\sin x) \frac{\cos h - 1}{h} + \frac{\sin h}{h} (\cos x) \right]$$

$$= \sin x \cdot 0 + 1 \cdot \cos x = \cos x. \quad \blacksquare$$

THEOREM 5-4.2: If $f(x)$ and $g(x)$ are differentiable at some point x in E^1 and c is a constant, then the following functions are also differentiable at x: $cf(x); f(x) + g(x); f(x) - g(x); f(x) \cdot g(x); f(x)/g(x)$ if $g(x) \neq 0$. Moreover, (i) $D_x[c \cdot f(x)] = c \cdot D_x f(x)$; (ii) $D_x[f(x) + g(x)] = D_x f(x) + D_x g(x)$; (iii) $D_x[f(x) - g(x)] = D_x f(x) - D_x g(x)$; (iv) $D_x[f(x) \cdot g(x)] = f(x) \cdot D_x g(x) + g(x) \cdot D_x f(x)$; and (v) $D_x[f(x)/g(x)] = [g(x) \cdot D_x f(x) - f(x) \cdot D_x g(x)]/(g(x))^2$, if $g(x) \neq 0$. (The proofs of parts (i), (ii), (iii), and (v) are left as exercises; the proof of part (iv) is presented here.)

Proof:

$$D_x[f(x) \cdot g(x)] = \lim_{h \to 0} \frac{f(x+h) \cdot g(x+h) - f(x) \cdot g(x)}{h}$$

$$= \lim_{h \to 0} \frac{f(x+h) \cdot g(x+h) - f(x+h) \cdot g(x) + f(x+h) \cdot g(x) - f(x) \cdot g(x)}{h}$$

$$= \lim_{h \to 0} f(x+h) \frac{g(x+h) - g(x)}{h} + g(x)\frac{f(x+h) - f(x)}{h}$$

$$= f(x) \cdot D_x g(x) + g(x) \cdot D_x f(x). \quad \blacksquare$$

EXERCISES

5-4.1. Using only the definition of a derivative, find $f'(x)$ for each of the following:
(a) $f(x) = x^3 + 2x + 4$; (b) $f(x) = 1/x^2$; (c) $f(x) = (3x + 2)/(5x - 4)$;
(d) $f(x) = \cos x$; (e) $f(x) = \sqrt[3]{x}$.

5-4.2. Prove parts (i), (ii), (iii), and (v) of Theorem 5-4.2.

5-4.3. Let $f: A \to E^1$ be a continuous function where $A \subset E^1$. Prove that

$$\lim_{h \to 0} [f(a + h) - f(a)] = 0$$

for every point a in A. This fact is often referred to in"delta" notation by the statement: "If f is continuous, then Δy approaches 0 when Δx approaches 0" or "$\Delta y \to 0$ when $\Delta x \to 0$".

5-4.4. Graph the function $f(x) = |x^2 + x - 2|$. Follow the pattern given in Example 5-4.2 to prove that $f'(1)$ and $f'(-2)$ do not exist. (Graph $g(h)$ in each case.)

5-5 THE CHAIN RULE

The "delta" notation mentioned on page 101 is especially useful in considerations relating to composition of functions. Let $f: E^1 \to E^1$ and $g: E^1 \to E^1$ be differentiable functions represented by $u = f(x)$ and $y = g(u)$, respectively. Then $y = g(u) = g[f(x)] = gf(x)$. Consider a change Δx in the variable x, with corresponding changes Δu and Δy in u and y, respectively. (See Figure 5-5.1.)

THEOREM 5-5.1: Under the conditions given above, $dy/dx = (dy/du)(du/dx)$. (This theorem can also be expressed by the equivalent formula $D_x[gf(x)] = D_u g(u) \cdot D_x f(x)$.)

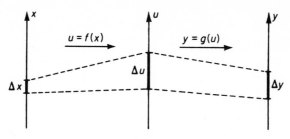

Figure 5-5.1

Proof: If we could assume that $\Delta u \neq 0$ when $\Delta x \neq 0$, the proof would be very simple: $dy/dx = \lim_{\Delta x \to 0} \Delta y/\Delta x = \lim_{\Delta x \to 0} (\Delta y/\Delta u) \cdot (\Delta u/\Delta x) =$ $\lim_{\Delta x \to 0} (\Delta y/\Delta u) \cdot \lim_{\Delta x \to 0} (\Delta u/\Delta x) = \lim_{\Delta u \to 0} (\Delta y/\Delta u) \cdot \lim_{\Delta x \to 0} (\Delta u/\Delta x) = dy/du \cdot du/dx.$ (Note that $\Delta x \to 0$ implies $\Delta u \to 0$ by Theorem 5-4.1 and Exercise 5-4.3.) If, however, $\Delta u = 0$ when $\Delta x \neq 0$, then the equation $\Delta y/\Delta x = \Delta y/\Delta u \cdot \Delta u/\Delta x$ cannot be used. To avoid this difficulty we define a function h of the variable Δu as follows:

Let

$h(\Delta u) = \Delta y/\Delta u - dy/du$ if $\Delta u \neq 0$, and $h(\Delta u) = 0$ if $\Delta u = 0$.

Then $\qquad \lim_{\Delta x \to 0} h(\Delta u) = \lim_{\Delta u \to 0} h(\Delta u) = dy/du - dy/du = 0.$

Now $\Delta y = (dy/du) \cdot \Delta u + h(\Delta u) \cdot \Delta u$ is valid whether Δu is 0 or not.

Therefore $\lim_{\Delta x \to 0} \Delta y/\Delta x = \lim_{\Delta x \to 0} [(dy/du) \cdot (\Delta u/\Delta x) + h(\Delta u) \cdot (\Delta u/\Delta x)]$

$= (dy/du) \cdot (du/dx) + 0 \cdot (du/dx)$ or $dy/dx = dy/du \cdot du/dx.$ ∎

EXAMPLE 5-5.1: Differentiate $y = (1 + x^3)^{40}$. Let $u = f(x) = 1 + x^3$ and $y = g(u) = u^{40}$. Then $y = gf(x) = (1 + x^3)^{40}$. From the equation $dy/dx = dy/du \cdot du/dx$, we get

$$dy/dx = 40 \cdot u^{39} \cdot (3x^2) = 40(1 + x^3)^{39}(3x^2) = 120x^2(1 + x^3)^{39}.$$

EXERCISE

5-5.1. Express each of the following as the composition of two functions $y = g(u)$ and $u = f(x)$, and find dy/dx by the chain rule: (a) $y = (4x^2 + 3x + 2)^{10}$; (b) $y = \sin(2x^3 + 3x)$; (c) $y = [\cos(2x)]^9$.

5-6 THE MEAN VALUE THEOREM FOR DERIVATIVES

In this section, f will denote a function from a subset of E^1 to E^1.

LEMMA 5-6.1: Assume f is differentiable at each point in the open interval (a,b). If there exists a point $v \in (a,b)$ such that $f(v) \geq f(x)$ for all $x \in (a,b)$, then $f'(v) = 0$; also, if there exists a point $u \in (a,b)$ such that $f(u) \leq f(x)$ for all $x \in (a,b)$, then $f'(u) = 0$.

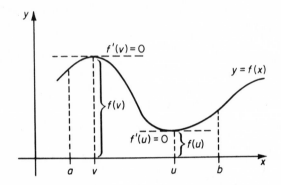

Proof: Consider

$$f'(v) = \lim_{h \to 0} \frac{f(v + h) - f(v)}{h}.$$

Since $f(v + h) \leq f(v)$ for all values $v + h \in (a,b)$, the quotient $\dfrac{f(v + h) - f(v)}{h}$ is negative or 0 for $h > 0$ and positive or 0 for $h < 0$. Therefore

$$f'(v) = \lim_{h \to 0} \frac{f(v + h) - f(v)}{h}$$

must equal zero. (The reader should furnish the proof of the second part of this lemma.) ▮

THEOREM 5-6.1: *Rolle's Theorem:* If (1) $f'(x)$ exists for every x in an open interval (a,b), (2) f is continuous at a and at b, and (3) $f(a) = f(b)$, then there exists a number $z \in (a,b)$ such that $f'(z) = 0$.

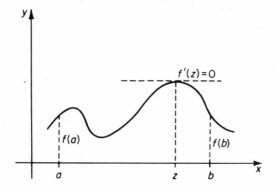

Proof: Case 1. If $f(x) = c$, where c is a constant, for all $x \in (a,b)$, then $f'(x) = 0$ for all $x \in (a,b)$ by the definition of the derivative.

Case 2. Suppose $f(x) > f(a)$ for some $x \in (a,b)$. By Hypotheses (1), (2), and Theorem 5-4.1 $f(x)$ is continuous in the closed interval $[a,b]$. Hence, by Corollary 5-2.1, there exists a point $v \in [a,b]$ such that $f(v) \geq f(x)$ for all $x \in [a,b]$. Moreover, since $f(a) = f(b)$ and $f(a)$ is not the maximum value of $f(x)$ in $[a,b]$, v must belong to (a,b). By the preceding lemma, $f'(v) = 0$.

Case 3. Suppose $f(x) < f(a)$ for some $x \in (a,b)$. Since $f(x)$ is continuous in the closed interval $[a,b]$, there exists a point $u \in [a,b]$ such that $f(u) \leq f(x)$ for all $x \in [a,b]$. Moreover, since $f(a) = f(b)$ and $f(a)$ is not the minimum value of $f(x)$ in $[a,b]$, u must belong to (a,b). By the preceding lemma, $f'(u) = 0$. ∎

The geometric interpretation of Rolle's Theorem is that the graph of the function f, under the stated conditions, has a horizontal tangent for *at least* one point $(z, f(z))$, where $z \in (a,b)$. In the figure accompanying Rolle's Theorem, there are two more points, not marked, in (a,b) which could serve as z.

THEOREM 5-6.2: *Mean Value Theorem for Derivatives:* If (1) $f'(x)$ exists for every x in the open interval (a,b), and (2) f is continuous at a and at b, then there exists a number $z \in (a,b)$ such that $f'(z) = \dfrac{f(b) - f(a)}{b - a}$.

Proof: Let function F be defined as follows: $F(x) = [f(b) - f(a)] \cdot x - [b - a] \cdot f(x)$. By Theorem 5-4.2, $F'(x)$ exists for every $x \in (a,b)$, and $F'(x) = [f(b) - f(a)] - (b - a) \cdot f'(x)$. By Theorem 5-1.1, the function $F(x)$ is continuous at a and at b. Also, $F(a) = F(b)$. The function F satisfies all the conditions of Rolle's Theorem; consequently there exists a

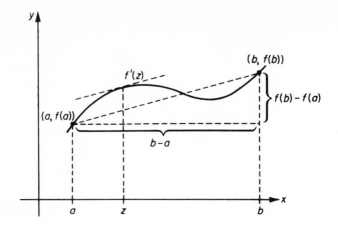

number $z \in (a,b)$ such that $F'(z) = 0$. Thus $[f(b) - f(a)] - (b - a) \cdot f'(z) = 0$, or $f'(z) = \dfrac{f(b) - f(a)}{b - a}$. ∎

The geometric interpretation of the mean value theorem for derivatives is that the graph of the function f, under the stated conditions, has a point $(z, f(z))$, where $z \in (a,b)$, at which the slope of the tangent to the curve is the same as the slope of the line joining points $(a, f(a))$ and $(b, f(b))$. There may, of course, be several such points on the graph of f.

An alternate, and slightly less general, form for this theorem is often used. Suppose $f'(x)$ exists for each point x in $[a,b]$. If $[x, x + \Delta x] \subset [a,b]$, then there exists a point $z \in (x, x + \Delta x)$ such that $\dfrac{f(x + \Delta x) - f(x)}{\Delta x} = f'(z)$, or $f(x + \Delta x) - f(x) = f'(z) \cdot \Delta x$.

5-7 TWO CONSEQUENCES OF THE MEAN VALUE THEOREM

THEOREM 5-7.1: Given any interval $[a,b] \subset E^1$ and any function $f: [a,b] \to E^1$ such that $f'(x) = 0$ for all $x \in [a,b]$. Then $f(x) = c$, a constant.

Proof: Let x be any point in (a,b). By the Mean Value Theorem, there exists a point $z \in (a,x)$ such that $f'(z) = \dfrac{f(x) - f(a)}{x - a}$; but $f'(z) = 0$, by hypothesis. Therefore $f(x) = f(a)$ for all $x \in [a,b]$. ∎

THEOREM 5-7.2: Let $f: [a,b] \to E^1$ and $g: [a,b] \to E^1$ be any two differentiable functions such that $f'(x) = g'(x)$ for all $x \in [a,b]$. Then $f(x) - g(x) = c$, a constant.

Proof: Let $h(x) = f(x) - g(x)$. Now $h'(x) = f'(x) - g'(x) = 0$ for all $x \in [a,b]$. By Theorem 5-7.1, $h(x) = c$. $\blacksquare$

EXERCISES

5-7.1. Complete the proof of Lemma 5-6.1.

5-7.2. Find z, as prescribed by Rolle's Theorem, for
  (a) $f(x) = \sin x$, $[0,\pi]$
  (b) $f(x) = x^3 - 3x^2 - x + 3$, $[1,3]$

5-7.3. Find z, as prescribed by the Mean Value Theorem, for
  (a) $f(x) = \ln x$, $[1,e]$
  (b) $f(x) = Ax^2 + Bx + C$, $[a,b]$

5-7.4. Let $f: [a,b] \to E^1$ be any function such that $f'(x)$ exists and $f'(x) \neq 0$ for all $x \in [a,b]$. Prove that f is strictly monotonic on $[a,b]$.

5-8 THE GENERALIZED MEAN VALUE THEOREM

THEOREM 5-8.1: Let $f(x)$ and $g(x)$ be differentiable in the open interval (a,b) and continuous at a and at b; then, if $g'(x) \neq 0$ for all x in (a,b), there exists a value $z \in (a,b)$ such that

$$\frac{f'(z)}{g'(z)} = \frac{f(b) - f(a)}{g(b) - g(a)}.$$

The reader can readily see that if $g(x) = x$, then $g'(x) = 1$, and $g(b) - g(a) = b - a$, giving the Mean Value Theorem in its original form—a special case of this *Generalized Form.*

Proof: Define a new function $H(x)$ as follows:

$$H(x) = [f(b) - f(a)] \cdot g(x) - [g(b) - g(a)] \cdot f(x).$$

Now $H'(x)$ exists and is equal to $[f(b) - f(a)] \cdot g'(x) - [g(b) - g(a)] \cdot f'(x)$ for all $x \in (a,b)$. The function $H(x)$ is continuous at a and at b, since $f(x)$ and $g(x)$ are continuous at these points. Moreover, $H(a) = H(b)$; therefore, by Rolle's Theorem, $H'(z) = 0$, or equivalently,

$$[f(b) - f(a)] \cdot g'(z) - [g(b) - g(a)] \cdot f'(z) = 0$$

for some $z \in (a,b)$. Note that $g(b) \neq g(a)$, since $g(b) = g(a)$ would imply that $g'(x) = 0$ for some value x in (a,b), contrary to hypothesis.

Hence $[f(b) - f(a)] \cdot g'(z) - [g(b) - g(a)] \cdot f'(z) = 0$

may be written in the form

$$\frac{f'(z)}{g'(z)} = \frac{f(b) - f(a)}{g(b) - g(a)}. \quad \blacksquare$$

THEOREM 5-8.2: *L'Hospital's Rule:* Let $f(x)$ and $g(x)$ represent functions which are differentiable at each point of a neighborhood $N(a,\varepsilon)$. Assume $f(a) = g(a) = 0$ and $g'(x) \neq 0$ for all $x \in N'(a,\varepsilon)$. If

$$\lim_{x \to a} \frac{f'(x)}{g'(x)}$$

exists, then

$$\lim_{x \to a} \frac{f(x)}{g(x)}$$

also exists and

$$\lim_{x \to a} \frac{f(x)}{g(x)} = \lim_{x \to a} \frac{f'(x)}{g'(x)}.$$

Proof: By the Generalized Mean Value Theorem (5-8.1), for each $x \in N'(a,\varepsilon)$ there exists a point z between a and x such that

$$\frac{f(x) - f(a)}{g(x) - g(a)} = \frac{f'(z)}{g'(z)}.$$

Since $f(a) = g(a) = 0$, $f(x)/g(x) = f'(z)/g'(z)$. Since z lies between a and x, $x \to a$ implies $z \to a$. Thus,

$$\lim_{x \to a} \frac{f(x)}{g(x)} = \lim_{x \to a} \frac{f'(z)}{g'(z)} = \lim_{z \to a} \frac{f'(z)}{g'(z)}.$$

The value of

$$\lim_{z \to a} \frac{f'(z)}{g'(z)}$$

does not depend on the choice of the letter representing the independent variable (i.e., z can be replaced by any letter); consequently,

$$\lim_{x \to a} \frac{f(x)}{g(x)} = \lim_{x \to a} \frac{f'(x)}{g'(x)}. \quad \blacksquare$$

EXAMPLE 5-8.1: Evaluate

$$\lim_{x \to 0} \frac{\sin x}{x}$$

by L'Hospital's Rule. Note that $f(x) = \sin x$ and $g(x) = x$ satisfy the necessary conditions.

$$\lim_{x \to 0} \frac{\sin x}{x} = \lim_{x \to 0} \frac{\cos x}{1} = 1.$$

EXERCISES

5-8.1. Find z as prescribed by the Generalized Mean Value Theorem for:
   (a) $f(x) = \sqrt{x}, g(x) = 2x + 1$; [1,4].
   (b) $f(x) = 2x + 5, g(x) = x^2$; $[a,b]$ where $a > 0$.

5-8.2. Use L'Hospital's Rule to evaluate the following:
   (a) $\lim_{x \to \pi/2} \dfrac{\cos x}{x - \pi/2}$ (b) $\lim_{x \to 2} \dfrac{3x^2 - 7x + 2}{x^2 + 2x - 8}$
   (c) $\lim_{x \to 0} \dfrac{\sin x - x}{x^3}$ [*Hint:* It is often necessary to apply the rule several times in succession.]

5-8.3. Criticize the following argument:
$$\lim_{x \to 1} \frac{2x^2 - x - 1}{x^2 - x} = \lim_{x \to 1} \frac{4x - 1}{2x - 1} = \lim_{x \to 1} \frac{4}{2} = 2$$

5-9 DIFFERENTIAL NOTATION

Consider $f: (a,b) \to E^1$, where $(a,b) \subset E^1$ and f is differentiable at each point of (a,b). Then

$$\lim_{h \to 0} \frac{f(x + h) - f(x)}{h} = f'(x)$$

implies that

$$\frac{f(x + h) - f(x)}{h} \sim f'(x)$$

if h is small. (The symbol $\sim$ means "approximately equal to".) Let

$$\varepsilon = \frac{f(x + h) - f(x)}{h} - f'(x);$$

then $f(x + h) - f(x) = (f'(x) + \varepsilon) \cdot h$. Figure 5-9.1 illustrates the difference between $f(x + h) - f(x)$ and $f'(x) \cdot h$.

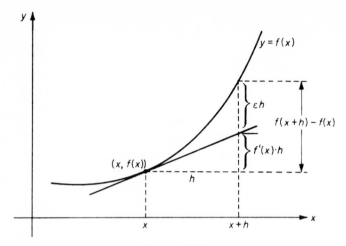

Figure 5-9.1

Geometrically, $|\varepsilon h|$ represents the distance between the curve and the tangent measured along the vertical line at $x + h$. Now

$$\lim_{h \to 0} \varepsilon = \lim_{h \to 0} \left[\frac{f(x + h) - f(x)}{h} - f'(x) \right] = f'(x) - f'(x) = 0;$$

hence $f(x + h) - f(x) = (f'(x) + \varepsilon)h \sim f'(x)h$ for small values of h.* Using delta notation, this approximation is written

$$\Delta y \sim f'(x)\, \Delta x.$$

The expression $f'(x) \cdot h$, used to approximate $f(x + h) - f(x)$, is called *the differential of f at x with increment h*, and is represented by the symbol $df(x;h)$, (or merely df); that is,

$$df(x;h) = f'(x) \cdot h$$

In more elementary texts, h is denoted dx, and $df(x;h)$ is represented by dy. The resulting formula is $dy = f'(x)\, dx$. The symbol dy/dx for the derivative introduced earlier did not attach separate meanings to either dy or dx.

EXERCISES

In Exercises 5-9.1 and 5-9.2, find both $\Delta y = f(x + h) - f(x)$ and the differential approximation $dy = df(x;h)$ for the function $y = f(x)$ and the values of x and h given:

5-9.1. $f(x) = 3x^2 - 2x + 1$; a. $x = 1$, $h = 1$; b. $x = 1$, $h = .1$; c. $x = 1$, $h = .01$; d. $x = 1, h = .001$.

---

* The product εh is small compared to h since $\varepsilon \to 0$ when $h \to 0$.

5-9.2. $f(x) = 1/(x + 2)$; a. $x = 3$, $h = 1$; b. $x = 3$, $h = .1$; c. $x = 3$, $h = .01$.

5-9.3. Approximate $\sqrt[5]{.98}$. [*Hint:* Consider $f(x) = \sqrt[5]{x}$ at $x = 1$, where $h = -.02$; solve for dy.]

5-9.4. Approximate $\sqrt[3]{8.01}$.

5-9.5. Approximate $\sin 31°$. [*Hint:* $x = \pi/6$, $h = \pi/180$.]

5-10 PARTIAL DIFFERENTIATION

Let A be an open subset of E^2, and let $f: A \to E^1$ be denoted by $z = f(x,y)$. Partial derivatives are defined by holding either x or y constant while the other varies. The formulas

$$f_x(x,y) = \lim_{h \to 0} \frac{f(x + h, y) - f(x,y)}{h} \quad \text{and} \quad f_y(x,y) = \lim_{k \to 0} \frac{f(x, y + k) - f(x,y)}{k}$$

define the partial derivative of f with respect to x and the partial derivative of f with respect to y, respectively. Other notations in common use for $f_x(x,y)$ are

$$f_x, \frac{\partial z}{\partial x}, \frac{\partial f}{\partial x}, \frac{\partial f(x,y)}{\partial x},$$

and similarly for $f_y(x,y)$.

EXAMPLE 5-10.1: Let $f: E^2 \to E^1$ be defined by $f(x,y) = x^2y + 3y^2 - 7$. Then

$$f_x(x,y) = \lim_{h \to 0} \frac{[(x + h)^2 y + 3y^2 - 7] - [x^2y + 3y^2 - 7]}{h}$$

$$= \lim_{h \to 0} \frac{x^2y + 2hxy + h^2y + 3y^2 - 7 - x^2y - 3y^2 + 7}{h}$$

$$= \lim_{h \to 0} \frac{2hxy + h^2y}{h} = \lim_{h \to 0} \frac{2xy + hy}{1} = 2xy.$$

EXERCISES

5-10.1. Use the definition for $f_y(x,y)$ to show that the partial derivative of $f(x,y) = x^2y + 3y^2 - 7$ with respect to y is equal to $x^2 + 6y$.

5-10.2. Let $f: E^3 \to E^1$ be denoted by $u = f(x,y,z)$. The partial derivatives f_x, f_y, f_z are defined by holding precisely two of the variables constant while the other, indicated as a subscript of f, varies. Provide (limit) formulas defining

$f_x(x,y,z), f_y(x,y,z)$, and $f_z(x,y,z)$, and evaluate each of these partial derivatives for $f(x,y,z) = x^2y^3z - 3xy - z^2$.

5-11 THE TOTAL DIFFERENTIAL

Let $z = f(x,y)$ be any function $f: A \to E^1$, where A is an open subset of E^2. Assume that the partial derivatives f_x and f_y exist at every point in some neighborhood of a fixed point (x_0,y_0) of A and that f_x and f_y are continuous at (x_0,y_0). The object of this section is to find an approximation for the change $f(x_0 + h,\ y_0 + k) - f(x_0,y_0)$ in functional value corresponding to small changes h and k in x and y, respectively. Now

(1) $f(x_0 + h, y_0 + k) - f(x_0,y_0) = [f(x_0 + h,\ y_0 + k) - f(x_0,\ y_0 + k)] +$
$\qquad [f(x_0,\ y_0 + k) - f(x_0,y_0)]$, (add and subtract $f(x_0,\ y_0 + k)$).

For the moment, hold k constant and apply the Mean Value Theorem to the function $f(x,\ y_0 + k)$ of the variable x to obtain a real number v between x_0 and $x_0 + h$ such that

(2) $\dfrac{f(x_0 + h,\ y_0 + k) - f(x_0,\ y_0 + k)}{h} = f_x(v,\ y_0 + k)$.

Apply the Mean Value Theorem to the function $f(x_0,y)$ of the variable y to obtain a real number w between y_0 and $y_0 + k$ such that

(3) $\dfrac{f(x_0,\ y_0 + k) - f(x_0,y_0)}{k} = f_y(x_0,w)$.

Multiply formula (2) by h and formula (3) by k and substitute into formula (1) to obtain

$\qquad f(x_0 + h, y_0 + k) - f(x,y_0) = f_x(v,\ y_0 + k) \cdot h + f_y(x_0,w) \cdot k$.

Let $\varepsilon_1 = f_x(v,\ y_0 + k) - f_x(x_0,y_0)$, or $f_x(v,\ y_0 + k) = f_x(x_0,y_0) + \varepsilon_1$. Let $\varepsilon_2 = f_y(x_0,w) - f_y(x_0,y_0)$, or $f_y(x_0,w) = f_y(x_0,y_0) + \varepsilon_2$. Then

(4) $f(x_0 + h, y_0 + k) - f(x_0,y_0) = [f_x(x_0,y_0) + \varepsilon_1] \cdot h + [f_y(x_0,y_0) + \varepsilon_2] \cdot k$

Since f_x and f_y are continuous at (x_0,y_0),

$\lim\limits_{(h,k) \to (0,0)} \varepsilon_1 = \lim\limits_{(h,k) \to (0,0)} [f_x(v,\ y_0 + k) - f_x(x_0,y_0)] = f_x(x_0,y_0) - f_x(x_0,y_0) = 0$

and

$\lim\limits_{(h,k) \to (0,0)} \varepsilon_2 = \lim\limits_{(h,k) \to (0,0)} [f_y(x_0,w) - f_y(x_0,y_0)] = f_y(x_0,y_0) - f_y(x_0,y_0) = 0$.

Hence,

(5) $f(x_0 + h, y_0 + k) - f(x_0,y_0) \sim f_x(x_0,y_0)h + f_y(x_0,y_0)k$.

This approximation is frequently expressed in delta notation where $\Delta z = f(x_0 + h, y_0 + k) - f(x_0,y_0)$, $\Delta x = h$, and $\Delta y = k$; that is,

(6) $\Delta z \sim f_x(x_0,y_0) \, \Delta x + f_y(x_0,y_0) \, \Delta y.$*

The subscripts on x_0 and y_0 may be omitted, since they only served to remind the reader that the point (x_0,y_0) is to remain fixed during the discussion.

The expression $f_x(x,y)h + f_y(x,y)k$ used to approximate $f(x + h, y + k) - f(x,y)$ is called the *total differential of f at* (x,y) *with increment* (h,k), and is represented by the symbol $df(x,y;h,k)$, or merely df:

(7) $df = df(x,y;h,k) = f_x(x,y)h + f_y(x,y)k$

In some texts, this differential is given by the formula $dz = f_x(x,y) \, dx + f_y(x,y) \, dy$, where $dx = h$, $dy = k$, and $dz = df(x,y;h,k)$.

EXERCISES

In Exercises 5-11.1 and 5-11.2, find both $\Delta z = f(x + h, y + k) - f(x,y)$ and the differential approximation $dz = df(x,y;h,k)$ for the function $z = f(x,y)$ and the values of x, y, h, and k given.

5-11.1. $f(x,y) = x^2y + xy^3 + 6$; a. $x = 1, y = 2, h = .3, k = .4$
    b. $x = 1, y = 2, h = .03, k = .04$

5-11.2. $f(x,y) = 1/(x + y^2)$; a. $x = 3, y = 2, h = .1, k = .1$
    b. $x = 3, y = 2, h = .01, k = .01$

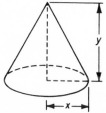

$V = \frac{1}{3}\pi x^2 y$

5-11.3. Find the exact (ΔV) and approximate (dV) change in the volume V of the cone illustrated, if x is changed from 4 to 4.02, and y is changed from 9 to 9.03.

5-11.4. Let $u = f(x,y,z)$ be any function $f: A \to E^1$, where A is a subset of E^3. Assume that the partial derivatives f_x, f_y, and f_z exist at every point in some neighborhood of a fixed point (x_0,y_0,z_0) of A and are continuous at (x_0,y_0,z_0). Prove that $f(x_0 + h, y_0 + k, z_0 + t) - f(x_0,y_0,z_0) = [f_x(x_0,y_0,z_0) + \varepsilon_1]h + [f_y(x_0,y_0,z_0) + \varepsilon_2]k + [f_z(x_0,y_0,z_0) + \varepsilon_3]t$, where $\lim_{(h,k,t) \to (0,0,0)} \varepsilon_i = 0$, for $i = 1, 2, 3$.

---

* From elementary calculus, the equation for the tangent plane to the surface $z = f(x,y)$ at (x_0,y_0,z_0), where $z_0 = f(x_0,y_0)$, is given by $z - z_0 = f_x(x_0,y_0) \cdot (x - x_0) + f_y(x_0,y_0) \cdot (y - y_0)$. Hence, the error in the approximation $\Delta z \sim f_x(x_0,y_0) \, \Delta x + f_y(x_0,y_0) \, \Delta y$ is equal to the distance between the tangent plane and the surface $z = f(x,y)$, measured along the vertical line at $(x_0 + x, y_0 + y)$.

Here, $df(x,y,z;h,k,t) = f_x(x,y,z)h + f_y(x,y,z)k + f_z(x,y,z)t$ is called the total differential of f at (x,y,z) with increment (h,k,t).

5-11.5. Let $f\colon E^3 \to E^1$ be defined by $u = xyz^2 + x^2y^3$. Find both
$$\Delta u = f(x + h,\, y + k,\, z + t) - f(x,y,z)$$
and the differential approximation
$$du = df(x,y,z;h,k,t)$$
for the values of x, y, z, h, k, and t given:
a. $x = 1, y = 2, z = 3, h = .1, k = .1, t = .1$
b. $x = 1, y = 2, z = 3, h = .01, k = .01, t = .01$

5-12 THE DIRECTIONAL DERIVATIVE

Let $f\colon A \to E^1$ be any function where A is an open subset of E^2; we will represent f by $z = f(x,y)$. Let (x_0,y_0) be any point in A. Consider a line segment L in the xy-plane, with one endpoint at (x_0,y_0). Let θ denote the angle of inclination of L with respect to the x-axis. Choose any point $p = (x_0 + h,\, y_0 + k)$ on L. The distance s from (x_0,y_0) to p is given by $s = \sqrt{h^2 + k^2}$. Note that $h = s \cdot \cos\theta$ and $k = s \cdot \sin\theta$. *The directional derivative*, $D[\theta, f(x_0,y_0)]$, *of f at (x_0,y_0) in the direction measured by θ is defined by*

$$D[\theta, f(x_0,y_0)] = \lim_{s \to 0} \frac{f(x_0 + s \cdot \cos\theta,\, y_0 + s \cdot \sin\theta) - f(x_0,y_0)}{s}.$$

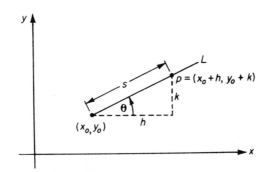

Assuming that the partial derivatives f_x and f_y exist in a neighborhood of (x_0,y_0) and that they are continuous at (x_0,y_0), the directional derivative can be evaluated as follows:

From formula (4), page 114,

$$f(x_0 + h,\, y_0 + k) - f(x_0,y_0) = (f_x(x_0,y_0) + \varepsilon_1)h + (f_y(x_0,y_0) + \varepsilon_2)k,$$

where $\lim_{(h,k)\to(0,0)} \varepsilon_1 = \lim_{(h,k)\to(0,0)} \varepsilon_2 = 0$. Divide by s to obtain

$$\frac{f(x_0 + h,\, y_0 + k) - f(x_0,y_0)}{s} = (f_x(x_0,y_0) + \varepsilon_1) \cdot \frac{h}{s} + (f_y(x_0,y_0) + \varepsilon_2) \cdot \frac{k}{s}.$$

Substitute $h = s \cdot \cos \theta$, $k = s \cdot \sin \theta$, and take the limit as s approaches 0:

$$D[\theta, f(x_0, y_0)] = \lim_{s \to 0} \frac{f(x_0 + s \cdot \cos \theta, \, y_0 + s \cdot \sin \theta) - f(x_0, y_0)}{s}$$

$$= \lim_{s \to 0} [(f_x(x_0, y_0) + \varepsilon_1) \cos \theta + (f_y(x_0, y_0) + \varepsilon_2) \sin \theta]$$

$$= f_x(x_0, y_0) \cos \theta + f_y(x_0, y_0) \sin \theta.$$

Note that $s \to 0$ implies $(h, k) \to (0, 0)$, which in turn implies $\varepsilon_1 \to 0$ and $\varepsilon_2 \to 0$. The geometrical interpretation is illustrated in Figure 5-12.1.

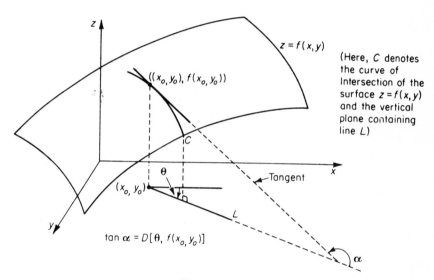

(Here, C denotes the curve of Intersection of the surface $z = f(x, y)$ and the vertical plane containing line L)

Figure 5-12.1

EXERCISES

5-12.1. Find $D[\theta, f(x_0, y_0)]$ where $f(x, y) = x^2 y + y^3$, $(x_0, y_0) = (1, 2)$ and $\theta = \pi/6$.

5-12.2. Given $f(x, y) = x^2 + y^{3/2}$.
   a. Find $D[\theta, f(3/4, 3)]$, where θ is not specified.
   b. Find the maximum value of $D[\theta, f(3/4, 3)]$. [*Hint:* Solve the equation $\dfrac{d}{d\theta} D[\theta, f(3/4, 3)] = 0$ to obtain the angle θ at which $D[\theta, f(3/4, 3)]$ is maximum.]

5-12.3. Given any function $f(x, y)$ such that the partial derivatives f_x and f_y exist in some neighborhood of the point (x_0, y_0) and are continuous at (x_0, y_0). Show that the maximum value of $D[\theta, f(x_0, y_0)]$ is $\sqrt{[f_x(x_0, y_0)]^2 + [f_y(x_0, y_0)]^2}$.

6

Integration

6-1 SIGMA NOTATION

The sum of n terms, $a_1 + a_2 + a_3 + \ldots + a_n$ is denoted by the symbol $\sum_{k=1}^{n} a_k$; that is, $\sum_{k=1}^{n} a_k = a_1 + a_2 + \ldots + a_n$.

EXAMPLES: $\displaystyle\sum_{k=1}^{4} k = 1 + 2 + 3 + 4 = 10$; $\displaystyle\sum_{k=1}^{3} c = c + c + c = 3c$;

$\displaystyle\sum_{k=2}^{5} k^2 = 2^2 + 3^2 + 4^2 + 5^2 = 54$; $\displaystyle\sum_{k=3}^{6} 1/k = 1/3 + 1/4 + 1/5 + 1/6 = 19/20$;

$\displaystyle\sum_{k=1}^{n} (k+1)k = (2)1 + (3)2 + \ldots + (n+1)n$.

THEOREM 6-1.1: $\displaystyle\sum_{k=1}^{n} k = n(n+1)/2$.

Proof: Consider the binomial

$$(1+x)^2 = 1 + 2x + x^2, \quad \text{or} \quad (1+x)^2 - x^2 = 1 + 2x.$$

Let
$$
\begin{aligned}
x &= 1: & 2^2 - 1^2 &= 1 + 2(1); \\
x &= 2: & 3^2 - 2^2 &= 1 + 2(2); \\
x &= 3: & 4^2 - 3^2 &= 1 + 2(3);
\end{aligned}
$$

$$
\begin{array}{cc}
\cdot & \cdot \\
\cdot & \cdot \\
\cdot & \cdot
\end{array}
$$

$$x = n: (n+1)^2 - n^2 = 1 + 2(n).$$

Adding all these expressions, we have

$$(n + 1)^2 - 1^2 = n + 2(1 + 2 + \ldots + n),$$

from which

$$1 + 2 + \ldots + n = [(1 + n)^2 - 1^2 - n]/2$$
$$= [1 + 2n + n^2 - 1 - n]/2 = n(n + 1)/2. \quad \blacksquare$$

THEOREM 6-1.2: $\sum_{k=1}^{n} k^2 = [n(n + 1)(2n + 1)]/6.$

Proof: Consider the binomial

$$(1 + x)^3 = 1 + 3x + 3x^2 + x^3, \quad \text{or} \quad (1 + x)^3 - x^3 = 1 + 3x + 3x^2.$$

Let

$$\begin{array}{lll} x = 1: & 2^3 - 1^3 = 1 + 3(1) + 3(1^2); \\ x = 2: & 3^3 - 2^3 = 1 + 3(2) + 3(2^2); \\ x = 3: & 4^3 - 3^3 = 1 + 3(3) + 3(3^2); \\ \quad \cdot & \quad \cdot \\ \quad \cdot & \quad \cdot \\ \quad \cdot & \quad \cdot \\ x = n: & (n + 1)^3 - n^3 = 1 + 3(n) + 3(n^2). \end{array}$$

Adding all of these expressions, we have

$$(n + 1)^3 - 1^3 = n + 3 \sum_{k=1}^{n} k + 3 \sum_{k=1}^{n} k^2;$$

and therefore

$$\sum_{k=1}^{n} k^2 = [(n + 1)^3 - 1^3 - n - 3 \sum_{k=1}^{n} k]/3$$
$$= [n^3 + 3n^2 + 3n + 1 - 1 - n - 3n(n + 1)/2]/3$$
$$= [n(n + 1)(2n + 1)]/6. \quad \blacksquare$$

EXERCISES

6-1.1. Evaluate (a) $\sum_{k=1}^{4} 2^k$;   (b) $\sum_{k=3}^{7} \frac{k + 2}{k}$.

6-1.2. Prove that $\sum_{k=1}^{n} k^3 = [n(n + 1)/2]^2$. [*Hint:* Start with the binomial $(1 + x)^4 = 1 + 4x + 6x^2 + 4x^3 + x^4$, and work as above.]

6-1.3. Show that $\sum_{k=1}^{n} ca_k = c \sum_{k=1}^{n} a_k$, where c is a constant.

6-1.4. Show that $\sum_{k=1}^{n} a_k + \sum_{k=1}^{n} b_k = \sum_{k=1}^{n} (a_k + b_k)$.

6-1.5. Evaluate $\sum_{k=1}^{n} k(k + 2)$.

6-2 HISTORICAL APPROACH TO THE PROBLEM OF AREA FINDING

In this section we shall deal with the problem of finding areas under certain curves. We begin with the intuitively simplest problem.

EXAMPLE 6-2.1: Let $f: E^1 \to E^1$ be defined by $f(x) = c$, where c is a positive constant. The area A of the rectangular region bounded by this curve, $x = 0$, $x = b$, and the x-axis, is given by the formula $A = cb$. (See Figure 6-2.1).

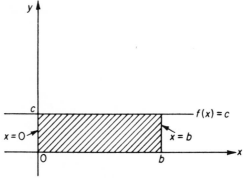

Figure 6-2.1

EXAMPLE 6-2.2: Let $f: E^1 \to E^1$ be the function defined by $f(x) = cx$, where $c > 0$. The area of the triangular region bounded by this curve, $x = b$, and the x-axis, is given by the formula $A = cb^2/2$. (Figure 6-2.2.)

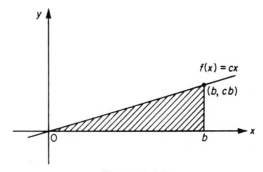

Figure 6-2.2

EXAMPLE 6-2.3: Let $f: E^1 \to E^1$ be defined by $f(x) = cx^2$, where $c > 0$. The following steps enable us to find the area of the region shown in Figure 6-2.3.

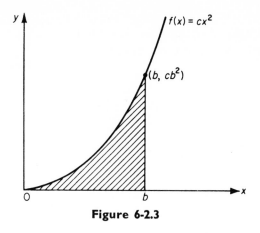

Figure 6-2.3

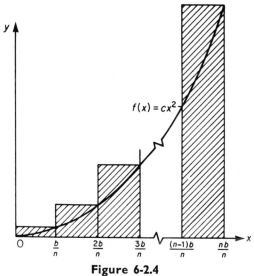

Figure 6-2.4

Step 1: Subdivide $[0,b]$ into n equal subintervals, the length of each being b/n.

Step 2: In each subinterval, construct a rectangle with height equal to the maximum height of the curve over the subinterval, and base equal to the length of the subinterval. (See Figure 6-2.4.) The sum T_n of the areas of these rectangles is:

$$T_n = c(b/n)^2(b/n) + c(2b/n)^2(b/n) + c(3b/n)^2(b/n) + \ldots + c(nb/n)^2(b/n)$$
$$= c(b^3/n^3) \cdot (1^2 + 2^2 + \ldots + n^2)$$
$$= c(b^3/n^3)[n(n+1)(2n+1)]/6 = [cb^3(1 + 1/n)(2 + 1/n)]/6.$$

Note that $T_n > A$ for all n.

Step 3: Consider the sequence $T_1, T_2, T_3, \ldots T_n, \ldots$; as n increases, T_n approaches the area A under the curve $f(x) = cx^2$ between 0 and b. That is,

$$A = \lim_{n \to \infty} T_n = \lim_{n \to \infty} [cb^3(1 + 1/n) \cdot (2 + 1/n)]/6 = [cb^3(1)(2)]/6 = cb^3/3.$$

In order to convince even the most skeptical reader that $A = cb^3/3$, the above three steps can be repeated using rectangles *under* the curve. (See Figure 6-2.5.)

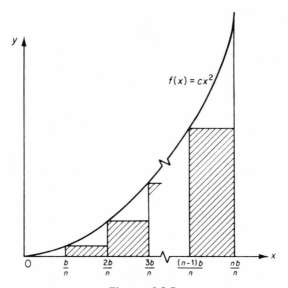

Figure 6-2.5

Step 1: Same as before.

Step 2: In each subinterval, construct a rectangle with height equal to the minimum height of the curve over the subinterval, and base equal to the length of the subinterval. The sum S_n of the areas of these rectangles is:

$$\begin{aligned} S_n &= c(0)^2(b/n) + c(b/n)^2(b/n) + c(2b/n)^2(b/n) + \ldots \\ &\quad + c[(n-1)b/n]^2(b/n) \\ &= c(b^3/n^3)(0^2 + 1^2 + 2^2 + \ldots + (n-1)^2) \\ &= c(b^3/n^3)[n(n+1)(2n+1)/6 - n^2]* \\ &= cb^3[(1 + 1/n)(2 + 1/n)/6 - 1/n]. \end{aligned}$$

Note that $S_n < A$ for all n.

---

* $1^2 + 2^2 + \ldots + (n-1)^2 = (1^2 + 2^2 + \ldots + (n-1)^2 + n^2) - n^2$
$$= n(n+1)(2n+1)/6 - n^2.$$

Step 3: Consider the sequence $S_1, S_2, S_3, \ldots, S_n, \ldots$; as n increases, S_n approaches the area A under the curve $f(x) = cx^2$ between 0 and b. That is,

$$A = \lim_{n \to \infty} S_n$$

$$= \lim_{n \to \infty} cb^3 \left[(1 + 1/n)(2 + 1/n)6 - 1/n\right] = cb^3[(1)(2)/6 - 0] = cb^3/3.$$

EXERCISE

6-2.1. Prove that the area A of the region bounded by the curve $f(x) = cx^3$ $(c > 0)$, $x = 0$, $x = b$, and the x-axis, is given by $A = cb^4/4$. [*Hint:* Follow the procedure of the preceding example and use $1^3 + 2^3 + 3^3 + \ldots + n^3 = [n(n + 1)/2]^2$. Approximate A by the sum of the areas of rectangles above and below the curve.]

6-3 PARTITIONS AND STEP FUNCTIONS

Before giving the general definition of the integral $\int_a^b f(x)\,dx$, where $f: [a,b] \to E^1$, it is first useful to discuss step functions.

Consider any closed interval $[a,b]$ in E^1. A subdivision of $[a,b]$ into n subintervals by $n - 1$ points of subdivision $x_1, x_2, \ldots, x_{n-1}$, where $a < x_1 < x_2 < \ldots < x_{n-1} < b$, is called a *partition P* of $[a,b]$. Symbolically,

$$P = \{x_0, x_1, x_2, \ldots, x_{n-1}, x_n\},$$

where $x_0 = a$ and $x_n = b$.

The n closed subintervals associated with P are $[x_0,x_1], [x_1,x_2], \ldots, [x_{n-1},x_n]$. We shall refer to $[x_{k-1},x_k]$ as the kth closed subinterval, where $1 \leq k \leq n$. Similarly, (x_{k-1},x_k) is called the kth open subinterval of P.

A function $h: [a,b] \to E^1$ is called a *step function* if for some partition $P = \{x_0, x_1, x_2, \ldots, x_n\}$ of $[a,b]$, $h(x)$ is equal to a constant in each open subinterval of P; that is, there exists a set of n constants $c_1, c_2, \ldots, c_n$ such that $h(x) = c_k$ for all $x \in (x_{k-1},x_k)$, $k = 1, 2, \ldots, n$. Figure 6-3.1 illustrates a step-function. The function h must be defined at each of the subdivision points $x_0, x_1, x_2, \ldots, x_n$ of P; however, the above definition places no restriction on the value of h at these points.

The "bracket function" $f(x) = [x]$, where $[x]$ is defined as the largest integer less than or equal to x is another example of a step function (Figure 5-1.1). The domain of f may be restricted to any closed interval $[a,b]$.

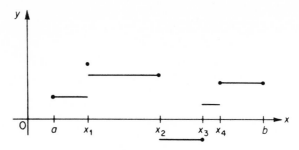

Figure 6-3.1

The *integral* of a step function $h(x)$ from a to b, denoted $\int_a^b h(x)\,dx$, is defined by the formula

$$\int_a^b h(x)\,dx = \sum_{k=1}^n c_k(x_k - x_{k-1}),$$

where $h(x) = c_k$ for all $x \in (x_{k-1}, x_k)$, $k = 1, 2, \ldots, n$. It should be noted here that the letter x used for the independent variable may be replaced by any other convenient letter without altering the definition of the integral. That is,

$$\int_a^b h(x)\,dx = \int_a^b h(t)\,dt = \int_a^b h(u)\,du, \text{ etc.}$$

EXAMPLE 6-3.1: Define $h: [1,5] \to E^1$ as follows: $h(x) = 3$ if $x \in [1,3/2)$, -2 if $x \in [3/2,4]$, 6 if $x \in (4,5]$. Then

$$\int_1^5 h(x)\,dx = 3(3/2 - 1) + (-2)(4 - 3/2) + 6(5 - 4) = 5/2.$$

EXERCISES

In each of the following exercises, graph the step function $h(x)$ for the interval $[a,b]$ given, and evaluate $\int_a^b h(x)\,dx$.

6-3.1. $h: [-2,7] \to E^1$, where $h(x) = 2$ if $x \in [-2,1]$, -3 if $x \in (1,2)$, 4 if $x \in [2,5)$, -1 if $x \in [5,7]$.

6-3.2. $h(x) = [x]$; $[a,b] = [1/2, 13/2]$.

6-3.3. $h(x) = |x|/x$ if $x \neq 0$, 0 if $x = 0$; $[a,b] = [-7/2, 1]$.

6-3.4. $h(x) = |2x^2 - 2x - 12|/(x^2 - x - 6)$ if $x \neq -2$ and $x \neq 3$, $h(-2) = h(3) = 5$; $[a,b] = [-3,8]$.

6-3.5. $h(x) = 3[x] - 2|x|/x$ if $x \neq 0$, $h(0) = 1$; $[a,b] = [-3/2,2]$.

6-3.6. $h(x) = [2x + 3]$; $[a,b] = [0,2]$. [Note that h is the composite of the functions $y = [u]$ and $u = 2x + 3$.]

6-3.7. $h(x) = [x^2]$; $[a,b] = [-1,2]$.

6-4 SEVERAL PROPERTIES OF INTEGRALS OF STEP FUNCTIONS

Let $h: [a,b] \to E^1$ be any step function with associated partition P. If P is replaced by a partition P' containing all the subdivision points of P together with additional points, the value of $\int_a^b h(x)\,dx$ is not altered, although some of the terms in the series used to evaluate $\int_a^b h(x)\,dx$ may change. For example, if $P = \{x_0, x_1, x_2, \ldots, x_{k-1}, x_k, \ldots, x_n\}$, and $P' = \{x_0, x_1, x_2, \ldots, x_{k-1}, x', x_k, \ldots, x_n\}$ contains exactly one more point, x', then the term $c_k(x_k - x_{k-1})$ in the series is replaced by the equal sum

$$c_k(x_k - x') + c_k(x' - x_{k-1}).$$

Consequently, the value of $\int_a^b h(x)\,dx$ does not depend on the partition P. We only require that $h(x)$ be constant on each open subinterval of P.

THEOREM 6-4.1: Let $h: [a,b] \to E^1$ be any step function. If r is a real number such that $a < r < b$, then

$$\int_a^b h(x)\,dx = \int_a^r h(x)\,dx + \int_r^b h(x)\,dx.$$

Proof: Let $P = \{x_0, x_1, \ldots, x_m, x_{m+1}, \ldots, x_{m+n}\}$ be a partition of $[a,b]$ associated with $h(x)$ such that $P_1 = \{x_0, x_1, \ldots, x_m\}$ is a partition of $[a,r]$ and $P_2 = \{x_m, x_{m+1}, \ldots, x_{m+n}\}$ is a partition of $[r,b]$. $\int_a^b h(x)\,dx =$

$$\sum_{k=1}^{m+n} c_k(x_k - x_{k-1}) = \sum_{k=1}^{m} c_k(x_k - x_{k-1}) + \sum_{k=m+1}^{m+n} c_k(x_k - x_{k-1}) = \int_a^r h(x)\,dx +$$

$\int_r^b h(x)\,dx$. ∎

THEOREM 6-4.2: Let $s: [a,b] \to E^1$ and $t: [a,b] \to E^1$ be any two step functions such that $s(x) \le t(x)$ for all $x \in [a,b]$. Then

$$\int_a^b s(x)\,dx \le \int_a^b t(x)\,dx.$$

Proof: Let P_1 and P_2 represent partitions of $[a,b]$ associated with $s(x)$ and $t(x)$ respectively. Let P be the partition of $[a,b]$ containing all of the points of subdivision of both P_1 and P_2. Using P to evaluate both integrals, we have

$$\int_a^b s(x)\,dx = \sum_{k=1}^n c_k'(x_k - x_{k-1}) \quad \text{and} \quad \int_a^b t(x)\,dx = \sum_{k=1}^n c_k''(x_k - x_{k-1}),$$

where $c_k' \leq c_k''$ for all k. Hence, by comparison of terms,

$$\int_a^b s(x)\,dx \leq \int_a^b t(x)\,dx. \quad \blacksquare$$

COROLLARY 6-4.1: Let $h: [a,b] \to E^1$ be any step function. Assume m and M are real numbers with the property $m \leq h(x) \leq M$ for all $x \in [a,b]$. Then

$$m(b-a) \leq \int_a^b h(x)\,dx \leq M(b-a).$$

Proof: Define step functions $s: [a,b] \to E^1$ and $t: [a,b] \to E^1$ by $s(x) = m$ and $t(x) = M$ for all $x \in [a,b]$. By Theorem 6-4.2,

$$\int_a^b s(x)\,dx \leq \int_a^b h(x)\,dx \leq \int_a^b t(x)\,dx$$

or

$$m(b-a) \leq \int_a^b h(x)\,dx \leq M(b-a). \quad \blacksquare$$

6-5   UPPER AND LOWER INTEGRALS
OF A BOUNDED FUNCTION

Let $f: [a,b] \to E^1$ be any *bounded function*; that is, there exist real numbers m and M such that $m \leq f(x) \leq M$ for all $x \in [a,b]$. The *lower integral of f from a to b* is represented by $\int_{\underline{a}}^b f(x)\,dx$, and defined as follows:

Let S_f denote the set of *all* step functions $s: [a,b] \to E^1$ such that $s(x) \leq f(x)$ for all $x \in [a,b]$. Then

$$\int_{\underline{a}}^b f(x)\,dx = \text{l.u.b.} \left\{ \int_a^b s(x)\,dx \mid s(x) \in S_f \right\}.$$

In Figure 6-5.1, the area of the shaded region represents $\int_a^b s(x)\,dx$. Note that for each function $s(x)$ in the set S_f, $s(x) \leq f(x) \leq M$. By Corollary 6-4.1, $\int_a^b s(x)\,dx \leq M(b-a)$. This means the set $\left\{ \int_a^b s(x)\,dx \mid s(x) \in S_f \right\}$ is

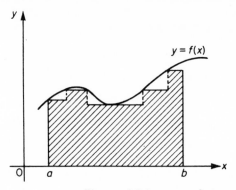

Figure 6-5.1

bounded above by $M(b - a)$; hence the least upper bound exists, by the completeness axiom for the real numbers.

The *upper integral of f from a to b* is represented by $\displaystyle\int_a^{\overline{b}} f(x)\, dx$, and defined similarly: Let T_f denote the set of all step functions $t: [a,b] \to E^1$ such that $t(x) \geq f(x)$ for all $x \in [a,b]$.

$$\int_a^{\overline{b}} f(x)\, dx = \text{g.l.b.} \left\{ \int_a^b t(x)\, dx \mid t(x) \in T_f \right\}.$$

In Figure 6-5.2, the area of the shaded region represents $\displaystyle\int_a^b t(x)\, dx$. Again citing Corollary 6-4.1, the set

$$\left\{ \int_a^b t(x)\, dx \mid t(x) \in T_f \right\}$$

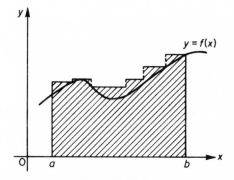

Figure 6-5.2

of real numbers is bounded below by $m(b-a)$; consequently, the greatest lower bound exists.

The upper and lower integrals $\overline{\int_a^b} f(x)\,dx$ and $\underline{\int_a^b} f(x)\,dx$ are not always equal, as is shown in the following example.

EXAMPLE 6-5.1: Consider the function $g\colon [0,1] \to E^1$ defined by

$$g(x) = \begin{cases} 2, & \text{if } x \text{ is a rational number;} \\ 1, & \text{if } x \text{ is an irrational number.} \end{cases}$$

Every open interval of the real line contains both rational and irrational numbers. Hence, if $s(x)$ is any step function belonging to S_g, then $s(x) \le 1$ for all $x \in [0,1]$. Moreover, if $t(x) \in T_g$, then $t(x) \ge 2$ for all $x \in [0,1]$. Thus,

$$\underline{\int_0^1} g(x)\,dx = 1 \qquad \text{and} \qquad \overline{\int_0^1} g(x)\,dx = 2.$$

However, it is always true that $\overline{\int_a^b} f(x)\,dx \ge \underline{\int_a^b} f(x)\,dx$ for any bounded function $f\colon [a,b] \to E^1$, as will be proved in Theorem 6-5.1.

We now prove two lemmas needed for Theorem 6-5.1.

LEMMA 6-5.1: If A is a real number with the property that $A < \varepsilon$ for every positive number ε, then $A \le 0$.

Proof: (Indirect) Suppose $A > 0$; then for $\varepsilon = A$, the statement $A < \varepsilon$, given in the hypothesis is false. We therefore conclude $A \le 0$. $\blacksquare$

LEMMA 6-5.2: Given any real number $\varepsilon > 0$, there exist step functions $s_0(x) \in S_f$ and $t_0(x) \in T_f$ such that

$$(1) \quad \underline{\int_a^b} f(x)\,dx - \int_a^b s_0(x)\,dx < \varepsilon/2,$$

and

$$(2) \quad \int_a^b t_0(x)\,dx - \overline{\int_a^b} f(x)\,dx < \varepsilon/2.$$

(See Figures 6-5.1 and 6-5.2.)

Proof: Part (1):

$$\underline{\int_a^b} f(x)\,dx - \varepsilon/2 < \underline{\int_a^b} f(x)\,dx = \text{l.u.b.} \left\{ \int_a^b s(x)\,dx \,\middle|\, s(x) \in S_f \right\}.$$

This means that $\underline{\int_a^b} f(x)\,dx - \varepsilon/2$ is not an upper bound for the set

$$\left\{ \int_a^b s(x)\,dx \,\middle|\, s(x) \in S_f \right\}.$$

Hence there exists a step function $s_0(x) \in S_f$ such that

$$\underline{\int_a^b} f(x)\, dx - \varepsilon/2 < \int_a^b s_0(x)\, dx.$$

Part (2) is proved in a similar manner (Ex. 6-5.3). ∎

THEOREM 6-5.1: For every bounded function $f: [a,b] \to E^1$,

$$\underline{\int_a^b} f(x)\, dx \le \overline{\int_a^b} f(x)\, dx.$$

Proof: Given any real number $\varepsilon > 0$; add the two inequalities of Lemma 6-5.2 to obtain

$$\left[\underline{\int_a^b} f(x)\, dx - \overline{\int_a^b} f(x)\, dx \right] + \left[\int_a^b t_0(x)\, dx - \int_a^b s_0(x)\, dx \right] < \varepsilon.$$

By Theorem 6-4.2,

$$\int_a^b t_0(x)\, dx - \int_a^b s_0(x)\, dx \ge 0;$$

therefore

$$\underline{\int_a^b} f(x)\, dx - \overline{\int_a^b} f(x)\, dx < \varepsilon,$$

for every $\varepsilon > 0$. Now, by Lemma 6-5.1,

$$\underline{\int_a^b} f(x)\, dx - \overline{\int_a^b} f(x)\, dx \le 0,$$

and the theorem is established. ∎

THEOREM 6-5.2: If $f: [a,b] \to E^1$ is a step function, then

$$\underline{\int_a^b} f(x)\, dx = \int_a^b f(x)\, dx = \overline{\int_a^b} f(x)\, dx.$$

Proof: Part 1. Since f is a step function, $f(x) \in S_f$ (see definition of S_f). Moreover, if $s(x) \in S_f$, then $s(x) \le f(x)$ for all $x \in [a,b]$, which implies

$$\int_a^b s(x)\, dx \le \int_a^b f(x)\, dx,$$

by Theorem 6-4.2. Therefore,

$$\underline{\int_a^b} f(x)\, dx = \text{l.u.b.} \left\{ \int_a^b s(x)\, dx \mid s(x) \in S_f \right\} = \int_a^b f(x)\, dx.$$

Part 2,

$$\int_a^b f(x)\, dx = \overline{\int_a^b} f(x)\, dx,$$

is proved in a similar manner (Ex. 6-5.4). ∎

EXERCISES

6-5.1. If $f: [a,b] \to E^1$ and $g: [a,b] \to E^1$ represent step functions, prove that $f + g: [a,b] \to E^1$ is also a step function and

$$\int_a^b f(x)\, dx + \int_a^b g(x)\, dx = \int_a^b [f(x) + g(x)]\, dx.$$

6-5.2. Assuming that $f: [a,b] \to E^1$ is any bounded function, and m and M are constants such that $m \leq f(x) \leq M$ for all $x \in [a,b]$, prove that

$$m(b - a) \leq \underline{\int_a^b} f(x)\, dx \qquad \text{and} \qquad M(b - a) \geq \overline{\int_a^b} f(x)\, dx.$$

6-5.3. Prove Part 2 of Lemma 6-5.2.

6-5.4. Prove Part 2 of Theorem 6-5.2.

6-6 DEFINITION OF THE INTEGRAL OF A BOUNDED FUNCTION

Let $f: [a,b] \to E^1$ be any bounded function. If

$$\underline{\int_a^b} f(x)\, dx = \overline{\int_a^b} f(x)\, dx,$$

then f is said to be *integrable* on $[a,b]$ and the symbol

$$\int_a^b f(x)\, dx,$$

called the *integral of f from a to b*, is used to denote the common value of $\underline{\int_a^b} f(x)\, dx$ and $\overline{\int_a^b} f(x)\, dx$.

Another way of stating that

$$\underline{\int_a^b} f(x)\, dx = \overline{\int_a^b} f(x)\, dx$$

is to say "the integral $\int_a^b f(x)\, dx$ exists". The function f is called the *integrand*, the numbers a and b are the *limits of integration*, and $[a,b]$ is called the *interval of integration*. According to Theorem 6-5.2 every step function is integrable; the function defined in Example 6-5.1 is not integrable.

Lemma 6-6.1: Given any bounded function $f: [a,b] \to E^1$. The function f is integrable on $[a,b]$ if, and only if, for every positive number ε there exist step functions $s_0(x) \in S_f$ and $t_0(x) \in T_f$, such that

$$\int_a^b t_0(x)\, dx - \int_a^b s_0(x)\, dx < \varepsilon.$$

(The Riemann condition for Integrability.)

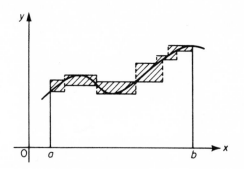

Figure 6-6.1

Proof: Part 1: Suppose f is integrable, and let ε denote any positive real number. By Lemma 6-5.2, there exist step functions $s_0(x) \in S_f$ and $t_0(x) \in T_f$ such that

$$\int_a^b f(x)\, dx - \int_a^b s_0(x)\, dx < \varepsilon/2, \quad \text{and} \quad \int_a^b t_0(x)\, dx - \int_a^b f(x)\, dx < \varepsilon/2.$$

Adding these inequalities, we obtain

$$\int_a^b t_0(x)\, dx - \int_a^b s_0(x)\, dx < \varepsilon.$$

Part 2: Assume that for every $\varepsilon > 0$, there exist step functions $s_0(x) \in S_f$ and $t_0(x) \in T_f$ such that

$$\int_a^b t_0(x)\, dx - \int_a^b s_0(x)\, dx < \varepsilon.$$

By the definitions of

$$\underline{\int_a^b} f(x)dx \quad \text{and} \quad \overline{\int_a^b} f(x)dx,$$

$s_0(x) \in S_f$ implies

$$\int_a^b s_0(x)\, dx \le \underline{\int_a^b} f(x)\, dx$$

and $t_0(x) \in T_f$ implies

$$\int_a^b t_0(x)\, dx \geq \overline{\int_a^b} f(x)\, dx.$$

Therefore

$$\overline{\int_a^b} f(x)\, dx - \underline{\int_a^b} f(x)\, dx \leq \int_a^b t_0(x)\, dx - \int_a^b s_0(x)\, dx < \varepsilon.$$

By Lemma 6-5.1,

$$\overline{\int_a^b} f(x)\, dx - \underline{\int_a^b} f(x)\, dx < \varepsilon,$$

· for every $\varepsilon > 0$, implies

$$\overline{\int_a^b} f(x)\, dx - \underline{\int_a^b} f(x)\, dx \leq 0.$$

By Theorem 6-5.1,

$$\overline{\int_a^b} f(x)\, dx - \underline{\int_a^b} f(x)\, dx \geq 0;$$

hence the upper and lower integrals are equal. ∎

THEOREM 6-6.1: If $f: [a,b] \to E^1$ is continuous on $[a,b]$, then $\displaystyle\int_a^b f(x)\, dx$ exists; (a sufficient condition for a function to be integrable on a closed interval $[a,b]$ is that the function be continuous on $[a,b]$).

Proof: Since $[a,b]$ is a closed and bounded subset of E^1, the function f is bounded (Theorem 5-2.6). Therefore both $\overline{\int_a^b} f(x)\, dx$ and $\underline{\int_a^b} f(x)\, dx$ exist. Moreover, by Theorem 5-3.1, f is uniformly continuous on $[a,b]$. Let $\varepsilon > 0$ be given, and define $\varepsilon' = \varepsilon/(b - a)$. By the definition of uniform continuity, there exists a $\delta > 0$, depending only upon ε', such that $|x' - x''| < \delta$ implies $|f(x') - f(x'')| < \varepsilon'$ for every pair of points x', $x'' \in [a,b]$. Let $P = \{x_0, x_1, \ldots, x_n\}$ be a partition of $[a,b]$ such that $x_k - x_{k-1} < \delta$ for all k, ($1 \leq k \leq n$). By the above property, $|f(x') - f(x'')| < \varepsilon'$ whenever x' and x'' belong to the same closed subinterval $[x_{k-1},x_k]$ of P.

Consider separately the subintervals $[x_{k-1},x_k]$ of P. By Corollary 5-2.1 there exist two fixed points $u_k \in [x_{k-1},x_k]$ and $v_k \in [x_{k-1},x_k]$ such that

(1) $f(u_k) \leq f(x) \leq f(v_k)$ for all $x \in [x_{k-1},x_k]$, $k = 1, 2, \ldots, n$,

and, since u_k and $v_k \in [x_{k-1},x_k]$,

(2) $f(v_k) - f(u_k) < \varepsilon'$.

Define step functions $s: [a,b] \to E^1$ and $t: [a,b] \to E^1$ as follows:

$$s(x) = \begin{cases} f(u_k), & \text{if } x \in (x_{k-1}, x_k], \quad k = 1, 2, \ldots, n; \\ f(a), & \text{if } x = a. \end{cases}$$

$$t(x) = \begin{cases} f(v_k), & \text{if } x \in (x_{k-1}, x_k], \quad k = 1, 2, \ldots, n; \\ f(a), & \text{if } x = a. \end{cases}$$

Note that $s(x) \le f(x) \le t(x)$ for all $x \in [a,b]$. Now,

$$\int_a^b t(x)\, dx - \int_a^b s(x)\, dx = \sum_{k=1}^n f(v_k)(x_k - x_{k-1}) - \sum_{k=1}^n f(u_k)(x_k - x_{k-1})$$

$$= \sum_{k=1}^n [f(v_k) - f(u_k)](x_k - x_{k-1})$$

$$< \sum_{k=1}^n \varepsilon'(x_k - x_{k-1}) \quad \text{(by statement (2) above)}$$

$$= \varepsilon' \sum_{k=1}^n (x_k - x_{k-1}) = \varepsilon'(b - a) = \varepsilon.$$

Hence, by Lemma 6-6.1, f is integrable. ∎

6-7 A REMARK CONCERNING GEOMETRY

If $f: [a,b] \to E^1$ is integrable on $[a,b]$ and $f(x) \ge 0$ for all $x \in [a,b]$, then the area of the region bounded by the curve $y = f(x)$, the lines $x = a$, $x = b$, and the x-axis, is defined to be the value of $\int_a^b f(x)\, dx$. (Figure 6-7.1.) Integration was motivated originally by the problem of finding area, and certainly this is still the most obvious application. However, the reader will recall from elementary calculus that there are many other applications of integration. For this reason, geometric intuition should be used only to conjecture, and all important properties of integration must be established by mathematical proof.

For clarity, the drawings in the sections which follow depict areas which lie entirely above the x-axis. If, however, $f(x) < 0$ for all x in the interval $[a,b]$, the area lies entirely below the x-axis, and the associated integral $\int_a^b f(x)\, dx$ has a negative value; that is, the value of $\int_a^b f(x)\, dx$ will be the

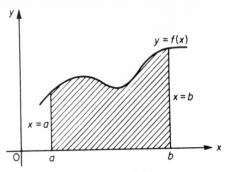

Figure 6-7.1

negative of the area bounded by the lines $x = a$, $x = b$, the x-axis, and the curve $y = f(x)$. See Figure 6-7.2.

If a continuous function f has positive and negative values in $[a,b]$, the value of $\int_a^b f(x)\,dx$ is the *difference* between the area above the x-axis and the area below it, as illustrated in Figure 6-7.3.

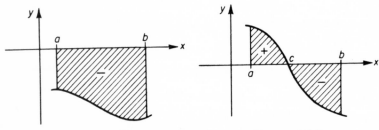

Figure 6-7.2   **Figure 6-7.3**

6-8 SEVERAL PROPERTIES OF THE INTEGRAL

THEOREM 6-8.1: If $f: [a,b] \to E^1$ is integrable on $[a,b]$, and m, M are real numbers such that $m \le f(x) \le M$ for all $x \in [a,b]$, then

$$m(b - a) \le \int_a^b f(x)\,dx \le M(b - a).$$

(The proof of Theorem 6-8.1 is left as an exercise. Figure 6-8.1 illustrates this property of the integral.)

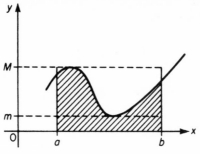

Figure 6-8.1

THEOREM 6-8.2: Let $f: [a,b] \to E^1$ be any bounded function, and let r denote any real number such that $a < r < b$. If $\int_a^r f(x)\,dx$ and $\int_r^b f(x)\,dx$ exist, then $\int_a^b f(x)\,dx$ exists, and

$$\int_a^b f(x)\,dx = \int_a^r f(x)\,dx + \int_r^b f(x)\,dx.$$

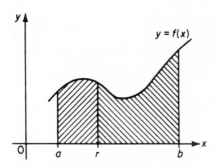

Figure 6-8.2

Proof: By Lemma 6-5.2, given any $\varepsilon > 0$, there exist step functions

$$s_1: [a,r] \to E^1,$$
$$t_1: [a,r] \to E^1,$$
$$s_2: [r,b] \to E^1,$$

and

$$t_2: [r,b] \to E^1$$

such that, for all $x \in [a,r]$, $s_1(x) \leq f(x) \leq t_1(x)$, and, for all $x \in [r,b]$, $s_2(x) \leq f(x) \leq t_2(x)$, and

(1) $\int_a^r f(x)\,dx - \int_a^r s_1(x)\,dx < \varepsilon/2,$

(2) $\int_a^r t_1(x)\,dx - \int_a^r f(x)\,dx < \varepsilon/2,$

(3) $\int_r^b f(x)\,dx - \int_r^b s_2(x)\,dx < \varepsilon/2,$

(4) $\int_r^b t_2(x)\,dx - \int_r^b f(x)\,dx < \varepsilon/2.$

Define step functions $s_0 : [a,b] \to E^1$ and $t_0 : [a,b] \to E^1$ by

$$s_0(x) = \begin{cases} s_1(x), & \text{if } x \in [a,r], \\ s_2(x), & \text{if } x \in (r,b]; \end{cases}$$

$$t_0(x) = \begin{cases} t_1(x), & \text{if } x \in [a,r], \\ t_2(x), & \text{if } x \in (r,b]. \end{cases}$$

Note that $s_0(x) \leq f(x) \leq t_0(x)$ for all $x \in [a,b]$. Moreover, by Theorem 6-4.1 and the definition of s_0 and t_0, we may write:

(5) $\displaystyle\int_a^b s_0(x)\,dx = \int_a^r s_0(x)\,dx + \int_r^b s_0(x)\,dx$

$\displaystyle = \int_a^r s_1(x)\,dx + \int_r^b s_2(x)\,dx,$

and

(6) $\displaystyle\int_a^b t_0(x)\,dx = \int_a^r t_0(x)\,dx + \int_r^b t_0(x)\,dx$

$\displaystyle = \int_a^r t_1(x)\,dx + \int_r^b t_2(x)\,dx.$

From lines (1), (3), and (5),

$$\int_a^r f(x)\,dx + \int_r^b f(x)\,dx < \int_a^r s_1(x)\,dx + \varepsilon/2 + \int_r^b s_2(x)\,dx + \varepsilon/2$$

$$= \int_a^b s_0(x)\,dx + \varepsilon \leq \int_a^b f(x)\,dx + \varepsilon.$$

By Lemma 6-5.1,

$$\left[\int_a^r f(x)\,dx + \int_r^b f(x)\,dx\right] - \int_a^b f(x)\,dx < \varepsilon,$$

for every $\varepsilon > 0$, implies

(7) $\displaystyle \int_a^r f(x)\,dx + \int_r^b f(x)\,dx \leq \underline{\int}_a^b f(x)\,dx.$

From lines (2), (4), and (6) we obtain

$$\int_a^r f(x)\,dx + \int_r^b f(x)\,dx > \int_a^r t_1(x)\,dx - \varepsilon/2 + \int_r^b t_2(x)\,dx - \varepsilon/2$$

$$= \int_a^b t_0(x)\,dx - \varepsilon \geq \overline{\int}_a^b f(x)\,dx - \varepsilon.$$

Again by Lemma 6-5.1,

$$\overline{\int}_a^b f(x)\,dx - \left[\int_a^r f(x)\,dx + \int_r^b f(x)\,dx\right] < \varepsilon,$$

for every $\varepsilon > 0$, implies

(8) $\displaystyle \overline{\int}_a^b f(x)\,dx \leq \int_a^r f(x)\,dx + \int_r^b f(x)\,dx.$

From lines (7), (8), and Theorem 6-5.1

$$\int_a^r f(x)\,dx + \int_r^b f(x)\,dx \leq \underline{\int}_a^b f(x)\,dx \leq \overline{\int}_a^b f(x)\,dx$$

$$\leq \int_a^r f(x)\,dx + \int_r^b f(x)\,dx.$$

Consequently, $\displaystyle \underline{\int}_a^b f(x)\,dx = \overline{\int}_a^b f(x)\,dx$, and this common value is equal

to $\displaystyle \int_a^r f(x)\,dx + \int_r^b f(x)\,dx.$ ∎

THEOREM 6-8.3: (*The Mean Value Theorem for Integrals*) If $f\colon [a,b] \to E^1$ is continuous on $[a,b]$, then there exists a real number $r \in [a,b]$ such that $(b - a)f(r) = \displaystyle\int_a^b f(x)\,dx.$ (Figure 6-8.3.)

Proof: By Theorem 6-6.1 $\displaystyle\int_a^b f(x)\,dx$ exists. By Corollary 5-2.1, there exist two fixed points $u \in [a,b]$ and $v \in [a,b]$ such that $f(u) \leq f(x) \leq f(v)$ for all $x \in [a,b]$. By Theorem 6-8.1, $(b - a)f(u) \leq \displaystyle\int_a^b f(x)\,dx \leq (b - a)f(v).$

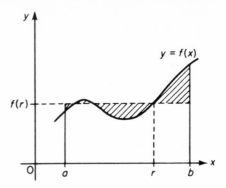

Figure 6-8.3

Case 1: If $(b - a)f(u) = \int_a^b f(x)\, dx$, let $r = u$. *Case 2:* If $\int_a^b f(x)dx = (b - a)f(v)$, let $r = v$. *Case 3:* Consider $(b - a)f(u) < \int_a^b f(x)dx < (b - a)f(v)$. Let $k = [1/(b - a)]\int_a^b f(x)\, dx$; then $f(u) < k < f(v)$. By Theorem 5-2.7, there exists a point r in the interval with end points u and v such that $f(r) = k$. Hence $f(r) = [1/(b - a)] \cdot \int_a^b f(x)\, dx$, and the proof is complete. ▌

6-9 INTERCHANGE OF LIMITS

Up to this point, the symbol $\int_a^b$ has only been used when $a < b$. We now define

$$\int_a^a f(x)\, dx = 0,$$

and we define

$$\int_b^a f(x)\, dx = -\int_a^b f(x)\, dx, \quad (a < b),$$

provided f is integrable on $[a,b]$.

Relating this definition to Theorem 6-8.3, we have

$$\int_b^a f(x)\, dx = -\int_a^b f(x)\, dx = -(b - a)f(r) = (a - b)f(r).$$

Therefore the formula, given in Theorem 6-8.3, remains valid even if a and b are interchanged (on both sides of the equation). This generalization is stated in the following corollary:

COROLLARY 6-9.1: Let A denote a closed interval with end points a and b (where either $a < b$ or $b < a$). If $f: A \to E^1$ is continuous on A, then there exists a point $r \in A$ such that

$$(b - a)f(r) = \int_a^b f(x)\, dx.$$

A useful modification of Theorem 6-8.2 is given in the following corollary:

COROLLARY 6-9.2: If $f: [a,b] \to E^1$ is continuous on $[a,b]$, and r_1, r_2, $r_3 \in [a,b]$, then

$$\int_{r_1}^{r_3} f(x)\, dx = \int_{r_1}^{r_2} f(x)\, dx + \int_{r_2}^{r_3} f(x)\, dx,$$

regardless of the relative order of r_1, r_2, and r_3. (To prove Corollary 6-9.2, one should consider all possible cases of relative order of the three points $r_1, r_2,$ and r_3; i.e., $r_1 \le r_2 \le r_3, r_3 \le r_1 \le r_2,$ and four others, and use Theorem 6-8.2.)

EXERCISES

6-9.1. Prove Theorem 6-8.1.

6-9.2. Prove Corollary 6-9.2.

6-9.3. If $f: [a,b] \to E^1$ and $g: [a,b] \to E^1$ are integrable on $[a,b]$, prove that $f + g: [a,b] \to E^1$ is integrable and that

$$\int_a^b f(x)\, dx + \int_a^b g(x)\, dx = \int_a^b [f(x) + g(x)]\, dx.$$

[*Hint:* Use Lemma 6-6.1.]

6-9.4. If $f: [a,b] \to E^1$ and $g: [a,b] \to E^1$ are integrable on $[a,b]$ and $f(x) \le g(x)$ for all $x \in [a,b]$, prove $\int_a^b f(x)\, dx \le \int_a^b g(x)\, dx.$

6-9.5. Let $f: [a,b] \to E^1$ be any bounded function. Prove that if $\int_a^b f(x)\, dx$ exists, then $\int_{r_1}^{r_2} f(x)\, dx$ exists for any subinterval $[r_1, r_2]$ of $[a,b]$; i.e., where $a \le r_1 \le r_2 \le b$. [*Hint:* Use Theorem 6-4.1 and Lemma 6-6.1.]

6-10 INFORMAL REMARKS ON INTEGRATION AND DIFFERENTIATION

Although we have proved that $\int_a^b f(x)\, dx$ exists if f is continuous on $[a,b]$, it is usually quite difficult to evaluate this integral using only the definition.

We shall use geometric intuition for the conjecture of a possible evaluation technique.

Consider the areas of the regions in Figures 6-2.1, 6-2.2, and 6-2.3 studied at the beginning of this chapter. In these examples, replace the letter "b" by "x", to obtain:

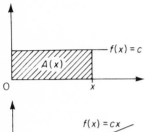

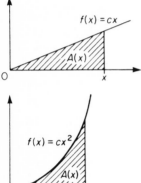

1. If $f(x) = c$, where $c > 0$, then $A(x) = cx$.

2. If $f(x) = cx$, $c > 0$, then $A(x) = cx^2/2$.

3. If $f(x) = cx^2$, $c > 0$, then $A(x) = cx^3/3$.

(See Figure 6-10.1.)

The important observation here is that

$$\frac{dA(x)}{dx} = f(x)$$

in each of the three examples. This leads us to an important question: Suppose $f: [a,b] \to E^1$ is continuous and the graph of f lies above the x-axis. Let $A(x)$ represent the area under the graph of f from a to x, where $a \leq x \leq b$. Is it always true that $dA(x)/dx = f(x)$? This question is answered in the affirmative, and the following is an intuitive "proof":

Figure 6-10.1

Consider a change Δx in the variable x, and let ΔA be the corresponding change in area (Figure 6-10.2.) (For this informal discussion, assume $\Delta x > 0$.) Let M equal the maximum value of f in $[x, x + \Delta x]$ and m equal the minimum value of f in $[x, x + \Delta x]$. Now, by comparison of

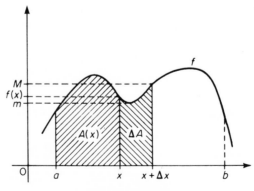

Figure 6-10.2

areas of rectangles having $[x, x + \Delta x]$ as base, with ΔA, we obtain $m\,\Delta x \leq \Delta A \leq M\,\Delta x$, or $m \leq \Delta A/\Delta x \leq M$. As $\Delta x \to 0$, it must be true that $m \to f(x)$ and $M \to f(x)$ by the continuity of f; hence the quantity $\Delta A/\Delta x$, bounded by m and M, approaches $f(x)$ as well:

$$\frac{dA(x)}{dx} = \lim_{\Delta x \to 0} \frac{\Delta A}{\Delta x} = f(x).$$

Thus, if the curve $f(x)$ is given, in order to find $A(x)$ look for a function which has a derivative equal to $f(x)$. It is also necessary that the area function have the value 0 at $x = a$.

The foregoing informal remarks will be used as a guide for a careful presentation of a similar result relating to integrals in general, given in Section 6-11 as "The Fundamental Theorem".

6-11 THE FUNDAMENTAL THEOREM OF DIFFERENTIAL AND INTEGRAL CALCULUS

Let $f\colon [a,b] \to E^1$ be any function which is integrable on $[a,b]$. The value of $\int_a^b f(x)\,dx$ depends only on the function f and the limits a, b of integration, and not on the choice of the letter representing the independent variable. Although x has been used extensively, another letter would serve equally well. Note that

$$\overline{\int}_a^b f(x)\,dx, \qquad \underline{\int}_a^b f(x)\,dx,$$

and consequently $\int_a^b f(x)\,dx$, were defined in terms of step functions, and we have observed (on page 124) that the value of the integral of a step function is independent of the choice of the letter representing this variable. Thus,

$$\int_a^b f(x)\,dx = \int_a^b f(u)\,du = \int_a^b f(t)\,dt,$$

etc. It is even acceptable to express an integral in the abbreviated form $\int_a^b f$.

If a function $f\colon [a,b] \to E^1$ is integrable on every closed subinterval of $[a,b]$, then we can define a new function $G\colon [a,b] \to E^1$ by

$$G(x) = \int_a^x f(u)\,du, \qquad \text{where } a \leq x \leq b.$$

The upper limit of integration is a variable; $\int_a^x f(u)\, du$ is called an *indefinite integral* of f. We avoid the notation $\int_a^x f(x)\, dx$, since the letter x would have two separate meanings, the variable of integration and the upper limit. It is acceptable to write $G(x) = \int_a^x f$.

THEOREM 6-11.1: *(The Fundamental Theorem)*: If $f: [a,b] \to E^1$ is continuous on $[a,b]$ and $G(x) = \int_a^x f(u)\, du$, then

$$D_x G(x) = f(x).$$

Proof:

$$D_x G(x) = \lim_{h \to 0} \frac{G(x + h) - G(x)}{h}$$

$$= \lim_{h \to 0} \frac{\int_a^{x+h} f(u)\, du - \int_a^x f(u)\, du}{h}$$

$$= \lim_{h \to 0} \frac{\int_x^{x+h} f(u)\, du}{h}, \qquad \text{by Corollary 6-9.2}$$

$$= \lim_{h \to 0} \frac{hf(r)}{h}, \qquad \text{by Corollary 6-9.1}$$

where r belongs to the closed interval with endpoints x and $x + h$. Now, because of the location of r, $h \to 0$ implies $r \to x$. Hence

$$\lim_{h \to 0} \frac{hf(r)}{h} = \lim_{h \to 0} f(r) = \lim_{r \to x} f(r) = f(x);$$

the last equality holds because of the continuity of f. ∎

6-12 PRIMITIVE FUNCTIONS

Given two functions $F: [a,b] \to E^1$ and $f: [a,b] \to E^1$, F is called a *primitive of f* if $D_x F(x) = f(x)$ for all $x \in [a,b]$. The following is a restatement of Theorem 5-7.2.

THEOREM 6-12.1: If $F: [a,b] \to E^1$ and $G: [a,b] \to E^1$ are primitives of a function $f: [a,b] \to E^1$, then, for some constant C, $F(x) - G(x) = C$, for all $x \in [a,b]$.

THEOREM 6-12.2: If $F: [a,b] \to E^1$ is any primitive of $f: [a,b] \to E^1$, and if f is continuous on $[a,b]$, then

$$F(b) - F(a) = \int_a^b f(x)\, dx.$$

Proof: By Theorem 6-11.1 and the hypothesis of the present theorem, both $\int_a^x f(u)\, du$ and $F(x)$ are primitives of $f(x)$. Hence, by Theorem 6-12.1, $F(x) - \int_a^x f(u)\, du = C$ for all $x \in [a,b]$. Now $C = F(a) - \int_a^a f(u)\, du = F(a)$; therefore $F(x) - F(a) = \int_a^x f(u)\, du$. Let $x = b$ to obtain

$$F(b) - F(a) = \int_a^b f(u)\, du = \int_a^b f(x)\, dx. \quad \blacksquare$$

Theorem 6-12.2 states that the integral of a continuous function may be evaluated by any primitive of f. However, this evaluation technique should not be regarded as an alternate definition of the integral.

EXAMPLE 6-12.1: Evaluate by Theorem 6-12.2: $\int_0^5 \sqrt{x + 4}\, dx.$

Since $F(x) = \frac{2}{3}(x + 4)^{3/2}$ is a primitive of $f(x) = \sqrt{x + 4}$,

$$\int_0^5 \sqrt{x + 4}\, dx = F(5) - F(0) = \tfrac{2}{3}(27) - \tfrac{2}{3}(8) = 38/3.$$

The following properties of the integral may be established using the Fundamental Theorem:

THEOREM 6-12.3: If $f: [a,b] \to E^1$ and $g: [a,b] \to E^1$ are continuous on $[a,b]$, then

1. $\displaystyle\int_a^b f(x)\, dx + \int_a^b g(x)\, dx = \int_a^b [f(x) + g(x)]\, dx$

2. $\displaystyle\int_a^b f(x)\, dx - \int_a^b g(x)\, dx = \int_a^b [f(x) - g(x)]\, dx$

3. $\displaystyle c\int_a^b f(x)\, dx = \int_a^b cf(x)\, dx$, for any constant c.

Proof: Part 1: Let

$$F(x) = \int_a^x f(u)\, du, \quad G(x) = \int_a^x g(u)\, du,$$

and

$$H(x) = \int_a^x [f(u) + g(u)]\, du.$$

By Theorem 6-11.1, $D_x[F(x) + G(x)] = D_xF(x) + D_xG(x) = f(x) + g(x)$, and $D_x[H(x)] = f(x) + g(x)$. By Theorem 6-12.1, $[F(x) + G(x)] - H(x) = C$. Now, $C = [F(a) + G(a)] - H(a) = 0$; hence $F(x) + G(x) = H(x)$ for all $x \in [a,b]$. At $x = b$, $F(b) + G(b) = H(b)$, or

$$\int_a^b f(u) \, du + \int_a^b g(u) \, du = \int_a^b [f(u) + g(u)] \, du.$$

Finally, we replace u by x to complete the proof of Part 1. ∎

The proofs of parts 2 and 3 are left as an exercise. (Ex. 6-13.1.)

6-13 CHANGE OF VARIABLE OF INTEGRATION

Let A denote a subset of E^1. If $g: [a,b] \to A$ and $f: A \to E^1$, then $fg: [a,b] \to E^1$ is a well defined composition. (See Figure 6-13.1.)

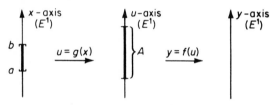

Figure 6-13.1

THEOREM 6-13.1: If f is continuous on A and if $g'(x)$ exists and is continuous for all $x \in [a,b]$, then

$$\int_{g(a)}^{g(b)} f(u) \, du = \int_a^b f[g(x)]g'(x) \, dx.$$

Proof: Note that all points between $g(a)$ and $g(b)$ belong to A by Corollary 5-2.2. Let $\phi(u) = \int_{g(a)}^u f(t) \, dt$ and $\psi(x) = \int_a^x f[g(t)]g'(t) \, dt$. Substitute $u = g(x)$ to obtain $\phi[g(x)] = \int_{g(a)}^{g(x)} f(t) \, dt$. Using the chain rule for differentiation and the Fundamental Theorem,

$$D_x\phi[g(x)] = D_u\phi(u) \cdot D_xg(x) = f(u) \cdot g'(x) = f[g(x)] \cdot g'(x);$$

$$D_x\psi(x) = f[g(x)]g'(x).$$

Now, since $\phi[g(x)]$ and $\psi(x)$ have the same derivative, $\phi[g(x)] - \psi(x) = C$, for some constant C. In particular,

$$C = \phi[g(a)] - \psi(a) = \int_{g(a)}^{g(a)} f(t) \, dt - \int_a^a f[g(t)]g'(t) \, dt = 0.$$

Thus, $\phi[g(x)] = \psi(x)$, or

$$\int_{g(a)}^{g(x)} f(t) \, dt = \int_{a}^{x} f[g(t)]g'(t) \, dt.$$

At $x = b$, $\int_{g(a)}^{g(b)} f(t) \, dt = \int_{a}^{b} f[g(t)]g'(t) \, dt$. The letter t representing the variable of integration may be replaced by any other convenient letter without changing the value of the integrals involved. Replacing t by x, the proof is complete. ∎

EXAMPLE 6-13.1: Evaluate $\int_{1}^{2} x\sqrt{x^2 + 3} \, dx$.

Let $g(x) = x^2 + 3$ and $f(u) = \sqrt{u}$; then $g'(x) = 2x$, $f[g(x)] = \sqrt{x^2 + 3}$, and $\int_{1}^{2} x\sqrt{x^2 + 3} \, dx = (1/2)\int_{1}^{2} f[g(x)]g'(x) \, dx$. By Theorem 6-13.1, this becomes

$(1/2)\int_{g(1)}^{g(2)} f(u) \, du = (1/2)\int_{4}^{7} \sqrt{u} \, du = (1/2)(2/3)u^{3/2}\Big|_{4}^{7} = (1/3)(7^{3/2} - 8)$.

EXERCISES

6-13.1. Prove parts 2 and 3 of Theorem 6-12.3, using the Fundamental Theorem.

6-13.2. Evaluate the following integrals using Theorem 6-13.1. In each case, state which functions $g(x)$ and $f(u)$ are used in the evaluation:

a. $\int_{1}^{2} x^2 \sqrt{x^3 + 2} \, dx$ e. $\int_{0}^{\pi/2} (x^2 \sin x \cos x + x \sin^2 x) \, dx$

b. $\int_{0}^{\pi/2} \sin^2 x \cos x \, dx$ f. $\int_{1}^{5} \sqrt{x + 4} \, dx$

c. $\int_{0}^{1} [x/(x^2 + 1)^5] \, dx$ g. $\int_{1}^{4} x\sqrt{1 + 2x} \, dx$

d. $\int_{0}^{1} x^3 \cos x^4 \, dx$

6-14 APPLICATION

In this section we give a simple application of integration which does not relate directly to area. Consider the problem of finding the volume of solids bounded by a surface of revolution.

In this discussion we shall assume that the volume V of a right circular cylinder is given by the formula $V = \pi r^2 h$, where h is the height of the cylinder and r denotes the radius of the base.

Let $f: [a,b] \to B$ be a continuous function where B represents the non-negative real numbers. Let S be the surface generated by revolving the curve

$y = f(x)$ about the x-axis, so that each point on the curve remains at its original distance from the x-axis. (The surface S is given by the equation $y^2 + z^2 = [f(x)]^2$.) Consider the solid K bounded by S and the planes $x = a$ and $x = b$ (Figure 6-14.1). Let $M > 0$ be an upper bound for the function $f(x)$ on the interval $[a,b]$. Then, given any $\varepsilon > 0$, there exist step functions $s: [a,b] \to [0,M]$ and $t: [a,b] \to [0,M]$ such that $s(x) \le f(x) \le t(x)$ and $\int_a^b t(x)\,dx - \int_a^b s(x)\,dx < \varepsilon$, by Lemma 6-6.1. (Since $0 \le f(x) \le M$ for all $x \in [a,b]$, it is clear $s(x)$ and $t(x)$ can be chosen so that $0 \le s(x) \le M$ and $0 \le t(x) \le M$.)

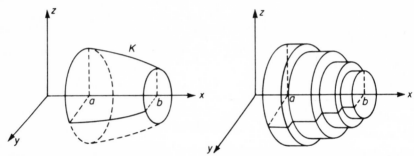

Figure 6-14.1   **Figure 6-14.2**

If the graph of $s(x)$ is revolved about the x-axis, we obtain a set of right circular cylinders, as shown in Figure 6-14.2. Let $P = \{x_0, x_1, x_2, \ldots, x_n\}$ be a partition associated with $s(x)$; let $s(x) = c_k$ in the kth subinterval, $k = 1, 2, \ldots, n$. Now the sum of the volumes of the cylinders described is

$$\sum_{k=1}^{n} \pi c_k^2 (x_k - x_{k-1}) = \int_a^b \pi s^2(x)\,dx.$$

Note that $\pi s^2(x)$ is also a step function. Moreover, since the cylinders lie inside K, $\int_a^b \pi s^2(x)\,dx \le V(K)$, where $V(K)$ represents the volume of K. Similarly, it can be shown that $\int_a^b \pi t^2(x)\,dx \ge V(K)$. The inequalities $0 \le s(x) \le f(x) \le t(x)$ imply $\pi s^2(x) \le \pi f^2(x) \le \pi t^2(x)$; hence

$$\pi \int_a^b s^2(x)\,dx \le \pi \int_a^b f^2(x)\,dx \le \pi \int_a^b t^2(x)\,dx.$$

Now

$$\pi \int_a^b t^2(x)\,dx - \pi \int_a^b s^2(x)\,dx = \pi \int_a^b [t^2(x) - s^2(x)]\,dx$$

$$= \pi \int_a^b (t(x) + s(x))(t(x) - s(x))\,dx \le \pi \int_a^b (2M)(t(x) - s(x))\,dx$$

$$= 2\pi M \left[\int_a^b t(x)\,dx - \int_a^b s(x)\,dx \right] < 2\pi M \varepsilon.$$

Since both $V(K)$ and $\pi \int_a^b f^2(x)\, dx$ lie between $\pi \int_a^b s^2(x)\, dx$ and $\pi \int_a^b t^2(x)\, dx$, it follows that

$$\left| V(K) - \pi \int_a^b f^2(x)\, dx \right| < 2\pi M\varepsilon$$

or

$$\frac{1}{2\pi M} \left| V(K) - \pi \int_a^b f^2(x)\, dx \right| < \varepsilon,$$

for every $\varepsilon > 0$. Thus, $V(K) = \pi \int_a^b f^2(x)\, dx$.

6-15 DOUBLE SUMMATION

Consider a rectangular array of real numbers:

$$
\begin{array}{cccccc}
a_{11} & a_{12} & a_{13} & \cdots & a_{1m} \\
a_{21} & a_{22} & a_{23} & \cdots & a_{2m} \\
a_{31} & a_{32} & a_{33} & \cdots & a_{3m} \\
\cdot & & & & \cdot \\
\cdot & & & & \cdot \\
\cdot & & & & \cdot \\
a_{n1} & a_{n2} & a_{n3} & \cdots & a_{nm}
\end{array}
$$

The sum of the elements in the ith row $(1 \le i \le n)$ is given by

$$\sum_{j=1}^m a_{ij} = a_{i1} + a_{i2} + a_{i3} + \ldots + a_{im}$$

The *double summation*

$$\sum_{i=1}^n \left(\sum_{j=1}^m a_{ij} \right) = \sum_{j=1}^m a_{1j} + \sum_{j=1}^m a_{2j} + \ldots + \sum_{j=1}^m a_{nj}$$

is obviously the sum of all elements a_{ij} in the rectangular array. Note that

$$\sum_{i=1}^n \left(\sum_{j=1}^m a_{ij} \right) = \sum_{j=1}^m \left(\sum_{i=1}^n a_{ij} \right),$$

since the sum is independent of the order in which the individual numbers are added. For brevity, the parentheses are usually omitted in expressions of double summation.

6-16 STEP FUNCTIONS DEFINED ON A RECTANGLE

Let R denote a closed rectangular region of the xy-plane bounded by the lines $x = a$, $x = b$, $y = c$, and $y = d$, as shown in Figure 6-16.1. Consider

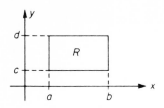

Figure 6-16.1

partitions $P_1 = \{x_0, x_1, \ldots x_n\}$ and $P_2 = \{y_0, y_1, \ldots, y_m\}$ of the intervals $[a,b]$ and $[c,d]$ respectively. If lines are drawn parallel to the x-axis through the points of P_2 and lines are drawn parallel to the y-axis through the points of P_1, then R is subdivided into smaller rectangles R_{ij}, as shown in Figure 6-16.2. Let $R_{ij} = \{(x,y) \mid x_{i-1} < x < x_i$ and $y_{j-1} < y < y_j\}$ and let $\bar{R}_{ij} = \{(x,y) \mid x_{i-1} \leq x \leq x_i$ and $y_{j-1} \leq y \leq y_j\}$. Define $|R_{ij}|$ to be the area of R_{ij}; that is, $|R_{ij}| = (x_i - x_{i-1})(y_j - y_{j-1})$; also define $|R| = (b - a)(d - c)$.

A subdivision of R of the type just described will be called a *partition of R*. The rectangles R_{ij} are called *subsets* of the partition. The partition itself is often denoted $P = P_1 \times P_2$.

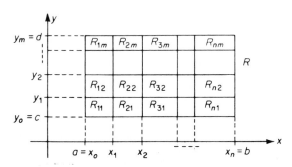

Figure 6-16.2

A function $h: R \to E^1$ is called a *step function on R* if there exists a partition of the rectangle R such that $h(x,y)$ is constant on each subset R_{ij} of P; i.e., if there exists a set of $n \times m$ constants c_{ij} such that $h(x,y) = c_{ij}$ when $(x,y) \in R_{ij}$. In this text, we will include the additional property that $h(x,y_j)$ be a step function of the variable x on each of the $m + 1$ lines $y = y_j$ of subdivision of P, $(y_j \in P_2, j = 0, 1, \ldots, m)$, and that $h(x_i,y)$ be a step function of the variable y on each of the $n + 1$ lines $x = x_i$ of subdivision of P, $(x_i \in P_1, i = 0, 1, \ldots, n)$. When defining a step function $h(x,y)$ it is often convenient to let h equal a constant on all such lines. See Figure 6-16.3.

The *double integral* $\iint\limits_{R} h(x,y)\, dA$ of a step function $h: R \to E^1$ is defined by

$$\iint\limits_{R} h(x,y)\, dA = \sum_{i=1}^{n} \sum_{j=1}^{m} c_{ij}(x_i - x_{i-1})(y_j - y_{j-1})$$

$$= \sum_{i=1}^{n} \sum_{j=1}^{m} c_{ij}\, |R_{ij}|.$$

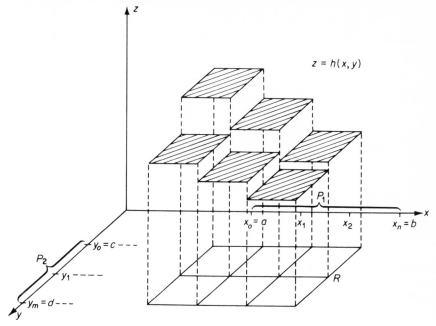

Figure 6-16.3

The value of a double integral is not altered if the partition P is replaced by a partition P' containing all the lines of subdivision of P together with additional lines parallel to the coordinate axes.

The definition of the double integral of a step function will now be related to repeated single integration.

Let $\bar{x}$ be any point in the ith open subinterval of partition P_1; $h(\bar{x},y)$ is a step function of the single real variable y, and $h(\bar{x},y) = c_{ij}$ if $y \in (y_{j-1},y_j)$, $j = 1, 2, \ldots, m$. Consequently

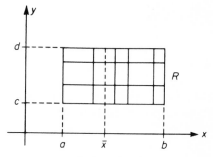

Figure 6-16.4

$$\int_c^d h(\bar{x},y)\, dy = \sum_{j=1}^m c_{ij}(y_j - y_{j-1})$$

(See Figure 6-16.4). Define $g(x) = \int_c^d h(x,y)\, dy$ for all $x \in [a,b]$. Note that $g: [a,b] \to E^1$ is also a step function, since it remains constant on each open subinterval of the partition P_1. If $u_i = \sum_{j=1}^m c_{ij}(y_j - y_{j-1})$, $i = 1, 2, \ldots, n$, then

$g(x) = u_i$ for all $x \in (x_{i-1}, x_i)$. Therefore

$$\int_a^b \left[\int_c^d h(x,y)\, dy \right] dx = \int_a^b g(x)\, dx = \sum_{i=1}^n u_i (x_i - x_{i-1})$$

$$= \sum_{i=1}^n \left[\sum_{j=1}^m c_{ij}(y_j - y_{j-1}) \right](x_i - x_{i-1}) = \iint_R h(x,y)\, dA.$$

This result is stated as a theorem for reference:

THEOREM 6-16.1: If $h: R \to E^1$ is any step function where $R = \{(x, y) \mid a \le x \le b$ and $c \le y \le d\}$, then $\int_a^b \left[\int_c^d h(x,y)\, dy \right] dx = \iint_R h(x,y)\, dA.$

EXERCISES

6-16.1. Let $R = \{(x,y) \mid 0 \le x \le 3$ and $5 \le y \le 9\}$, and let $P_1 = \{0, 1, 2, 3\}$ and $P_2 = \{5, 6, 7, 8, 9\}$ be partitions of $[0,3]$ and $[5,9]$ respectively. Define a step function $h: R \to E^1$ by $h(x,y) = [x][y]$, where $P = P_1 \times P_2$. (See definition of the "bracket function" on page 90.)

a. Evaluate $\iint_R h(x,y)\, dA$ using the definition of a double integral.

b. Tabulate the values of $g(x) = \int_c^d h(x,y)\, dy$.

c. Show that $\int_a^b g(x)\, dx = \iint_R h(x,y)\, dA$.

6-16.2. If $s: R \to E^1$ and $t: R \to E^1$ are step functions such that $s(x,y) \le t(x,y)$ for all $(x,y) \in R$, prove that $\iint_R s(x,y)\, dA \le \iint_R t(x,y)\, dA$. (See Theorem 6-4.2.)

6-16.3. If $h: R \to E^1$ is any step function such that $|h(x,y)| < M$ for all $(x,y) \in R$, where M is a positive constant, prove that $-M\,|R| \le \iint_R h(x,y)\, dA \le M\,|R|$.

6-17 UPPER AND LOWER DOUBLE INTEGRALS OF A BOUNDED FUNCTION

Given any bounded function $f: R \to E^1$ where $R = \{(x,y) \mid a \le x \le b$ and $c \le y \le d\}$ and $|f(x,y)| \le M$ for all $(x,y) \in R$. Let S_f denote the set of all step functions $s: R \to E^1$ such that $s(x,y) \le f(x,y)$ for all $(x,y) \in R$ and let T_f represent the set of all step functions $t: R \to E^1$ such that $t(x,y) \geq f(x,y)$ for all $(x,y) \in R$. Define the lower and upper integrals of f as follows:

$$\underline{\iint_R} f(x,y)\, dA = \text{l.u.b.}\left\{ \iint_R s(x,y)\, dA \mid s(x,y) \in S_f \right\}$$

and

$$\overline{\iint_R} f(x,y)\, dA = \text{g.l.b.}\left\{ \iint_R t(x,y)\, dA \mid t(x,y) \in T_f \right\}.$$

Both of these integrals exist since f is bounded.

The next lemma and the subsequent two theorems can be proved by following the patterns of proof given in Lemma 6-5.2, Theorem 6-5.1, and Theorem 6-5.2.

LEMMA 6-17.1: Given any number $\varepsilon > 0$, there exist step functions $s_0(x,y) \in S_f$ and $t_0(x,y) \in T_f$ such that

(1)
$$\underline{\iint_R} f(x,y)\, dA - \iint_R s_0(x,y)\, dA < \varepsilon/2$$

and

(2)
$$\iint_R t_0(x,y)\, dA - \overline{\iint_R} f(x,y)\, dA < \varepsilon/2,$$

THEOREM 6-17.1: For any bounded function $f: R \to E^1$

$$\underline{\iint_R} f(x,y)\, dA \leq \overline{\iint_R} f(x,y)\, dA.$$

THEOREM 6-17.2: If $f: R \to E^1$ is a step function, then

$$\underline{\iint_R} f(x,y)\, dA = \iint_R f(x,y)\, dA = \overline{\iint_R} f(x,y)\, dA.$$

A simplified notation for the subsets of a partition is often useful. Double subscripts, together with double summation, were needed to prove Theorem 6-16.1 only. If P is a partition of a rectangle R, then we can number the subsets determined by P in any convenient order to obtain $R_1, R_2, R_3, \ldots, R_n$. (Here n denotes the total number of subsets defined by P, and not the number of subintervals on the x-axis.) If $h: R \to E^1$ is a step function and P is the associated partition, then the constant values of h on each subset R_k can be denoted c_k, $(k = 1, 2, \ldots, n)$. Using this notation,

$$\iint\limits_R h(x,y)\, dA = \sum_{k=1}^{n} c_k\, |R_k|.$$

6-18 DEFINITION OF THE DOUBLE INTEGRAL OF A BOUNDED FUNCTION

Whenever $\underline{\iint\limits_R} f(x,y)\, dA = \overline{\iint\limits_R} f(x,y)\, dA$, we say that f is *integrable* on R, or equivalently, "the double integral exists", and the symbol $\iint\limits_R f(x,y)\, dA$ is used to denote this common value.

So far, double integrals have only been defined on rectangles. Now suppose $f: D \rightarrow E^1$, where D is any closed and bounded subset of E^2 and $f(D)$ is bounded. Let $a = $ g.l.b. $\{x \mid (x,y) \in D\}$, $b = $ l.u.b. $\{x \mid (x,y) \in D\}$, $c = $ g.l.b. $\{y \mid (x,y) \in D\}$, and $d = $ l.u.b. $\{y \mid (x,y) \in D\}$. Let $R_D = \{(x,y) \mid a \le x \le b$ and $c \le y \le d\}$; obviously, $D \subset R_D$. Define $\tilde{f}: R_D \rightarrow E^1$ by

$$\tilde{f}(x,y) = \begin{cases} f(x,y) \text{ if } (x,y) \in D \\ \quad 0 \quad \text{ if } (x,y) \in R_D - D \end{cases}$$

Also define

$$\underline{\iint\limits_D} f(x,y)\, dA = \underline{\iint\limits_{R_D}} \tilde{f}(x,y)\, dA$$

and

$$\overline{\iint\limits_D} f(x,y)\, dA = \overline{\iint\limits_{R_D}} \tilde{f}(x,y)\, dA$$

By Theorem 6-17.1, $\underline{\iint\limits_D} f(x,y)\, dA \le \overline{\iint\limits_D} f(x,y)\, dA$. If equality holds, then we say that f is integrable on D and the double integral $\iint\limits_D f(x,y)\, dA$ exists.

LEMMA 6-18.1: $\iint\limits_D f(x,y)\, dA \left(\text{or, equivalently, } \iint\limits_{R_D} \tilde{f}(x,y)\, dA \right)$ exists if, and only if, for every real number $\varepsilon > 0$ there exist step functions $s_0: R_D \rightarrow E^1$

and $t_0: R_D \to E^1$, where $s_0(x,y) \le \tilde{f}(x,y) \le t_0(x,y)$ for all $(x,y) \in R_D$, such that $\displaystyle\iint\limits_{R_D} t_0(x,y)\,dA - \iint\limits_{R_D} s_0(x,y)\,dA < \varepsilon$.

(The proof of this lemma is similar to the proof of Lemma 6-6.1, and is left as an exercise.)

EXERCISES

6-18.1. Prove Lemma 6-17.1.

6-18.2. Prove Theorem 6-17.1.

6-18.3. Prove Theorem 6-17.2.

6-18.4. Prove Lemma 6-18.1.

6-19 THE DOUBLE INTEGRAL OF A CONTINUOUS FUNCTION

Let D be a closed and bounded subset of E^2. The set of all boundary points of D, designated $B(D)$, is said to *satisfy the Riemann Condition* if, and only if, for every $\varepsilon > 0$ there exists a partition P of R_D such that the sum of the areas of all open subsets R_{ij} of P which intersect $B(D)$ is less than ε (see Figure 6-19.1).

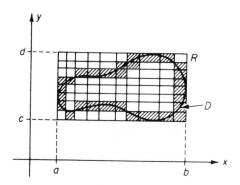

Figure 6-19.1

THEOREM 6-19.1: Assume D is a closed subset of E^2 bounded by curves $y = f(x)$, $y = g(x)$, and lines $x = a$ and $x = b$. If $f: [a,b] \to E^1$ and $g: [a,b] \to E^1$ are continuous functions and $f(x) \le g(x)$ for all $x \in [a,b]$, then $B(D)$ satisfies the Riemann Condition. (Figure 6-19.2.)

The proof of this theorem is left to the reader. (See Lemma 6-6.1, and Figure 6-6.1.)

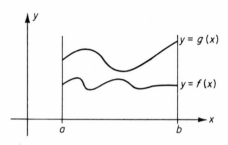

Figure 6-19.2

THEOREM 6-19.2: Assume D is a closed and bounded subset of E^2 such that $B(D)$ satisfies the Riemann Condition. If $f: D \to E^1$ is continuous on D, then $\iint\limits_{D} f(x,y)\, dA$ exists.

Proof: Since $f: D \to E^1$ is continuous, the function is bounded. (Theorem 5-2.6.) Consequently, $\tilde{f}: R_D \to E^1$ is also bounded. Let $M > 0$ denote a real number such that $|\tilde{f}(x,y)| \le M$ for all $(x,y) \in R_D$. Given any $\varepsilon > 0$, let $\varepsilon' = \varepsilon/(2M + |R_D|)$. Since f is continuous on the closed and bounded set D, f is also uniformly continuous on D. (Theorem 5-3.1.) This implies that it is possible to find a partition P of R_D such that if points (x',y') and (x'',y'') of D belong to the same closed subset of P, then

$$|f(x',y') - f(x'',y'')| < \varepsilon'.$$

Let P' be a partition of R_D such that the total area of all open subsets of P' which intersect $B(D)$ is less than ε' (the Riemann Condition). We shall work with the partition P'' of R_D which contains all of the lines of subdivision of both P and P'. Simplified notation for the subsets of P'' will be used, that is, consecutive numbering with single subscripts. It is convenient to start our numbering with the open subsets which intersect $B(D)$. Therefore assume that $R_1, R_2, \ldots, R_q, R_{q+1}, \ldots, R_n$ are all the subsets of R_D determined by P'', and that $R_k \cap B(D) \ne \varnothing$ if and only if $1 \le k \le q$. Note that since P'' contains all the lines of subdivision of P', $\sum_{k=1}^{q} |R_k| < \varepsilon'$.

For each closed subset $\bar{R}_k$ of P'' which lies entirely in D, let $(\check{x}_k, \check{y}_k)$ and $(\hat{x}_k, \hat{y}_k)$ be two points of $\bar{R}_k$ such that $f(\check{x}_k, \check{y}_k) \le f(x,y) \le f(\hat{x}_k, \hat{y}_k)$ for all

$(x,y) \in \bar{R}_k$. (Corollary 5-2.1.) Since P'' contains all the lines of sub-division of P, $f(\hat{x}_k, \hat{y}_k) - f(\check{x}_k, \check{y}_k) < \varepsilon'$. Define step functions $s: R_D \to E^1$ and $t: R_D \to E^1$ as follows:

$$s(x,y) = \check{c}_k \text{ for all } (x,y) \in R_k, \text{ where}$$

$$\check{c}_k = \begin{cases} 0 \text{ if } R_k \subset R_D - D, \\ -M \text{ if } R_k \cap B(D) \neq \varnothing, \\ f(\check{x}_k, \check{y}_k) \text{ if } R_k \subset D - B(D). \end{cases}$$

Also define $s(x,y) = -M$ if (x,y) lies on a line of subdivision of P''.

$$t(x,y) = \hat{c}_k \text{ for all } (x,y) \in R_k, \text{ where}$$

$$\hat{c}_k = \begin{cases} 0 \text{ if } R_k \subset R_D - D \\ M \text{ if } R_k \cap B(D) \neq \varnothing \\ f(\hat{x}_k, \hat{y}_k) \text{ if } R_k \subset D - B(D) \end{cases}$$

Also, let $t(x,y) = M$ if (x,y) lies on a line of subdivision of P''.

Note that
$$\hat{c}_k - \check{c}_k = 0 \text{ if } R_k \subset R_D - D,$$
$$\hat{c}_k - \check{c}_k = 2M \text{ if } R_k \cap B(D) \neq \varnothing, 1 \leq k \leq q$$
$$\hat{c}_k - \check{c}_k < \varepsilon' \text{ if } R_k \subset D - B(D)$$
and
$$s(x,y) \leq \tilde{f}(x,y) \leq t(x,y) \text{ for all } (x,y) \in R_D.$$

Now

$$\iint\limits_{R_D} t(x,y)\, dA - \iint\limits_{R_D} s(x,y)\, dA = \sum_{k=1}^{n} \hat{c}_k |R_k| - \sum_{k=1}^{n} \check{c}_k |R_k|$$

$$= \sum_{k=1}^{n} (\hat{c}_k - \check{c}_k) |R_k|$$

$$= \sum_{k=1}^{q} (\hat{c}_k - \check{c}_k) |R_k| + \sum_{k=q+1}^{n} (\hat{c}_k - \check{c}_k) |R_k|$$

$$\leq \sum_{k=1}^{q} (2M) |R_k| + \sum_{k=q+1}^{n} \varepsilon' |R_k|$$

$$= 2M \sum_{k=1}^{q} |R_k| + \varepsilon' \sum_{k=q+1}^{n} |R_k|$$

$$< 2M\varepsilon' + \varepsilon' |R_D| = (2M + |R_D|)\varepsilon' = \varepsilon.$$

Therefore, by Lemma 6-18.1, $\iint\limits_{D} f(x,y)\, dA$ exists. ∎

6-20 THE EVALUATION OF DOUBLE INTEGRALS

The statement of Theorem 6-16.1 relating to step functions motivates the following more general question: "How does repeated integration

$$\int_a^b \int_c^d \tilde{f}(x,y)\, dy\, dx$$

compare in value with the double integral $\iint\limits_{R_D} \tilde{f}(x,y)\, dA = \iint\limits_{D} f(x,y)\, dA$ for an integrable function $f: D \to E^1$?" In order to study this question, two preliminary lemmas will be given.

LEMMA 6-20.1: Let $f(x,y)$ be a function defined on a subset D of the xy-plane. If f is continuous at a point (x_0,y_0) of D and if every neighborhood of (x_0,y_0) contains other points of D on the line $y = y_0$, then the function $f(x_0,y)$ of the single variable y is also continuous at y_0.

Proof: Since $f(x,y)$ is continuous at (x_0,y_0), given any $\varepsilon > 0$ there exists a $\delta > 0$ such that $d((x,y),(x_0,y_0)) < \delta$ implies $|f(x,y) - f(x_0,y_0)| < \varepsilon$. Now if $|y - y_0| < \delta$, then

$$d((x_0,y), (x_0,y_0)) = \sqrt{(x_0 - x_0)^2 + (y - y_0)^2} = |y - y_0| < \delta.$$

Hence $|f(x_0,y) - f(x_0,y_0)| < \varepsilon$, and the lemma is established. ∎

LEMMA 6-20.2: If $f: [a,b] \to E^1$ is a function of a single real variable x, where (1) f is continuous on a closed subinterval $[r_1,r_2]$ of $[a,b]$, ($a \le r_1 < r_2 \le b$), and (2) $f(x) = 0$ for all $x \in [a,b] - [r_1,r_2]$, then $\int_a^b f(x)\, dx$ exists and is equal to $\int_{r_1}^{r_2} f(x)\, dx$.

Proof: Since f is continuous on $[r_1,r_2]$, the integral $\int_{r_1}^{r_2} f(x)\, dx$ exists. Given any real number $\varepsilon > 0$, there exist step functions $s: [r_1,r_2] \to E^1$ and $t: [r_1,r_2] \to E^1$ such that $s(x) \le f(x) \le t(x)$ for all $x \in [r_1,r_2]$ and

$$\int_{r_1}^{r_2} t(x)\, dx - \int_{r_1}^{r_2} s(x)\, dx < \varepsilon.$$

(Lemma 6-6.1.)
Define step function $\bar{s}: [a,b] \to E^1$ and $\bar{t}: [a,b] \to E^1$ as follows:

$$\bar{s}(x) = \begin{cases} s(x) & \text{if } x \in [r_1,r_2], \\ 0 & \text{if } x \in [a,b] - [r_1,r_2], \end{cases}$$

and

$$\bar{t}(x) = \begin{cases} t(x) & \text{if } x \in [r_1, r_2], \\ 0 & \text{if } x \in [a,b] - [r_1, r_2]. \end{cases}$$

Directly from the definition of the integral of a step function we obtain

$$\int_a^b \bar{s}(x)\,dx = \int_{r_1}^{r_2} s(x)\,dx \quad \text{and} \quad \int_a^b \bar{t}(x)\,dx = \int_{r_1}^{r_2} t(x)\,dx.$$

Note also that $\bar{s}(x) \leq f(x) \leq \bar{t}(x)$ for all $x \in [a,b]$. Now,

$$\int_a^b \bar{t}(x)\,dx - \int_a^b \bar{s}(x)\,dx = \int_{r_1}^{r_2} t(x)\,dx - \int_{r_1}^{r_2} s(x)\,dx < \varepsilon.$$

Therefore $\int_a^b f(x)\,dx$ exists, by Lemma 6-6.1.

Since both

$$\int_a^b f(x)\,dx \qquad \text{and} \qquad \int_{r_1}^{r_2} f(x)\,dx$$

are bounded by

$$\int_a^b \bar{s}(x)\,dx \qquad \text{and} \qquad \int_a^b \bar{t}(x)\,dx$$

or, equivalently, by

$$\int_{r_1}^{r_2} s(x)\,dx \qquad \text{and} \qquad \int_{r_1}^{r_2} t(x)\,dx$$

it must be true that

$$\left| \int_a^b f(x)\,dx - \int_{r_1}^{r_2} f(x)\,dx \right| < \varepsilon$$

for every $\varepsilon > 0$. Hence

$$\int_a^b f(x)\,dx = \int_{r_1}^{r_2} f(x)\,dx. \quad \blacksquare$$

THEOREM 6-20.1: Let D be a closed subset of the xy-plane bounded by curves $y = g_1(x)$, $y = g_2(x)$ and lines $x = a$ and $x = b$, where $g_1 : [a,b] \to E^1$ and $g_2 : [a,b] \to E^1$ are continuous, and $g_1(x) \leq g_2(x)$ for all $x \in [a,b]$. Let c equal the minimum value of $g_1(x)$ and d equal the maximum value of $g_2(x)$ on $[a,b]$, so that $R_D = \{(x,y) \mid a \leq x \leq b \text{ and } c \leq y \leq d\}$. If $f : D \to E^1$ is continuous, then

$$\iint_D f(x,y)\,dA = \int_a^b \left[\int_c^d \tilde{f}(x,y)\,dy \right] dx.$$

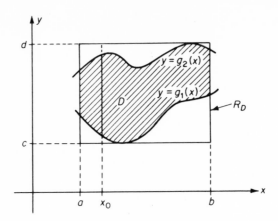

Figure 6-20.1

Proof: Let $x_0 \in [a,b]$ be any fixed value. Now $\tilde{f}(x_0,y)$ is a function of the real variable y, which is continuous for all y such that $g_1(x_0) \le y \le g_2(x_0)$, (Lemma 6-20.1), and equal to 0 at all other points in the interval $[c,d]$. Hence, by Lemma 6-20.2, $\int_c^d \tilde{f}(x_0,y)\,dy$ exists. (Obviously, it does not matter if the variable is represented by the letter x or by the letter y.) By Theorems 6-19.1 and 6-19.2, $\iint_D f(x,y)\,dA$ exists. Let $\varepsilon > 0$ be given.

According to Lemma 6-18.1, there are step functions $s\colon R_D \to E^1$ and $t\colon R_D \to E^1$ such that $s(x,y) \le \tilde{f}(x,y) \le t(x,y)$ for all $(x,y) \in R_D$ and

$$(1) \qquad \iint_{R_D} t(x,y)\,dA - \iint_{R_D} s(x,y)\,dA < \varepsilon.$$

By Theorem 6-16.1,

$$\int_a^b \left[\int_c^d s(x,y)\,dy \right] dx = \iint_{R_D} s(x,y)\,dA$$

and

$$\int_a^b \left[\int_c^d t(x,y)\,dy \right] dx = \iint_{R_D} t(x,y)\,dA.$$

Thus

$$(2) \qquad \int_a^b \left[\int_c^d t(x,y)\,dy \right] dx - \int_a^b \left[\int_c^d s(x,y)\,dy \right] dx < \varepsilon.$$

Since $s(x,y) \le \tilde{f}(x,y) \le t(x,y)$ and $s(x,y)$, $t(x,y)$ are step functions for each fixed $x \in [a,b]$, we have

$$(3) \qquad \int_c^d s(x,y)\,dy \le \int_c^d \tilde{f}(x,y)\,dy \le \int_c^d t(x,y)\,dy.$$

By the discussion preceding Theorem 6-16.1 (see pages 149–150) both $\int_c^d s(x,y)\,dy$ and $\int_c^d t(x,y)\,dy$ are step functions of the variable x, where the domain of definition is $[a,b]$. Hence, by lines (2) and (3) and Lemma 6-6.1, the function $\int_c^d \tilde{f}(x,y)\,dy$ of x is integrable on $[a,b]$—that is, $\int_a^b \left[\int_c^d \tilde{f}(x,y)\,dy \right] dx$ exists. Moreover, from statement (3) and the definition of $\int_a^b$ we have

$$\int_a^b \left[\int_c^d s(x,y)\,dy \right] dx \leq \int_a^b \left[\int_c^d \tilde{f}(x,y)\,dy \right] dx \leq \int_a^b \left[\int_c^d t(x,y)\,dy \right] dx$$

Consequently, both

$$\int_a^b \left[\int_c^d \tilde{f}(x,y)\,dy \right] dx \qquad \text{and} \qquad \iint_{R_D} \tilde{f}(x,y)\,dA$$

are bounded by $\iint_{R_D} s(x,y)\,dA$ and $\iint_{R_D} t(x,y)\,dA$. This, and line (1), imply

$$\left| \iint_{R_D} \tilde{f}(x,y)\,dA - \int_a^b \left[\int_c^d \tilde{f}(x,y)\,dy \right] dx \right| < \varepsilon$$

for every real number $\varepsilon > 0$. Hence

$$\iint_{R_D} \tilde{f}(x,y)\,dA = \int_a^b \left[\int_c^d \tilde{f}(x,y)\,dy \right] dx.$$

Since

$$\iint_D f(x,y)\,dA = \iint_{R_D} \tilde{f}(x,y)\,dA,$$

the proof is complete. $\blacksquare$

COROLLARY 6-20.1: Under the conditions given in Theorem 6-20.1,

$$\iint_D f(x,y)\,dA = \int_a^b \left[\int_{g_1(x)}^{g_2(x)} f(x,y)\,dy \right] dx.$$

Proof: By Lemmas 6-20.1 and 6-20.2,

$$\int_c^d \tilde{f}(x,y)\,dy = \int_{g_1(x)}^{g_2(x)} \tilde{f}(x,y)\,dy = \int_{g_1(x)}^{g_2(x)} f(x,y)\,dy$$

for every $x \in [a,b]$. Substitute $\int_{g_1(x)}^{g_2(x)} f(x,y)\,dy$ for $\int_c^d \tilde{f}(x,y)\,dy$ in the formula given in Theorem 6-20.1. $\blacksquare$

The following corollary is established by merely interchanging the roles of x and y.

COROLLARY 6-20.2: Let D be a closed subset of the xy-plane bounded by curves $x = g_1(y)$, $x = g_2(y)$, and lines $y = c$, $y = d$, where $g_1\colon [c,d] \to E^1$ and $g_2\colon [c,d] \to E^1$ are continuous, and $g_1(y) \le g_2(y)$ for all $y \in [c,d]$. Let a equal the minimum value of $g_1(y)$ and b equal the maximum value of $g_2(y)$ on $[c,d]$. Then $R_D = \{(x,y) \mid a \le x \le b \text{ and } c \le y \le d\}$. If $f\colon D \to E^1$ is continuous, then

$$\iint_D f(x,y)\, dA = \int_c^d \left[\int_{g_1(y)}^{g_2(y)} f(x,y)\, dx \right] dy.$$

The double integral can be used to find the volume of solids. This is the most obvious application (see the definition of $\iint$).

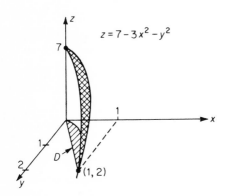

$z = 7 - 3x^2 - y^2$

Figure 6-20.2

EXAMPLE 6-20.1: Find the volume of the solid below the surface $z = 7 - 3x^2 - y^2$ and above the closed region D of the xy-plane bounded by the curves $y = 2x$ and $y = 2x^2$, as shown in Figure 6-20.2.

Method 1: Let $g_1(x) = 2x^2$ and $g_2(x) = 2x$; $f(x,y) = 7 - 3x^2 - y^2$; $a = 0$, and $b = 1$. Now

$$\iint_D f(x,y)\, dA$$

$$= \int_0^1 \left[\int_{g_1(x)}^{g_2(x)} f(x,y)\, dy \right] dx = \int_0^1 \left[\int_{2x^2}^{2x} (7 - 3x^2 - y^2)\, dy \right] dx$$

$$= \int_0^1 (7y - 3x^2 y - y^3/3) \Big|_{2x^2}^{2x} \, dx$$

$$= \int_0^1 (14x - 6x^3 - 8x^3/3 - 14x^2 + 6x^4 + 8x^6/3)\, dx$$

$$= [7x^2 - 3x^4/2 - 2x^4/3 - 14x^3/3 + 6x^5/5 + 8x^7/21] \Big|_0^1 = 367/210.$$

Method 2: Let $g_1(y) = y/2$ and $g_2(y) = \sqrt{y/2}$; $f(x,y) = 7 - 3x^2 - y^2$; $c = 0$, $d = 2$.

$$\iint\limits_D f(x,y)\, dA$$

$$= \int_0^2 \left[\int_{g_1(y)}^{g_2(y)} f(x,y)\, dx \right] dy$$

$$= \int_0^2 \left[\int_{y/2}^{\sqrt{y/2}} (7 - 3x^2 - y^2)\, dx \right] dy$$

$$= \int_0^2 [7x - x^3 - y^2 x]\Big|_{y/2}^{\sqrt{y/2}}\, dy$$

$$= \int_0^2 (7\sqrt{y/2} - y\sqrt{y/2}/2 - y^2\sqrt{y/2} - 7(y/2) + y^3/8 + y^3/2)\, dy$$

$$= 367/210.$$

EXERCISES

6-20.1. Prove Theorem 6-19.1.

6-20.2. Evaluate $\iint\limits_D f(x,y)\, dA$ for the following closed regions D of the xy-plane and functions $f: D \to E^1$:

a. D is bounded by $y = x^2$ and $y = 3x$; $f(x,y) = x + y$.
b. D is bounded by $y = 2x^2 - 2$ and $y = x^2 + x$; $f(x,y) = 2xy$.
c. Let D be the region in the first quadrant of the xy-plane bounded by $x = 0$, $y = 0$, and $4x^2 + y^2 = a^2$; let $f(x,y) = my$.
d. D is bounded by $y^2 = x$ and $x^2 = y$; $f(x,y) = x^2 + 4y^2$.

Project: Let K denote a closed and bounded subset of E^3 and let $f: K \to E^1$ be a bounded function. Carefully define $\iiint\limits_K f(x,y,z)\, dV$ in terms of step functions of three real variables, and find a method of evaluation. Follow the pattern given for double integrals.

Answers

to

Selected

Exercises

Pages 8–9

1-7.1: $R' = \{e, f, g\}; S' = T; T' = S; R - S = \{a, b\}; S - R = \{e, f\}; R \cap S = \{c, d\}; S \cup T = \mathscr{U}; S \cap T = \varnothing; R' - T = \{e, f\}; R' \cap T' = \{e, f\}.$

1-7.3: Subsets of S_1: $\varnothing$, S_1; subsets of S_2: $\varnothing$; $\{1\}$, $\{2\}$, S_2; subsets of S_3: $\varnothing$, $\{1\}$, $\{2\}$, $\{3\}$, $\{1, 2\}$, $\{1, 3\}$, $\{2, 3\}$, S_3; subsets of S_4: $\varnothing$, $\{1\}$, $\{2\}$, $\{3\}$, $\{4\}$, $\{1, 2\}$, $\{1, 3\}$, $\{1, 4\}$, $\{2, 3\}$, $\{2, 4\}$, $\{3, 4\}$, $\{1, 2, 3\}$, $\{1, 2, 4\}$, $\{1, 3, 4\}$, $\{2, 3, 4\}$, S_4; $S_n = \{1, 2, 3, \ldots, n\}$ has 2^n subsets.

1-7.4:

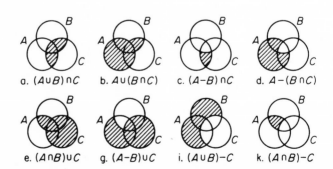

a. $(A \cup B) \cap C$ b. $A \cup (B \cap C)$ c. $(A - B) \cap C$ d. $A - (B \cap C)$

e. $(A \cap B) \cup C$ g. $(A - B) \cup C$ i. $(A \cup B) - C$ k. $(A \cap B) - C$

Only sets k and l are equal.

1-7.5:

Proof	Reason
1. Let $x \in (A - B) \cap C$	Arbitrary choice
2. $x \in A - B$ and $x \in C$	Definition of $\cap$ (1)
3. $x \in A$ and $x \notin B$	Definition of $-$ (2)
4. $x \notin B \cap C$	Definition of $\cap$ (3)
5. $x \in A - (B \cap C)$	Definition of $-$ (3,4)

Let $A = \{1, 4, 5, 7\}$, $B = \{2, 4, 6, 7\}$, $C = \{3, 5, 6, 7\}$;
then $(A - B) \cap C = \{5\}$ and $A - (B \cap C) = \{1, 4, 5\}$.

1-7.7:

Proof	Reason
1. Let $x \in (A - B) \cap (A - C)$	Arbitrary choice
2. $x \in A - B$ and $x \in A - C$	Definition of $\cap$ (1)
3. $x \in A$, $x \notin B$, $x \notin C$	Definition of $-$ (2)
4. $x \notin B \cap C$	Definition of $\cap$ (3)
5. $x \in A - (B \cap C)$	Definition of $-$ (3,4)

Let $A = \{1, 4, 5, 7\}$, $B = \{2, 4, 6, 7\}$, $C = \{3, 5, 6, 7\}$;
then $(A - B) \cap (A - C) = \{1\}$ and $A - (B \cap C) = \{1, 4, 5\}$.

1-7.9:

Proof	Reason
1. Let $x \in A \cap (B \cup C)$	Arbitrary choice
2. $x \in A$ and $x \in B \cup C$	Definition of $\cap$ (1)
3. $x \in B$ or $x \in C$	Definition of $\cup$ (2)
4. $x \in A \cap B$ or $x \in C$	Definition of $\cap$ (2,3)
5. $x \in (A \cap B) \cup C$	Definition of $\cup$ (4)

Take A, B, C as in 1-7.7; then $A \cap (B \cup C) = \{4, 5, 7\}$ and
$(A \cap B) \cup C = \{3, 4, 5, 6, 7\}$.

1-7.11:

Proof	Reason
1. Let $x \in (A - C) \cup (B - D)$	Arbitrary choice
2. $x \in A - C$ or $x \in B - D$	Definition of $\cup$ (1)
3. Case 1: $x \in A$ and $x \notin C$	Definition of $-$ (2)
or	
Case 2: $x \in B$ and $x \notin D$	
4. $x \in A \cup B$	Definition of $\cup$ (3)
5. $x \notin C \cap D$	Definition of $\cap$ (3)
6. $x \in (A \cup B) - (C \cap D)$	Definition of $-$ (4,5)

Let $A = \{1, 2, 3\}$, $B = \{3, 4, 5\}$, $C = \{2, 3, 4\}$, $D = \{4, 5, 6\}$;
then $(A - C) \cup (B - D) = \{1, 3\}$ and $(A \cup B) - (C \cap D) =$
$\{1, 2, 3, 5\}$.

1-7.13: *Proof (Part I)*

---

1. Let $x \in (A \cap B) - C$
2. $x \in A \cap B$ and $x \notin C$
3. $x \in A$ and $x \in B$ and $x \notin C$
4. $x \in A$ and $x \in B - C$
5. $x \in A \cap (B - C)$

Read this proof in reverse order to obtain Part II.

1-7.15: *Proof (Part I)*

---

1. Let $x \in (A \cap B) - (A \cap C)$
2. $x \in A \cap B$ and $x \notin A \cap C$
3. $x \in A$ and $x \in B$ and $x \notin C$
4. $x \in A$ and $x \in B - C$
5. $x \in A \cap (B - C)$

Read this proof in reverse order to obtain Part II.

1-7.17: *Proof (Part I)*

---

1. Let $x \in A - (B \cup C)$
2. $x \in A$ and $x \notin B \cup C$
3. $x \in A$ and $x \notin B$ and $x \notin C$
4. $x \in A - B$ and $x \in A - C$
5. $x \in (A - B) \cap (A - C)$

Read the proof in reverse order to obtain Part II.

1-7.19: *Proof (Part I)*

---

1. Let $x \in B - \bigcap_{i=1}^{n} A_i$
2. $x \in B$ and $x \notin \bigcap_{i=1}^{n} A_i$
3. $x \in B$ and x does not belong to at least one A_i
4. x belongs to at least one $B - A_i$
5. $x \in \bigcup_{i=1}^{n} (B - A_i)$

Read the proof in reverse order to obtain Part II.

Page 14

2-2.1: a, d, f

2-2.2:

A	B	a	c	e	g	i	k	m
T	T	T	F	F	F	T	T	F
T	F	T	F	T	F	T	T	T
F	T	F	F	F	F	T	F	T
F	F	T	T	F	T	F	T	F

Equivalent statements are (a,k), (c,g), (d,f,h), (e,j) and (l,m).

2-2.3:   a. No horse is white.

        b. Some horses are white.

        c. At least one horse is not white.

        d. Either the owl or the pussycat did not go to sea.

        e. I won't pass this course and I won't know the reason why.

2-2.4:   a. If a person is a philosopher, then he is wise. (Restatement)

        If a person is wise, then he is a philosopher. (Converse)

        If a person is not a philosopher, then he is not wise. (Inverse)

        If a person is not wise, then he is not a philosopher. (Contrapositive).

Pages 17–18

2-3.1:

Proof	*Reason*
1. $a + b = a$	Hypothesis
2. $a + b = a + 0$	A-4
3. $b = 0$	A-2, Theorem 2-3.1

2-3.2:

Proof	*Reason*
1. $b + (-b) = 0$	A-5
2. $(-b) + b = 0$	A-2
3. $b = -(-b)$	Theorem 2-3.3

2-3.5: Restatement: "If a number b has the property $ab = 1$, $(a \neq 0)$, then $b = a^{-1}$".

Proof	*Reason*
1. $ab = 1$	Hypothesis
2. $aa^{-1} = 1$	M-5
3. $ab = aa^{-1}$	Equality of (1) and (2)
4. $b = a^{-1}$	M-2, Exercise 2-3.4

2-3.7:

Proof	*Reason*
1. $1(1^{-1}) = 1$	M-5
2. $1 \cdot 1 = 1$	M-4
3. $1^{-1} = 1$	Exercise 2-3.5

2-3.9:

Proof	*Reason*
1. $a + (-a) = 0$	A-5
2. $b + (-b) = 0$	A-5
3. $[a + (-a)] + [b + (-b)] = 0$	A-1, A-4
4. $[a + b] + [(-a) + (-b)] = 0$	A-2, A-3
5. $[a + b] + [-a - b] = 0$	Abbreviation
6. $[a + b] + [-(a + b)] = 0$	A-5
7. $-(a + b) = -a - b$	Theorem 2-3.3

Page 19

2-4.1: *Proof*	*Reason*
1. $(a^{-1})(a^{-1})^{-1} = 1$	M-5, Corollary 2-4.2,
2. $(a^{-1})a = 1$	M-2, M-5
3. $(a^{-1})^{-1} = a$	Ex. 2-3.5

2-4.3: *Proof*	*Reason*
1. $1/a = (a^{-1}) \cdot 1$	Definition of $1/a$
2. $(a^{-1}) \cdot 1 = a^{-1}$	M-4
3. $1/a = a^{-1}$	Equality, lines (1) and (2)

2-4.5: *Proof*	*Reason*
1. $b^{-1}d^{-1} = (bd)^{-1}$	Exercise 2-4.4
2. $(ad)(b^{-1}d^{-1}) = (ad)(bd)^{-1}$	M-1
3. $(ab^{-1})(dd^{-1}) = (ad)(bd)^{-1}$	M-2, M-3
4. $(ab^{-1}) \cdot 1 = (ad)(bd)^{-1}$	M-5
5. $ab^{-1} = (ad)(bd)^{-1}$	M-4
6. $a/b = ad/bd$	Reciprocal form

2-4.7: *Proof*	*Reason*
1. $(bd)^{-1}(ad + bc) =$ $(bd)^{-1}(ad) + (bd)^{-1}(bc)$	D
2. $\dfrac{ad + bc}{bd} = \dfrac{ad}{bd} + \dfrac{bc}{bd}$	Reciprocal form
3. $\dfrac{ad + bc}{bd} = \dfrac{a}{b} + \dfrac{c}{d}$	M-2, Exercise 2-4.5

Page 20

2-5.1: *Proof*	*Reason*
1. $1 + (-1) = 0$	A-5
2. $a[1 + (-1)] = a \cdot 0$	M-1
3. $a \cdot 1 + a(-1) = 0$	D, Theorem 2-4.1
4. $a + (-1)a = 0$	M-2, M-4
5. $(-1)a = -a$	Theorem 2-3.3

2-5.3: *Proof*	*Reason*
1. $[(-1)a]b = (-1)(ab)$	M-3
2. $(-a)b = -(ab)$	Exercise 2-5.1

2-5.5: *Proof* | *Reason*

1. $(-a)b^{-1} = -(ab^{-1})$ — Exercise 2-5.3
2. $(-a)/b = -(a/b)$ — Reciprocal form

2-5.7: *Proof* | *Reason*

1. $a[b + (-c)] = ab + a(-c)$ — D
2. $a[b + (-c)] = ab + [-(ac)]$ — Exercise 2-5.4
3. $a(b - c) = ab - ac$ — Abbreviation

Pages 21–22

2-6.1: By O-2, one and only one of the following statements is true: $a - b = 0$, $a - b$ is positive, $-(a - b)$ is positive. Now $a - b = 0$ means that $a = b$ (additive inverse is unique); $a - b$ positive is equivalent to $a > b$ (by definition of $>$); $-(a - b)$ positive is equivalent to $a < b$ (since $-(a - b) = b - a$, Theorem 2-3.4, and definition of $<$).

2-6.3: $a > b$ means that $a - b$ is positive.
Since $c > 0$, $c(a - b)$ is positive by O-4.
$c(a - b) = ca - cb$ by D.
Therefore $ca - cb$ is positive, which implies $ca > cb$.
Also, $ac > bc$ by M-2.

2-6.5: Suppose a is positive and b is negative. By the definition of negative number, $(-b)$ is positive. By O-4, $a(-b)$ is positive, and by Exercise 2-5.4, $a(-b) = -(ab)$. This means that $-(ab)$ is positive and consequently ab is negative. [By M-2, ba must also be negative.]

2-6.7: $x = 0$ is not a solution since $1 > 0$. If $x \neq 0$, then $x^2 > 0$ by Exercise 2-6.6, and $x^2 + 1 > 0$ by O-3.

2-6.9: If $a \neq 0$, then $a^{-1} \neq 0$, by Corollary 2-4.2. Now consider $a^{-1} = a^{-1}(1) = a^{-1}(aa^{-1}) = (a^{-1})^2a$. By Exercise 2-6.6, $(a^{-1})^2$ is positive. Thus a^{-1} can be represented as the product of two positive numbers if a is positive and the product of a positive and a negative number if a is negative. Referring now to O-4 and Exercise 2-6.5, the proof is established.

2-6.11: $a < b$ implies $a + c < b + c$, by Exercise 2-6.2;
$c < d$ implies $b + c < b + d$, by Exercise 2-6.2;
now $a + c < b + c$ and $b + c < b + d$ imply $a + c < b + d$, by Theorem 2-6.2.

2-6.13: *Part 1.* Suppose $a > b$; then $(a - b) > 0$ and $(a + b) > 0$. (The latter inequality follows from O-3.) Hence, $a^2 - b^2 = (a - b)(a + b)$ is positive by O-4. By definition, $a^2 > b^2$.

Part 2. Using the same reasoning, $b \leq a$ implies $b^2 \leq a^2$. The contrapositive of this implication reads, "$a^2 < b^2$ implies $a < b$". (See Exercise 2-6.1, the law of trichotomy.)

Page 23

2-7.1: $-6 < x < -2$

2-7.3: $-5/3 < x < 3$

2-7.5: $\{x \mid x < -1 \text{ or } x > 7/3\}$

2-7.7: Case 1: $x \geq 0$, $y \geq 0$, then $|xy| = xy = |x| \cdot |y|$
Case 2: $x \geq 0$, $y < 0$, then $|xy| = -(xy) = x(-y) = |x| \cdot |y|$
Case 3: $x < 0$, $y \geq 0$, then $|xy| = -(xy) = (-x)y = |x| \cdot |y|$
Case 4: $x < 0$, $y < 0$, then $|xy| = xy = (-x)(-y) = |x| \cdot |y|$

2-7.9: Case 1: $x = 0$, then $|x| = 0$ and $|-x| = 0$
Case 2: $x > 0$, then $|x| = x$ and $|-x| = -(-x) = x$
Case 3: $x < 0$, then $|x| = -x$ and $|-x| = -x$

2-7.11: $|x - y| = |x + (-y)| \leq |x| + |-y| = |x| + |y|$

Page 25

2-8.1: (a) If a and b are even integers, then $a = 2m$ and $b = 2n$, where m and n are integers. Since $a + b = 2m + 2n = 2(m + n)$ and $m + n$ is an integer, $a + b$ is even.
(b) If a and b are odd integers, then $a = 2m + 1$ and $b = 2n + 1$, where m and n are integers. Since $a + b = 2m + 1 + 2n + 1 = 2(m + n + 1)$ and $m + n + 1$ is an integer, $a + b$ is even.
(c) If a is even and b is odd, then $a = 2m$ and $b = 2n + 1$, where m and n are integers. Since $a + b = 2m + 2n + 1 = 2(m + n) + 1$ and $m + n$ is an integer, $a + b$ is odd.
(d) (Part 1): If a and b are odd, $a = 2m + 1$ and $b = 2n + 1$, and $ab = (2m + 1)(2n + 1) = 2(2mn + m + n) + 1$ must be odd.
(Part 2): If a is even, then $a = 2m$, and $ab = (2m)b = 2(mb)$ is even. Similarly, if b is even then $b = 2n$ and $ab = a(2n) = 2(an)$ is even.

2-8.3: Indirect proof: Suppose a is rational, b is irrational and $a + b$ is rational. Then $a = p/q$ and $a + b = r/s$, where p, q, r, and s are integers and $q \neq 0, s \neq 0$. Now $b = (a + b) - a = r/s - p/q = r/s + [-(p/q)] = r/s + (-p)/q = [rq + s(-p)]/sq$; hence b must be rational.

Pages 29–30

2-9.1: a. All upper bounds are ≥ 8; all lower bounds are ≤ -3.

2-9.3: By Corollary 2-9.3, there exists a natural number n such that $1/n < d/c$; hence $c/n < d$.

2-9.5: Let b denote a lower bound for set S and let $T = \{x \mid -x \in S\}$.

CLAIM 1: $-b$ is an upper bound for T.

Proof: If $x \in T$, then $-x \in S$; hence $b \leq -x$ which implies $-b \geq x$.

Let c be the least upper bound of T.

CLAIM 2: $-c = $ g.l.b. S.

Proof: $-c$ is a lower bound for S since $x \in S$ implies $-x \in T$; consequently, $-x \leq c$ and $x \geq -c$. Now suppose a is any lower bound for S; by Claim 1, $-a$ is an upper bound for T. Since c is the least upper bound of T, $c \leq -a$ and consequently $-c \geq a$.

2-9.7: Let $c = $ g.l.b. S. If $d > c$, then d is not a lower bound for S. Therefore $x < d$ for at least one $x \in S$.

2-9.9: From $a < b$, we obtain $a - \sqrt{2} < b - \sqrt{2}$. By Theorem 2-9.3 there exists a rational number r such that $a - \sqrt{2} < r < b - \sqrt{2}$. Hence $a < r + \sqrt{2} < b$.

2-9.11: Since $a < b$, there exists a natural number n such that $1/10^n < b - a$ (Exercise 2-9.10) or equivalently, $a < b - 1/10^n$. By Theorem 2-9.2, there exists an integer k such that $10^n b - 1 \leq k < 10^n b$; hence $b - 1/10^n \leq k/10^n < b$. Combining the appropriate inequalities, we obtain $a < b - 1/10^n \leq k/10^n < b$.

Page 32

2-10.1: $1 < \sqrt{2} < 2$ since $1^2 < (\sqrt{2})^2 < 2^2$;

$1 + 4/10 < \sqrt{2} < 1 + 5/10$ since $(1.4)^2 < (\sqrt{2})^2 < (1.5)^2$;

$1 + 4/10 + 1/10^2 < \sqrt{2} < 1 + 4/10 + 2/10^2$ since $(1.41)^2 < (\sqrt{2})^2 < (1.42)^2$; etc.

Page 34

2-11.1: a. 40/9;   c. 67/111;   e. 1/8.

2-11.2: Divide to obtain these answers (note the eventual repetition):
a. .428571428571428571...; c. 5.333...; e. .171717....

2-11.3: *Proof:* From the preceding section (Section 2-11) it should be clear that a decimal expansion ending in all zeros can be replaced by an expansion ending in all 9's; the last non-zero digit is replaced by the digit one less than itself.

Suppose $x = a_0 . a_1 a_2 a_3 \cdots a_k \cdots$ and $x = b_0 . b_1 b_2 b_3 \cdots b_k \cdots$ where neither expansion ends in all zeros, $a_k > b_k$, and $a_n = b_n$ for all $n < k$.
Now $x = b_0 . b_1 b_2 b_3 \cdots b_k \cdots \leq b_0 . b_1 b_2 b_3 \cdots b_k 999 \cdots = b_0 . b_1 b_2 b_3 \cdots (b_k + 1) \leq a_0 . a_1 a_2 a_3 \cdots a_k < x$ since $a_k \geq b_k + 1$. Note the contradiction $x < x$.

Pages 43–44

3-6.1: a. $R = \{(1,1), (2,1), (3,3), (4,7)\}$
b. $R = \{(i,s), (i,t), (l,o), (n,o)\}$

3-6.3:   The relations in parts b and c are functions; the others are not.

3-6.4:

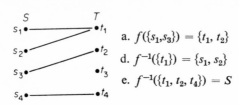

a. $f(\{s_1,s_3\}) = \{t_1, t_2\}$

d. $f^{-1}(\{t_1\}) = \{s_1, s_2\}$

e. $f^{-1}(\{t_1, t_2, t_4\}) = S$

3-6.5:   a. $f([0,1]) = [1,4]$
c. $f([3,4]) = [1,4]$
e. $f^{-1}((1,2)) = (2 - \sqrt{2},1) \cup (3,2 + \sqrt{2})$

3-6.7:

Proof	*Reason*
1. Let $x \in f^{-1}(D)$	Arbitrary choice
2. For some y in D, $(x,y) \in f$	Definition of inverse image
3. $y \in D$ and $D \subset E$ imply $y \in E$	Definition of $\subset$
4. $y \in E$ and $(x,y) \in f$ imply $x \in f^{-1}(E)$	Definition of inverse image

The following is also an acceptable proof of Ex. 3-6.7:

Proof	*Reason*
1. Let $x \in f^{-1}(D)$	Arbitrary choice
2. $f(x) \in D$	Definition of inverse image
3. Since $D \subset E$, $f(x) \in E$	Definition of $\subset$
4. $x \in f^{-1}(E)$	Definition of inverse image

3-6.8:

Proof	*Reason*
1. Let $x \in f^{-1}(D \cup E)$	Arbitrary choice
2. For some $y \in D \cup E$, $(x,y) \in f$	Definition of inverse image
3. $y \in D$ or $y \in E$	Definition of $\cup$
4. $x \in f^{-1}(D)$ or $x \in f^{-1}(E)$	Definition of inverse image
5. $x \in f^{-1}(D) \cup f^{-1}(E)$	Definition of $\cup$

The following is also acceptable:

Proof	*Reason*
1. Let $x \in f^{-1}(D \cup E)$	Arbitrary choice
2. $f(x) \in D \cup E$	Definition of inverse image
3. $f(x) \in D$ or $f(x) \in E$	Definition of $\cup$
4. $x \in f^{-1}(D)$ or $x \in f^{-1}(E)$	Definition of inverse image
5. $x \in f^{-1}(D) \cup f^{-1}(E)$	Definition of $\cup$

3-6.10: *Part I:* To show that $f^{-1}(D) \cap f^{-1}(E) \subseteq f^{-1}(D \cap E)$.

1. Let $x \in f^{-1}(D) \cap f^{-1}(E)$	Arbitrary choice
2. $x \in f^{-1}(D)$ and $x \in f^{-1}(E)$	Definition of $\cap$
3. For some $y \in D$, $(x,y) \in f$ and for some $y' \in E$, $(x,y') \in f$	Definition of inverse image
4. $(x,y) \in f$ and $(x,y') \in f$ imply $y = y'$	Definition of function
5. $y \in D \cap E$	Definition of $\cap$
6. $y \in D \cap E$ and $(x,y) \in f$ imply $x \in f^{-1}(D \cap E)$	Definition of inverse image

Part II: To show that $f^{-1}(D \cap E) \subseteq f^{-1}(D) \cap f^{-1}(E)$.

1. Let $x \in f^{-1}(D \cap E)$	Arbitrary choice
2. For some $y \in D \cap E$ $(x,y) \in f$	Definition of inverse image
3. $y \in D$ and $y \in E$	Definition of $\cap$
4. $x \in f^{-1}(D)$ and $x \in f^{-1}(E)$	Definition of inverse image
5. $x \in f^{-1}(D) \cap f^{-1}(E)$	Definition of $\cap$

Alternate proof for Exercise 3-6.10:

Part I:

1. Let $x \in f^{-1}(D) \cap f^{-1}(E)$	Arbitrary choice
2. $x \in f^{-1}(D)$ and $x \in f^{-1}(E)$	Definition of $\cap$
3. $f(x) \in D$ and $f(x) \in E$	Definition of inverse image
4. $f(x) \in D \cap E$	Definition of $\cap$
5. $x \in f^{-1}(D \cap E)$	Definition of inverse image

Part II:

1. Let $x \in f^{-1}(D \cap E)$	Arbitrary choice
2. $f(x) \in D \cap E$	Definition of inverse image
3. $f(x) \in D$ and $f(x) \in E$	Definition of $\cap$
4. $x \in f^{-1}(D)$ and $x \in f^{-1}(E)$	Definition of inverse image
5. $x \in f^{-1}(D) \cap f^{-1}(E)$	Definition of $\cap$

3-6.11: | *Proof* | *Reason* |
|---|---|
| 1. Let $y \in f[f^{-1}(D)]$ | Arbitrary choice |
| 2. For some $x \in f^{-1}(D)$, $(x,y) \in f$ | Definition of image |
| 3. $x \in f^{-1}(D)$ implies for some $y' \in D$, $(x,y') \in f$ | Definition of inverse image |
| 4. $(x,y) \in f$ and $(x,y') \in f$ imply $y = y'$ | Definition of function |
| 5. $y \in D$ | Lines (3) and (4) |

Alternate proof of Exercise 3-6.11:

1. Let $y \in f[f^{-1}(D)]$	Arbitrary choice
2. For some $x \in f^{-1}(D)$, $f(x) = y$	Definition of image
3. $x \in f^{-1}(D)$ implies $f(x) \in D$	Definition of inverse image
4. $y \in D$	Lines (2) and (3)

In general, $f[f^{-1}(D)] \neq D$. Consider sets $S = \{s_1, s_2, s_3\}$ and $T = \{t_1, t_2, t_3\}$ where $f: S \to T$ is defined by $f(s_1) = t_1$, $f(s_2) = t_1$, and $f(s_3) = t_2$. Let $D = \{t_2, t_3\}$; then $f[f^{-1}(D)] = f[\{s_3\}] = \{t_2\} \neq D$.

3-6.13: *Part I*: To show that $f^{-1}(D) - f^{-1}(E) \subseteq f^{-1}(D - E)$.

1. Let $x \in f^{-1}(D) - f^{-1}(E)$	Arbitrary choice
2. $x \in f^{-1}(D)$ and $x \notin f^{-1}(E)$	Definition of $-$
3. $x \in f^{-1}(D)$ implies for some $y \in D$, $(x,y) \in f$	Definition of inverse image
4. $x \notin f^{-1}(E)$ implies if $(x,y) \in f$ then $y \notin E$	Definition of inverse image
5. $y \in D - E$	Definition of $-$, lines (3), (4)
6. $y \in D - E$ and $(x,y) \in f$ imply $x \in f^{-1}(D - E)$	Definition of inverse image

Part II: To show that $f^{-1}(D - E) \subseteq f^{-1}(D) - f^{-1}(E)$.

1. Let $x \in f^{-1}(D - E)$	Arbitrary choice
2. For some $y \in D - E$, $(x,y) \in f$	Definition of inverse image
3. $y \in D$ and $y \notin E$	Definition of $-$
4. $y \in D$ and $(x,y) \in f$ imply $x \in f^{-1}(D)$	Definition of inverse image
5. If $(x,y') \in f$, then $y = y'$, so $y' \notin E$	Definition of function
6. $x \notin f^{-1}(E)$	Definition of inverse image (from line (5))
7. $x \in f^{-1}(D) - f^{-1}(E)$	Definition of $-$

Alternate proof of Exercise 3-6.13:

Part I:

1. Let $x \in f^{-1}(D) - f^{-1}(E)$	Arbitrary choice
2. $x \in f^{-1}(D)$ and $x \notin f^{-1}(E)$	Definition of $-$
3. $f(x) \in D$ and $f(x) \notin E$	Definition of inverse image
4. $f(x) \in D - E$	Definition of $-$
5. $x \in f^{-1}(D - E)$	Definition of inverse image

Part II:

1. Let $x \in f^{-1}(D - E)$	Arbitrary choice
2. $f(x) \in D - E$	Definition of inverse image
3. $f(x) \in D$ and $f(x) \notin E$	Definition of $-$
4. $x \in f^{-1}(D)$ and $x \notin f^{-1}(E)$	Definition of inverse image
5. $x \in f^{-1}(D) - f^{-1}(E)$	Definition of $-$

3-6.15: $z \in [0,1]$ if and only if $0 \le y^2 - x \le 1$

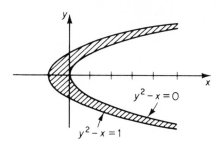

Page 45

3-7.1: Range $R = \{y \mid (x,y) \in R\} = \{y \mid (y,x) \in R^{-1}\}$ = Domain R^{-1}
Domain $R = \{x \mid (x,y) \in R\} = \{x \mid (y,x) \in R^{-1}\}$ = Range R^{-1}

Pages 52–53

3-8.1: $f(1/4,1/3) = .2343939393\ldots = \dfrac{1547}{6600}$; $f(1,1) = .99999\ldots = 1$;

$f(.63072517008\ldots, .202130074091\ldots) = .62302071235007147090081\ldots$

3-8.2: a. $x = .721003085\ldots, y = .32094502\ldots$

3-8.3: $s = \varnothing \to f_s(a_1) = 0, f_s(a_2) = 0, f_s(a_3) = 0$;
$s = \{a_1\} \to f_s(a_1) = 1, f_s(a_2) = 0, f_s(a_3) = 0$;
$s = \{a_1, a_2\} \to f_s(a_1) = 1, f_s(a_2) = 1, f_s(a_3) = 0$;
$s = A \to f_s(a_1) = 1, f_s(a_2) = 1, f_s(a_3) = 1$.
The functions relating to subsets $\{a_2\}$, $\{a_3\}$, $\{a_1, a_3\}$, and $\{a_2, a_3\}$ are defined similarly.

3-8.5: $f: C \to (0,1]$ is defined by representing each of the numbers x, y, and z by a non-terminating decimal (using a repetition of 9's rather than 0's whenever two representations are possible). For every $(x,y,z) \in C$, mark off subsets of digits in the decimal expansions of x, y, and z by going up to the next non-zero digit. To express $f(x,y,z)$, start with the first portion of x, followed by the first portion of y, the first portion of z, the second portion of x, etc.; Example: If $x = .400215\ldots$, $y = .03102\ldots$, and $z = .29090\ldots$, then $f(x,y,z,) = .40320021910209\ldots$

3-8.7: $f: S \to Q$ can be defined by $f(x,y) = \left(\dfrac{x}{1-x}, \dfrac{y}{1-y} \right)$

3-8.9: If simple alternation of digits is used to define $f: S \to (0,1]$, then the only (x,y) in S with image $z_1 = .1290909\ldots$ is $x = .1999\ldots, y = .2000\ldots$; but the decimal expansion for y does not satisfy the rule given for unique decimal representation. If this rule is not invoked, then f ceases to be a function since
$(.1999\ldots, .2000\ldots)$ is related to $z_1 = .12909090\ldots$
$(.2000\ldots, .1999\ldots)$ is related to $z_2 = .21090909\ldots$
$(.1999\ldots, .2000\ldots) = (.2000\ldots, .1999\ldots)$ but $z_1 \ne z_2$.

Page 56

3-9.1: $gf = \{(a_1,c_3), (a_2,c_3), (a_3,c_3), (a_4,c_1)\}$;
Range $gf = \{c_1, c_3\}$.

3-9.3: $gf(x) = g\,[f(x)] = f(x) - 1 = 3x^2 + 2x - 1$;
$fg(x) = f[g(x)] = 3[g(x)]^2 + 2[g(x)] = 3(x - 1)^2 + 2(x - 1) = 3x^2 - 4x + 1$.

3-9.5: $gf(x,y) = g[f(x,y)] = |f(x,y) - 1/2| = \left| \dfrac{1}{x^2 + y^2 + 1} - \dfrac{1}{2} \right|$
Range $f = (0,1]$;
Range g = non-negative real numbers;
Range $gf = [0,1/2]$.

Page 57

3-10.1: For each $x \in A$, $a \le x \le b$ by hypothesis. Hence $f(a) \ge f(x) \ge f(b)$, or equivalently, $f(x) \in [f(b), f(a)]$ for all $x \in A$, by the definition of a decreasing function. This proves that $f(A) \subset [f(b), f(a)]$.

3-10.3: If $0 \le x_1 < x_2$, then $|x_1| < |x_2|$; $|x_1| + |x_1| \cdot |x_2| < |x_2| + |x_1| \cdot |x_2|$;
$|x_1| (1 + |x_2|) < |x_2| (1 + |x_1|); \dfrac{|x_1|}{1 + |x_1|} < \dfrac{|x_2|}{1 + |x_2|}$, and so $f(x_1) < f(x_2)$.
If $x_1 < x_2 \le 0$, then $-x_1 > -x_2$ and $|x_1| > |x_2|$; $|x_1| + |x_1| \cdot |x_2| > |x_2| + |x_1| \cdot |x_2|$; $|x_1| (1 + |x_2|) > |x_2| (1 + |x_1|)$; thus $\dfrac{|x_1|}{1 + |x_1|} > \dfrac{|x_2|}{1 + |x_2|}$; hence $f(x_1) > f(x_2)$.

Graph:

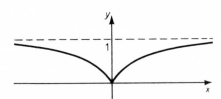

Page 60

4-1.1: Properties 1, 2, and 3 required of metrics are easy to verify in each of the examples. We will establish property 4 in each case:
Part 1: (Example 4-1.1): $d(p,q) + d(q,r) = |x_1 - x_2| + |x_2 - x_3| \ge |x_1 - x_2 + x_2 - x_3| = |x_1 - x_3| = d(p,r)$.
Part 2: (Example 4-1.2): Let $a = |x_1 - x_2|$, $b = |y_1 - y_2|$, $c = |x_2 - x_3|$, $d = |y_2 - y_3|$, $e = |x_1 - x_3|$, and $f = |y_1 - y_3|$. In order to establish $d(p,q) + d(q,r) \ge d(p,r)$, we must prove $\sqrt{a^2 + b^2} + \sqrt{c^2 + d^2} \ge \sqrt{e^2 + f^2}$.
Now, $(bc - ad)^2 \ge 0$; $b^2c^2 - 2abcd + a^2d^2 \ge 0$; $2abcd \le b^2c^2 + a^2d^2$;
$$a^2c^2 + 2abcd + b^2d^2 \le a^2c^2 + b^2c^2 + a^2d^2 + b^2d^2;$$
$$(ac + bd)^2 \le (a^2 + b^2)(c^2 + d^2);$$
$$ac + bd \le \sqrt{a^2 + b^2} \cdot \sqrt{c^2 + d^2};$$
$$2(ac + bd) \le 2\sqrt{a^2 + b^2} \cdot \sqrt{c^2 + d^2} \qquad \text{(I)}.$$

Moreover $a + c = |x_1 - x_2| + |x_2 - x_3| \geq |x_1 - x_3| = e,$
$\qquad b + d = |y_1 - y_2| + |y_2 - y_3| \geq |y_1 - y_3| = f.$
Therefore $a^2 + 2ac + c^2 \geq e^2$; $b^2 + 2bd + d^2 \geq f^2$. Add these last two inequalities to obtain $a^2 + b^2 + c^2 + d^2 + 2(ab + cd) \geq e^2 + f^2$ (II). From inequalities (I) and (II), we obtain

$$a^2 + b^2 + c^2 + d^2 + 2\sqrt{a^2 + b^2}\sqrt{c^2 + d^2} \geq e^2 + f^2$$

or
$$(\sqrt{a^2 + b^2} + \sqrt{c^2 + d^2})^2 \geq e^2 + f^2,$$

and finally
$$\sqrt{a^2 + b^2} + \sqrt{c^2 + d^2} \geq \sqrt{e^2 + f^2}.$$

Part 3: (Example 4-1.5): Solution partially given in hint. To establish the last inequality, note that $\dfrac{m}{1 + m} \geq \dfrac{k}{1 + k}$ whenever $m \geq k \geq 0$.

4-1.3: d_1 is not a metric since for $p = 1$ and $q = -1$, $d_1(p,q) = 0$ but $p \neq q$. d_2 and d_3 are metrics.

4-1.5: Properties 1, 2, and 3 required of metrics are easy to verify. To establish property 4 we must show
$$\sqrt{[d_A(x_1,x_2)]^2 + [d_B(y_1,y_2)]^2} + \sqrt{[d_A(x_2,x_3)]^2 + [d_B(y_2,y_3)]^2} \geq$$
$\sqrt{[d_A(x_1,x_3)]^2 + [d_B(y_1,y_3)]^2}$, where $p = (x_1,y_1)$, $q = (x_2,y_2)$, and $r = (x_3,y_3)$. Let $a = d_A(x_1,x_2)$, $b = d_B(y_1,y_2)$, $c = d_A(x_2,x_3)$, $d = d_B(y_2,y_3)$, $e = d_A(x_1,x_3)$, $f = d_B(y_1,y_3)$ and follow the pattern of proof given for Exercise 4-1.1. Only two lines need be changed:
$a + c = d_A(x_1,x_2) + d_A(x_2,x_3) \geq d_A(x_1,x_3) = e,$
$b + d = d_B(y_1,y_2) + d_B(y_2,y_3) \geq d_B(y_1,y_3) = f.$
Note that $E^2 = E^1 \times E^1$, $E^3 = E^1 \times E^2$, $E^4 = E^1 \times E^3$.

Pages 65–66

4-5.1: Interior of A is A itself.
Exterior of A is $\{(x, y) \mid x^2 + 4y^2 > 4\}$.
Boundary of A is $\{(x, y) \mid x^2 + 4y^2 = 4\}$.
The set of all limit points of A is $\{(x, y) \mid x^2 + 4y^2 \leq 4\}$.
The set A is open; A is not closed.

4-5.3: The only limit point is $(0,1)$.
There are no interior points.
The set itself together with the point $(0,1)$ is the set of all boundary points.
The set is neither open nor closed.

4-5.5: a. Separated; b. not separated; c. not separated; d. not separated.

4-5.7: The set of all boundary points of a finite set is the set itself; therefore every finite set is closed.

4-5.9: The set of all boundary points of $\varnothing$ is $\varnothing$.
The null set $\varnothing$ is closed since $\varnothing \supset$ (the set of all boundary points of $\varnothing$).
The null set is open since $\varnothing \cap$ (the set of all boundary points of $\varnothing$) $= \varnothing$.

A note on logic: Consider the two implications:

1. If p is a boundary point of $\varnothing$, then $p \in \varnothing$.
2. If p is a boundary point of $\varnothing$, then $p \notin \varnothing$.

Both implications are true since the hypothesis is false; i.e., $H \to C$ is true if H is false.

4-5.11: Solution is partially given in hint. Let ε be the smallest number in the finite set $\{\varepsilon_1, \varepsilon_2, \ldots, \varepsilon_n\}$. Note that $\varepsilon > 0$. Now, $N(p,\varepsilon) \subset A_i$, $i = 1, 2, \ldots, n$, and hence $N(p,\varepsilon) \subset \bigcap_{i=1}^{n} A_i$. This proves that every point in $\bigcap_{i=1}^{n} A_i$ is an interior point of this set.

4-5.13: Let $A_1, A_2, \ldots, A_n$ be a finite collection of closed sets in a metric set M. By Theorem 4-4.1, $M - A_1$, $M - A_2$, $\ldots$, $M - A_n$ are open. By Exercise 4-5.11, $\bigcap_{i=1}^{n} (M - A_i)$ is open. Now $M - \bigcup_{i=1}^{n} A_i = \bigcap_{i=1}^{n} (M - A_i)$. Since $M - \bigcup_{i=1}^{n} A_i$ is open, $\bigcup_{i=1}^{n} A_i$ is closed, [Theorem 4-4.1].

Pages 68–69

4-7.1: a. $f(n) = 1/2^n$; c. $f(n) = -n/(3n - 1)$;

e. $f(n) = \begin{cases} 1/[\sqrt{2}]^{n+1} & \text{if } n \text{ is odd,} \\ 1/[\sqrt{3}]^n & \text{if } n \text{ is even;} \end{cases}$ g. $f(n) = \dfrac{2n - 1}{3n + 1}$;

i. $f(n) = ((-1)^{n+1}, 1 - 1/n))$.

4-7.2: a. converges to 0; c. converges to $-1/3$; e. converges to 0; g. converges to $2/3$; i. diverges.

4-7.3: Let $b = \lim_{n \to \infty} f(n)$; then $N(b,1)$ contains all but a finite number of elements of set A. If $N(b,1)$ contains A, then there is nothing more to prove. If elements of A lie outside $N(b,1)$, let $r_1, r_2, r_3, \ldots, r_n$ represent the distances between b and each of the finitely many elements of A outside $N(b,1)$. Let r be the largest of the numbers $r_1, r_2, \ldots, r_n$. Then $A \subset N(b,r + 1)$.

4-7.5: The divergent sequence $1/2$, $-2/3$, $3/4$, $-4/5$, $5/6$, $-6/7$, $\ldots$ has convergent subsequences $1/2$, $3/4$, $5/6$, $7/8$, $\ldots$ and $-2/3$, $-4/5$, $-6/7$, $-8/9$, $\ldots$.

Page 70

4-8.1: By Exercise 2-9.5, there exists a real number c such that $c = $ g.l.b. $\{f(n) \mid n \in I\}$. Given any positive number ε, there exists an integer J such that $f(J) < c + \varepsilon$ since $c + \varepsilon$ is greater than the greatest lower bound. Now $c + \varepsilon > f(n) \geq c$ for all $n \geq J$, since f is decreasing and c is a lower bound. Thus $N(c,\varepsilon)$ confines $\{f(n)\}$ and we have $\lim_{n \to \infty} f(n) = c$.

Page 74

4-9.1: The sequences in parts a, b, c, e, g, and j are Cauchy sequences. (See Theorems 4-9.1 and 4-9.4.)

4-9.2: $a_{2n} - a_n = 1/(n+1) + 1/(n+2) + \ldots + 1/2n \geq n(1/2n) = 1/2$. Hence for every integer N there are terms a_n and a_m where n, $m > N$ and $|a_m - a_n| \geq 1/2$.

4-9.4: In E^1 use repeated bisection of intervals.
In E^3 use repeated subdivision of cubes into 8 parts.

Page 83

4-11.1: $\left| \dfrac{4x^2 - 17x + 15}{x - 3} - 7 \right| = \left| \dfrac{4x^2 - 24x + 36}{x - 3} \right| = \dfrac{4|x - 3|^2}{|x - 3|}$. If $\delta = \varepsilon/4$, then $0 < |x - 3| < \delta$ implies $|f(x) - 7| = 4(|x - 3|^2)/(|x - 3|) = 4|x - 3| < 4\delta = \varepsilon$.

4-11.3: a. Largest $\delta = \dfrac{3\sqrt{2}}{2} - 2$; b. Largest $\delta = \sqrt{3/2} - 1$; c. Largest $\delta = \sqrt{19/2} - 3$.

4-11.4: Proof of part (b):
Case 1: $a \geq 0$.
$|f(x) - f(a)| = |x^2 - a^2| = |x - a| \cdot |x + a|$. Note that if $|x - a| < \delta$, then $-\delta < x - a < \delta$; $2a - \delta < x + a < 2a + \delta$. Since $a \geq 0$, $-2a \leq 2a$; $-(2a + \delta) < x + a < 2a + \delta$; $|x + a| < 2a + \delta$. Therefore $|x - a| < \delta$ where $\delta = \sqrt{a^2 + \varepsilon} - a$ implies $|f(x) - f(a)| = |x - a| \cdot |x + a| < \delta(2a + \delta) = \varepsilon$.
Case 2: $a < 0$.
If $|x - a| < \delta$, then $-\delta < x - a < \delta$; $2a - \delta < x + a < 2a + \delta$. Since $a < 0$, $-2a > 2a$; $-(\delta - 2a) < x + a < \delta - 2a$; $|x + a| < \delta - 2a$. Therefore $|x - a| < \delta$ where $\delta = \sqrt{a^2 + \varepsilon} + a$ implies $|f(x) - f(a)| = |x - a| \cdot |x + a| < \delta(\delta - 2a) = \varepsilon$.

Since
$$\sqrt{a^2 + \varepsilon} - |a| = \begin{cases} \sqrt{a^2 + \varepsilon} - a \text{ if } a \geq 0 \\ \sqrt{a^2 + \varepsilon} + a \text{ if } a < 0, \end{cases}$$
the proof is complete.

4-11.7: Solution to Part (b).
Suppose $(x,y) \in N'[(a,b),\delta]$ where $\delta = \sqrt{a^2 + b^2 + \varepsilon} - \sqrt{a^2 + b^2}$. Then $d[(x,y),(a,b)] < \delta$. Now $d[(x,y),(0,0)] \leq d[(x,y),(a,b)] + d[(a,b),(0,0)]$; or $\sqrt{x^2 + y^2} < \delta + \sqrt{a^2 + b^2}$; $\sqrt{x^2 + y^2} < \sqrt{a^2 + b^2 + \varepsilon}$; $x^2 + y^2 < a^2 + b^2 + \varepsilon$; $f(x,y) < f(a,b) + \varepsilon$; hence $f(x,y) - f(a,b) < \varepsilon$. In order to prove that $f(a,b) - f(x,y) < \varepsilon$, we consider two cases:
Case I: $\varepsilon > a^2 + b^2$.
$a^2 + b^2 - (x^2 + y^2) \leq a^2 + b^2 < \varepsilon$; hence $f(a,b) - f(x,y) < \varepsilon$.
Case II: $\varepsilon \leq a^2 + b^2$.
First prove that
$\sqrt{a^2 + b^2} - \sqrt{a^2 + b^2 - \varepsilon} \geq \sqrt{a^2 + b^2 + \varepsilon} - \sqrt{a^2 + b^2} = \delta$. Then $d[(a,b), (0,0)] \leq d[(a,b), (x,y)] + d[(x,y), (0,0)] < \delta + d[(x,y), (0,0)]$ implies $\sqrt{a^2 + b^2} - \sqrt{x^2 + y^2} < \delta \leq \sqrt{a^2 + b^2} - \sqrt{a^2 + b^2 - \varepsilon}$; $\sqrt{x^2 + y^2} > \sqrt{a^2 + b^2 - \varepsilon}$; $x^2 + y^2 > a^2 + b^2 - \varepsilon$; $a^2 + b^2 - (x^2 + y^2) < \varepsilon$; $f(a,b) - f(x,y) < \varepsilon$.

Now since $f(x,y) - f(a,b) < \varepsilon$ and $f(a,b) - f(x,y) < \varepsilon$, we have $|f(x,y) - f(a,b)| < \varepsilon$. Therefore $f(x,y) \in N[f(a,b),\varepsilon]$.

Pages 87–88

4-12.1: Suppose $r \in N(p,\varepsilon/2)$ and $s \in N(q,\varepsilon/2)$; then $|r - p| < \varepsilon/2$ and $|s - q| < \varepsilon/2$. By Exercise 2-7.11, $|(r - s) - (p - q)| = |(r - p) - (s - q)| \leq |r - p| + |s - q| < \varepsilon/2 + \varepsilon/2 = \varepsilon$. Hence $r - s \in N(p - q,\varepsilon)$.

4-12.5: To prove parts 2, 3, and 4, replace $+$ by $-$, $\cdot$, and $\div$, respectively, in the proof given for part 1.

4-12.7: Consider any neighborhood $N(b/c,\varepsilon)$ of b/c in E^1 ($c \neq 0$). Let ε' be chosen subject to the conditions $\varepsilon' \leq |c|/2$ and $\varepsilon' \leq c^2\varepsilon/2(|b| + |c|)$. Replace $\cdot$ by $\div$ in the latter portion of the proof of Theorem 4-12.4. Cite Lemma 4-12.4 instead of Lemma 4-12.3.

Page 88

4-13.1: $\delta = \varepsilon$ will suffice in both cases.

4-13.2: a. $\lim\limits_{x \to 0^-} f(x) = 4$

$\lim\limits_{x \to 0^+} f(x) = 6$

The graph of $f(x)$ is:

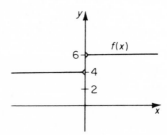

4-13.3: Let $\varepsilon > 0$ be given. Since $\lim\limits_{x \to a^-} f(x) = b$, there exists a positive number δ_1 such that $a - \delta_1 < x < a$ implies $|f(x) - b| < \varepsilon$. Since $\lim\limits_{x \to a^+} f(x) = b$, there exists a positive number δ_2 such that $a < x < a + \delta_2$ implies $|f(x) - b| < \varepsilon$. Let δ be the lesser of the two values δ_1 and δ_2; then $0 < |x - a| < \delta$ implies $|f(x) - b| < \varepsilon$; hence $\lim\limits_{x \to a} f(x) = b$.

Page 92

5-1.1: $f(x) = c$ is continuous at each point a of E^1 since, for every neighborhood $N(c,\varepsilon) = N(f(a),\varepsilon)$, $f(N(a,1)) = \{c\} \subset N(f(a),\varepsilon)$. ($\delta = 1$ suffices).

$g(x) = x$ is continuous at each point a of E^1 since for every neighborhood $N(a,\varepsilon) = N(g(a),\varepsilon)$ we can choose $\delta = \varepsilon$ to obtain $g(N(a,\delta)) = N(g(a),\varepsilon)$.

5-1.3: $f(x)$ is the quotient of two continuous functions; therefore $f(x)$ is continuous at each point x where $x - 2 \neq 0$. The discontinuity at $x = 2$ is not removable.

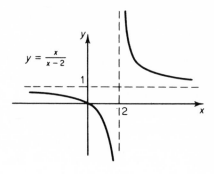

$$y = \frac{x}{x-2}$$

5-1.5: The graph has jump discontinuities at $x = -3$ and $x = 4$.

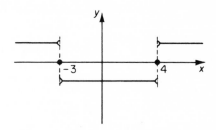

5-1.7: For $\varepsilon = 1/2$ and any real number a, it is impossible to find a $\delta > 0$ such that $f(N(a,\delta)) \subset N(f(a),1/2)$ since $N(a,\delta)$ contains both rational and irrational points and therefore $f(N(a,\delta)) = \{0, 1\}$. [No neighborhood with radius 1/2 can contain the two points 0 and 1; $d(0,1) = 1$.] Hence $\lim_{x \to a} f(x)$ does not exist.

Page 96

5-2.1: Given any neighborhood $N(M,\varepsilon)$, since $M - \varepsilon < M$, the number $M - \varepsilon$ is not an upper bound for C; hence there exists a point x in C such that $M - \varepsilon < x \leq M$. Moreover, since M is an upper bound for C, the interval $(M, M + \varepsilon)$ does not contain any points of C. Therefore every neighborhood $N(M,\varepsilon)$ contains a point in C and points not in C. M must be a boundary point of C and consequently M belongs to the closed set C. A similar argument proves that $m \in C$.

5-2.3: Since 0 is a real number between $f(a)$ and $f(b)$, there exists a point $c \in [a,b]$ such that $f(c) = 0$, by Theorem 5-2.7. Now, by hypothesis, $f(a) \neq 0$ and $f(b) \neq 0$; hence $c \in (a,b)$.

Page 99

5-3.1: Given any $\varepsilon > 0$ and point $a \in E^1$, the largest δ such that $f(N(a,\delta)) \subset N(f(a),\varepsilon)$ is given by max $\delta = \sqrt{a^2 + \varepsilon} - |a|$ (see Exercise 4-11.4). Now for integral values of a ($a = n$; $n = 1, 2, 3, \ldots$), $\lim\limits_{n \to \infty} \sqrt{n^2 + \varepsilon} - |n| =$

$$\lim_{n \to \infty} \frac{(\sqrt{n^2 + \varepsilon} - |n|)(\sqrt{n^2 + \varepsilon} + |n|)}{\sqrt{n^2 + \varepsilon} + |n|} = \lim_{n \to \infty} \frac{\varepsilon}{\sqrt{n^2 + \varepsilon} + |n|} = 0.$$

This proves that for any given $\varepsilon > 0$, there exists no $\delta > 0$ small enough such that $f(N(a,\delta)) \subset N(f(a),\varepsilon)$ for all $a \in E^1$.

5-3.3: Given any $\varepsilon > 0$ and point $(a,b) \in E^2$, the largest δ such that $f[N((a,b),\delta)] \subset N(f(a,b),\varepsilon)$ is given by max $\delta = \sqrt{a^2 + b^2 + \varepsilon} - \sqrt{a^2 + b^2}$ (see Exercise 4-11.7). Let S denote a bounded subset of E^2, i.e., $S \subset N((0,0),r)$ for some real number r. Let $\bar{\delta} = \sqrt{r^2 + \varepsilon} - \sqrt{r^2}$. Since $\bar{\delta} \le \sqrt{a^2 + b^2 + \varepsilon} - \sqrt{a^2 + b^2}$ for every point $(a,b) \in S$, we have $f[N((a,b),\bar{\delta}] \subset N(f(a,b),\varepsilon)$ for all $(a,b) \in S$.

$f(x,y)$ is not uniformly continuous on the entire plane E^2. Consider integral values of a ($a = n$; $n = 1, 2, 3, \ldots$) and let $b = 0$. Then $\lim\limits_{n \to \infty} \sqrt{n^2 + \varepsilon} - \sqrt{n^2} =$

$$\lim_{n \to \infty} \frac{(\sqrt{n^2 + \varepsilon} - \sqrt{n^2})(\sqrt{n^2 + \varepsilon} + \sqrt{n^2})}{\sqrt{n^2 + \varepsilon} + \sqrt{n^2}} = \lim_{n \to \infty} \frac{\varepsilon}{\sqrt{n^2 + \varepsilon} + \sqrt{n^2}} = 0.$$

This proves that for any given $\varepsilon > 0$, there exists no $\delta > 0$ small enough such that $f(N((a,b),\delta)) \subset N(f(a,b),\varepsilon)$ for all $(a,b) \in E^2$.

Page 104

5-4.1: a. $f'(x) = \lim\limits_{h \to 0} \dfrac{[(x + h)^3 + 2(x + h) + 4] - [x^3 + 2x + 4]}{h}$

$\qquad = \lim\limits_{h \to 0} 3x^2 + 3xh + h^2 + 2 = 3x^2 + 2.$

c. $f'(x) = \lim\limits_{h \to 0} \dfrac{\dfrac{3(x + h) + 2}{5(x + h) - 4} - \dfrac{3x + 2}{5x - 4}}{h}$

$\qquad = \lim\limits_{h \to 0} \dfrac{[5x - 4][3(x + h) + 2] - [5(x + h) - 4][3x + 2]}{h[5(x + h) - 4][5x - 4]}$

$\qquad = \lim\limits_{h \to 0} \dfrac{-22}{[5(x + h) - 4][5x - 4]} = \dfrac{-22}{[5x - 4]^2}.$

5-4.2: (i) $D_x[cf(x)] = \lim\limits_{h \to 0} \dfrac{cf(x + h) - cf(x)}{h}$

$\qquad = \lim\limits_{h \to 0} c \dfrac{f(x + h) - f(x)}{h} = c \lim\limits_{h \to 0} \dfrac{f(x + h) - f(x)}{h} = cD_x f(x)$

(see Exercise 4-12.8).

(v) $D_x \dfrac{f(x)}{g(x)} = \lim\limits_{h \to 0} \dfrac{\dfrac{f(x+h)}{g(x+h)} - \dfrac{f(x)}{g(x)}}{h}$

$= \lim\limits_{h \to 0} \dfrac{g(x)[f(x+h) - f(x)] - f(x)[g(x+h) - g(x)]}{h[g(x+h)]g(x)}$

$= \lim\limits_{h \to 0} \left[\dfrac{1}{g(x+h)g(x)} \right] \cdot \left[g(x)\dfrac{f(x+h) - f(x)}{h} - f(x)\dfrac{g(x+h) - g(x)}{h} \right]$

$= \dfrac{g(x)D_x f(x) - f(x)D_x g(x)}{[g(x)]^2}$.

[Note: Theorems 4-12.3, 4-12.4, 4-12.5, and 5-4.1 were used.]

5-4.3: Let $x = a + h$. Since $f(x)$ is continuous at a,
$\lim\limits_{h \to 0} f(a + h) = \lim\limits_{x \to a} f(x) = f(a)$. Now
$\lim\limits_{h \to 0} [f(a + h) - f(a)] = \lim\limits_{h \to 0} f(a + h) - \lim\limits_{h \to 0} f(a) =$
$f(a) - f(a) = 0$. [See Theorem 4-12.3.]

Page 105

5-5.1: c. $y = g(u) = u^9$, $u = f(x) = \cos(2x)$.
First consider $u = \cos(2x)$; let $u = \cos v$ and $v = 2x$.
$\dfrac{du}{dx} = \dfrac{du}{dv}\dfrac{dv}{dx} = (-\sin v)(2) = -2\sin(2x)$.
$\dfrac{dy}{dx} = \dfrac{dy}{du}\dfrac{du}{dx} = 9\,u^8[-2\sin(2x)] = -18[\sin(2x)][\cos(2x)]^8$.

Page 109

5-7.1: Consider $f'(u) = \lim\limits_{h \to 0} \dfrac{f(u+h) - f(u)}{h}$. Since $f(u+h) \ge f(u)$ for all
values $u + h \in (a,b)$, the quotient $\dfrac{f(u+h) - f(u)}{h}$ is positive or 0 for
$h > 0$, and negative or 0 for $h < 0$. Therefore $f'(u) = \lim\limits_{h \to 0} \dfrac{f(u+h) - f(u)}{h}$
must equal 0.

5-7.3: a. $z = e - 1$ b. $z = (a + b)/2$

Page 111

5-8.1: a. $z = 9/4$;   b. $z = (b + a)/2$

5-8.3: L'Hospital's Rule cannot be used to evaluate $\lim\limits_{x \to 1} \dfrac{4x - 1}{2x - 1}$ since the numerator
and the denominator are not 0 when $x = 1$.

Pages 112–113

5-9.1: a. $\Delta y = 7$, $dy = 4$ c. $\Delta y = .0403$, $dy = .04$

5-9.2: b. $\Delta y = -.00392\ldots$, $dy = -.004$

5-9.3: $dy = f'(x)h = \dfrac{1}{5x^{4/5}} h = -.004$ when $x = 1$ and $h = -.02$. Therefore,
$\sqrt[5]{.98} \sim \sqrt[5]{1} - .004 = .996$.

5-9.5: Consider $f(x) = \sin x$; $dy = f'(x) h = (\cos x)h = \dfrac{\sqrt{3}}{2}\left(\dfrac{\pi}{180}\right)$ when $x = \pi/6$
and $h = \pi/180$ radians.

Therefore $\sin 31° \sim \sin 30° + \sqrt{3}\pi/360 = 1/2 + \dfrac{\sqrt{3}\pi}{360}$.

Page 113

5-10.2: $f_y(x,y,z) = \lim\limits_{k \to 0} \dfrac{f(x,y + k,z) - f(x,y,z)}{k}$; for the function given, $f_y(x,y,z) = 3x^2y^2z - 3x$.

Pages 115–116

5-11.1: a. $\Delta z = 12.0272$, $dz = 8.8$
b. $\Delta z = .90858992$, $dz = .88$

5-11.3: $\Delta V = (.642804)\pi$, $dV = (.64)\pi$

5-11.5: b. $\Delta u = .6767340901$, $du = .67$

Page 117

5-12.1: $D[\theta, f(x_0, y_0)] = 13/2 + 2\sqrt{3}$

5-12.2: a. $D[\theta, f(x_0, y_0)] = \tfrac{3}{2}[\cos \theta + \sqrt{3} \sin \theta]$

5-12.3: $\dfrac{d}{d\theta} D[\theta, f(x_0, y_0)] = \dfrac{d}{d\theta} [f_x(x_0,y_0) \cos \theta + f_y(x_0,y_0) \sin \theta] = -f_x(x_0,y_0) \sin \theta + f_y(x_0,y_0) \cos \theta = 0$; $f_x(x_0,y_0) \sin \theta = f_y(x_0,y_0) \cos \theta$;
$\tan \theta = \dfrac{f_y(x_0,y_0)}{f_x(x_0,y_0)}$.

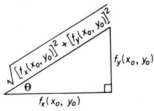

The angle θ for which $D[\theta, f(x_0,y_0)]$ is maximum is illustrated in the above triangle. Using this angle we have
Max $D[\theta, f(x_0,y_0)] = f_x(x_0,y_0) \cos \theta + f_y(x_0,y_0) \sin \theta = \sqrt{[f_x(x_0,y_0)]^2 + [f_y(x_0,y_0)]^2}$.

Page 119

6-1.1: a. 30;   b. $7\frac{13}{70}$

6-1.3: $\sum_{k=1}^{n} ca_k = ca_1 + ca_2 + \ldots + ca_n$

$= c(a_1 + a_2 + \ldots + a_n) = c\sum_{k=1}^{n} a_k.$

6-1.5: $\sum_{k=1}^{n} k(k+2) = \sum_{k=1}^{n} (k^2 + 2k) = \sum_{k=1}^{n} k^2 + 2\sum_{k=1}^{n} k =$

$\dfrac{n(n+1)(2n+1)}{6} + 2\dfrac{n(n+1)}{2} = \dfrac{n(n+1)(2n+7)}{6}.$

Pages 124–125

6-3.1: $\displaystyle\int_{-2}^{7} h(x)\,dx = 13$

6-3.3: $\displaystyle\int_{-7/2}^{1} h(x)\,dx = -2\frac{1}{2}$

6-3.5: $\displaystyle\int_{-3/2}^{2} h(x)\,dx = -4$

6-3.7: $\displaystyle\int_{-1}^{2} h(x)\,dx = 5 - \sqrt{2} - \sqrt{3}$

Page 130

6-5.1: Let P_1 and P_2 be partitions of $[a,b]$ associated with f and g respectively. Let $P = \{x_0, x_1, \ldots, x_n\}$ be the partition of $[a,b]$ containing all the points of subdivision of both P_1 and P_2. Let c'_k and c''_k be the constant values of f and g respectively on the kth open subinterval of P; $k = 1, 2, \ldots, n$. $f(x) + g(x) = c'_k + c''_k$ for all x in (x_{k-1}, x_k); $k = 1, 2, \ldots, n$. Consequently, $f + g$ is a step function and $\displaystyle\int_a^b [f(x) + g(x)]\,dx = \sum_{k=1}^{n} (c'_k + c''_k)(x_k - x_{k-1})$

$= \displaystyle\sum_{k=1}^{n} c'_k(x_k - x_{k-1}) + \sum_{k=1}^{n} c''_k(x_k - x_{k-1}) = \int_a^b f(x)\,dx + \int_a^b g(x)\,dx.$

Page 139

6-9.1: By Exercise 6-5.2, $m(b-a) \le \displaystyle\int_{\underline{a}}^{b} f(x)\,dx$ and $M(b-a) \ge \displaystyle\overline{\int_a^b} f(x)\,dx.$

Since f is integrable on $[a,b]$, $\displaystyle\overline{\int_a^b} f(x)\,dx = \int_{\underline{a}}^{b} f(x)\,dx = \int_a^b f(x)\,dx.$

6-9.2: Consider six cases depending upon the relative values of r_1, r_2, and r_3. For instance, if $r_1 \le r_2 \le r_3$, then $\displaystyle\int_{r_1}^{r_3} = \int_{r_1}^{r_2} + \int_{r_2}^{r_3}$ by Theorem 6-8.2;

if $r_1 \le r_3 \le r_2$, then $\displaystyle\int_{r_1}^{r_2} = \int_{r_1}^{r_3} + \int_{r_3}^{r_2} = \int_{r_1}^{r_3} - \int_{r_2}^{r_3}$, etc.

6-9.3: Let $\varepsilon > 0$ be given; by Lemma 6-6.1, there exist step functions $s_1(x) \in S_f$, $t_1(x) \in T_f$, $s_2(x) \in S_g$, $t_2(x) \in T_g$ such that $\int_a^b t_1(x)\,dx - \int_a^b s_1(x)\,dx < \varepsilon/2$ and $\int_a^b t_2(x)\,dx - \int_a^b s_2(x)\,dx < \varepsilon/2$. Now, $s_0(x) = s_1(x) + s_2(x) \in S_{f+g}$, $t_0(x) = t_1(x) + t_2(x) \in T_{f+g}$ (see Exercise 6-5.1). $\int_a^b t_0(x)\,dx - \int_a^b s_0(x)\,dx = \int_a^b t_1(x)\,dx + \int_a^b t_2(x)\,dx - \int_a^b s_1(x)\,dx - \int_a^b s_2(x)\,dx < \varepsilon/2 + \varepsilon/2 = \varepsilon$. Hence $f + g \colon [a,b] \to E^1$ is integrable by Lemma 6-6.1. Moreover, $\int_a^b s_0(x)\,dx \leq \int_a^b [f(x) + g(x)]\,dx \leq \int_a^b t_0(x)\,dx$ and $\int_a^b s_0(x)\,dx = \int_a^b s_1(x)\,dx + \int_a^b s_2(x)\,dx \leq \int_a^b f(x)\,dx + \int_a^b g(x)\,dx \leq \int_a^b t_1(x)\,dx + \int_a^b t_2(x)\,dx = \int_a^b t_0(x)\,dx$.

Therefore: $\left| \int_a^b f(x)\,dx + \int_a^b g(x)\,dx - \int_a^b [f(x) + g(x)]\,dx \right| < \varepsilon$.

Since this last inequality holds for all $\varepsilon > 0$,

$$\int_a^b f(x)\,dx + \int_a^b g(x)\,dx = \int_a^b [f(x) + g(x)]\,dx.$$

6-9.5: Let $\varepsilon > 0$ be given. Since $f\colon [a,b] \to E^1$ is integrable, there exist step functions $s_0(x) \in S_f$ and $t_0(x) \in T_f$ such that $\int_a^b t_0(x)\,dx - \int_a^b s_0(x)\,dx < \varepsilon$, (see Lemma 6-6.1). By Theorem 6-4.1,

$$\int_a^b t_0(x)\,dx = \int_a^{r_1} t_0(x)\,dx + \int_{r_1}^{r_2} t_0(x)\,dx + \int_{r_2}^b t_0(x)\,dx \text{ and } \int_a^b s_0(x)\,dx = \int_a^{r_1} s_0(x)\,dx + \int_{r_1}^{r_2} s_0(x)\,dx + \int_{r_2}^b s_0(x)\,dx.$$

Now, $\int_{r_1}^{r_2} t_0(x)\,dx - \int_{r_1}^{r_2} s_0(x)\,dx \leq \left(\int_a^{r_1} t_0(x)\,dx - \int_a^{r_1} s_0(x)\,dx \right) + \left(\int_{r_1}^{r_2} t_0(x)\,dx - \int_{r_1}^{r_2} s_0(x)\,dx \right) + \left(\int_{r_2}^b t_0(x)\,dx - \int_{r_2}^b s_0(x)\,dx \right) = \int_a^b t_0(x)\,dx - \int_a^b s_0(x)\,dx < \varepsilon$. Therefore, by Lemma 6-6.1, $\int_{r_1}^{r_2} f(x)\,dx$ exists.

Page 145

6-13.1: *Part 2:* Let $F(x) = \int_a^x f(u)\,du$, $G(x) = \int_a^x g(u)\,du$, and

$$H(x) = \int_a^x [f(u) - g(u)]\,du.$$

By Theorem 6-11.1, $D_x[F(x) - G(x)] = D_x F(x) - D_x G(x) = f(x) - g(x)$, and $D_x H(x) = f(x) - g(x)$. By Theorem 6-12.1, $[F(x) - G(x)] - H(x) = C$. Now, $C = [F(a) - G(a)] - H(a) = 0$. Hence $F(x) - G(x) = H(x)$ for all $x \in [a,b]$. At $x = b$, $F(b) - G(b) = H(b)$, or $\int_a^b f(u)\,du - \int_a^b g(u)\,du = \int_a^b [f(u) - g(u)]\,du$. Replace u by x to complete the proof.

6-13.2: a. Let $g(x) = x^3 + 2$ and $f(u) = \sqrt{u}$; then $g'(x) = 3x^2$ and $f[g(x)] = \sqrt{x^3 + 2}$.

$\int_1^2 x^2 \sqrt{x^3 + 2}\, dx = \frac{1}{3} \int_1^2 f[g(x)]g'(x)\, dx$. By Theorem 6-13.1, this becomes

$\frac{1}{3} \int_{g(1)}^{g(2)} f(u)\, du = \frac{1}{3} \int_3^{10} \sqrt{u}\, du = \frac{1}{3} \cdot \frac{2}{3} u^{3/2} \Big|_3^{10} = \frac{2}{9} (10\sqrt{10} - 3\sqrt{3})$.

c. $g(x) = x^2 + 1$, $f(u) = 1/u^5$; Answer, $15/128$.

e. $g(x) = x \sin x$, $f(u) = u$; Answer, $\pi^2/8$.

g. $g(x) = \sqrt{1 + 2x}$, $f(u) = (u^4 - u^2)/2$; Answer, $\dfrac{99 - 2\sqrt{3}}{5}$.

Page 150

6-16.1: The values of $h(x,y)$ on each subset R_{ij} are illustrated.

a. $\displaystyle\iint_R h(x,y)\, dA = 5 + 6 + 7 + 8 + 10 + 12 + 14 + 16 = 78$

c. $\displaystyle\int_0^3 g(x)\, dx = 0 + 26 + 52 = 78 = \iint h(x,y)\, dA$

6-16.3: Define step functions $s: R \to E^1$ and $t: R \to E^1$ by $s(x,y) = -M$ and $t(x,y) = M$ for all $(x,y) \in R$. Now, $|h(x,y)| \le M$ implies $s(x,y) = -M \le h(x,y) \le M = t(x,y)$ for all $(x,y) \in R$. By Exercise 6-16.2, $\displaystyle\iint_R s(x,y)\, dA \le \iint_R h(x,y)\, dA \le \iint_R t(x,y)\, dA$.

Since $\displaystyle\iint_R s(x,y)\, dA = -M\,|R|$ and $\displaystyle\iint_R t(x,y)\, dA = M\,|R|$, the proof is complete.

Page 153

6-18.1: Part 1: $\displaystyle\iint_R f(x,y)\, dA - \varepsilon/2 < \iint_R f(x,y)\, dA = \text{l.u.b.} \left\{ \iint_R s(x,y)\, dA \,\middle|\, s(x,y) \in S_f \right\}$.

This means that $\displaystyle\iint_R f(x,y)\, dA - \varepsilon/2$ is not an upper bound for the set

$\left\{ \iint\limits_R s(x,y)\, dA \mid s(x,y) \in S_f \right\}$. Hence there exists a step function $s_0(x,y) \in S_f$ such that $\displaystyle\iint\limits_{\underline{R}} f(x,y)\, dA - \varepsilon/2 < \iint\limits_R s_0(x,y)\, dA.$

Part 2: $\displaystyle\iint\limits_{\overline{R}} f(x,y)\, dA + \varepsilon/2 > \iint\limits_{\overline{R}} f(x,y)\, dA = \text{g.l.b.}\left\{ \iint\limits_R t(x,y)\, dA \mid t(x,y) \in T_f \right\}.$

This means that $\displaystyle\iint\limits_{\overline{R}} f(x,y)\, dA + \varepsilon/2$ is not a lower bound of the set $\left\{ \iint\limits_R t(x,y)\, dA \mid t(x,y) \in T_f \right\}$. Hence there exists a step function $t_0(x,y) \in T_f$ such that $\displaystyle\iint\limits_{\overline{R}} f(x,y)\, dA + \varepsilon/2 > \iint\limits_R t_0(x,y)\, dA.$

6-18.3: Since f is a step function, $f(x,y) \in S_f$ and $f(x,y) \in T_f$ (see the definitions of S_f and T_f).

$f(x,y) \in S_f$ implies $\displaystyle\iint\limits_R f(x,y)\, dA \le \iint\limits_{\overline{R}} f(x,y)\, dA;$

$f(x,y) \in T_f$ implies $\displaystyle\iint\limits_R f(x,y)\, dA \ge \iint\limits_{\overline{R}} f(x,y)\, dA;$

By Theorem 6-17.1, $\displaystyle\iint\limits_{\underline{R}} f(x,y)\, dA \le \iint\limits_{\overline{R}} f(x,y)\, dA.$ These three inequalities establish Theorem 6-17.2.

Page 161

6-20.1: Since $f: [a,b] \to E^1$ and $g: [a,b] \to E^1$ are continuous and therefore integrable on $[a,b]$, there exist step functions $s_0(x) \in S_f$, $t_0(x) \in T_f$, $s_1(x) \in S_g$, and $t_1(x) \in T_g$ such that (I) $\displaystyle\int_a^b t_0(x)\, dx - \int_a^b s_0(x)\, dx < \varepsilon/2$ and (II) $\displaystyle\int_a^b t_1(x)\, dx - \int_a^b s_1(x)\, dx < \varepsilon/2.$ Let P_1 be a partition of $[a,b]$ containing all the points of subdivision of the partitions associated with $s_0(x)$, $t_0(x)$, $s_1(x)$, and $t_1(x)$. Let d be the maximum value of $g(x)$ and c be the minimum value of $f(x)$ for all x in $[a,b]$. Let P_2 be the partition of $[c,d]$ containing, as points of subdivision, all values of the step functions $s_0(x)$, $t_0(x)$, $s_1(x)$, $t_1(x)$. Let $P = P_1 \times P_2$. All open subsets R_{ij} of P which intersect $B(D)$ are contained in at least one of the following two regions:

   (1) The region bounded by $s_0(x)$, $t_0(x)$, $x = a$, $x = b$;
   (2) The region bounded by $s_1(x)$, $t_1(x)$, $x = a$, $x = b$.
The total area of these two regions is less than ε, by lines I and II.

6-20.2: a. 22.95;   c. $(m\,|a|^3)/6.$

Index